H±
TRANSHUMANISM
AND ITS CRITICS

H±
Transhumanism and Its Critics

Edited by

Gregory R. Hansell and William Grassie

Contributors

Russell Blackford
Nick Bostrom
Jean-Pierre Dupuy
William Grassie
Aubrey de Grey
Katherine Hayles
Don Ihde
Michael LaTorra
Sky Marsen
Max More
Ted Peters
Andrew Pickering
Martine Rothblatt
Hava Tirosh-Samuelson
Natasha Vita-More
Mark Walker

Metanexus

This book was printed in the United States of America.

Published by:

Metanexus Institute
1616 Walnut Street, Suite 1112
Philadelphia, PA 19103 USA
www.metanexus.net
+1.484.592.0304

Printing and distribution by xlibris.com

74149

Contents

Edited by Gregory R. Hansell and William Grassie

IV. H-: Critical Perspectives on Transhumanism

Contributors

Russell Blackford is a writer, philosopher, lawyer, and literary critic based in Newcastle, Australia. He is a conjoint lecturer in the School of Humanities and Social Science at the University of Newcastle, the editor-in-chief of *The Journal of Evolution and Technology*, and a fellow of the Institute for Ethics and Emerging Technologies. His academic specializations include philosophical bioethics and legal/political philosophy. Blackford's work has appeared in a wide range of magazines, academic journals, and other publications, including *Quadrant, Journal of Medical Ethics, The Monist, Journal of Law and Medicine, American Journal of Bioethics*, and many others. He is also an internationally prominent critic and scholar of the science fiction and fantasy genres and a widely published author of novels and short stories.

Nick Bostrom is director of the Future of Humanity Institute at Oxford University. He previously taught at Yale University in the Department of Philosophy and in the Yale Institute for Social and Policy Studies. He has more than 140 publications to his name, including three scholarly books: *Anthropic Bias* (Routledge, 2002), *Global Catastrophic Risks* (ed., Oxford University Press, 2008), and *Enhancing Humans* (ed., Oxford University Press, 2008). He has a background in physics, computational neuroscience, and mathematical logic, as well as analytic philosophy. Bostrom is a leading thinker on big picture questions for humanity, occasionally serves as an expert consultant for various governmental agencies in the UK, Europe, and the USA, and is a frequent commentator in the media.

Aubrey de Grey is a biomedical gerontologist based in Cambridge, UK, whose research focuses on whether regenerative medicine can thwart the aging process. De Grey is the chief science officer of SENS Foundation, a nonprofit charity dedicated to combating the aging process. He is editor-in-chief of *Rejuvenation Research*, the world's leading peer-reviewed journal focused on intervention in aging. In 1999 his book *The Mitochondrial Free Radical Theory of Aging* (Landes Bioscience) was published, and on the basis of the book, he was awarded a PhD from Cambridge University in 2000. He also coauthored *Ending Aging: The Rejuvenation Breakthroughs That Could Reverse Human Aging in Our Lifetime* (St. Martin's, 2007).

Jean-Pierre Dupuy is professor of French and political science at Stanford University and professor emeritus of social and political philosophy at Ecole Polytechnique, Paris. He is a member of the French Academy of Technology and chairs the Ethics Committee of the French High Authority on Nuclear Safety and Security. He is the director of research of Imitatio, a new foundation devoted to the dissemination and discussion of René Girard's mimetic theory. His most recent work has dealt with the topic of catastrophe and is being translated and collected in a volume to be published in English. Among his most recent publications are *Retour de Tchernobyl: Journal d'un homme en colère* (Paris, Seuil, 2006), *On the Origins of Cognitive Science: The Mechanization of the Mind* (The MIT Press, 2009), *La Marque du sacré* (Paris, Carnets Nord, 2009).

William Grassie is founder and executive director of Metanexus Institute, which works to promote the constructive engagement of religion and science. He received his doctorate in religion from Temple University in 1994. Grassie is the author of *Politics by Other Means: Science and Religion in the 21st Century* (Metanexus, 2010) and *The New Sciences of Religion: Exploring Spirituality from the Outside In and Bottom Up* (forthcoming from Palgrave Macmillan). Grassie is the recipient of a number of academic awards and grants from the American Friends Service Committee, the Roothbert Fellowship, and the John Templeton Foundation. In 2007-2008, Grassie served as a senior Fulbright fellow in the Department of Buddhist Studies at the University of Peradeniya in Kandy, Sri Lanka.

Gregory R. Hansell received his MA in theology from Union Theological Seminary, specializing in the philosophy of religion, and his BA in religion from Swarthmore College with an interdisciplinary concentration in interpretation theory. He is currently working on his PhD in philosophy from Villanova University. Hansell juxtaposes academic training in philosophical theology and philosophy of religion with technical training and extensive career experience in computer networking, programming, and hardware. From 2002 until 2010, Hansell directed publications and information technology at Metanexus Institute. He also served as the managing editor of Metanexus Institute's award-winning online publication, *The Global Spiral*.

N. Katherine Hayles is professor of literature at Duke University. With degrees in both chemistry and English literature, Hayles is one of the foremost scholars of the relationship between literature and science in the late twentieth century. She is the author of six books, including *How We Became Posthuman: Virtual Bodies* *in Cybernetics, Literature and Informatics* (University of Chicago, 1999), which won the Rene Wellek Prize for the Best Book in Literary Theory for 1998-1999, and *Writing Machines* (MIT, 2001), which won the Suzanne Langer Award for Outstanding Scholarship. Her recent book is *Electronic Literature: New Horizons for the Literary* (2007). She is currently completing a book entitled *How We Think: Transforming Power and Digital Technologies.*

Don Ihde is distinguished professor of philosophy and the director of the Technoscience Research Group in the Philosophy Department at Stonybrook (SUNY). His research interests center around the philosophy of science and technology with a recent focus on imaging technologies. Ihde is the author of twenty original books and the editor of many others. Recent examples include *Chasing Technoscience* (Indiana University, 2003), edited with Evan Selinger, and *Bodies in Technology* (University of Minnesota, 2002). Some of his books and articles have appeared in a dozen languages. Together with Indiana University Press, Ihde initiated a monograph series in philosophy of technology that has become one of the most influential collections in the field. He is currently working on *Imaging Technologies: Plato Upside Down.*

Michael LaTorra is college assistant professor of English at New Mexico State University, where he has taught since 2000. Previous to his teaching appointment, he worked in information technology in California's Silicon Valley and in other states. He is the author of the 1993 book *A Warrior Blends with Life: A Modern Tao* (North Atlantic Books, 1993) and is an ordained Soto Zen Buddhist priest at the Zen Center of Las Cruces / Daibutsuji Zen Temple. LaTorra serves on the board of directors of the World Transhumanist Association and on the board of the Institute for Ethics and Emerging Technologies.

Sky Marsen is a linguist and literary theorist and has published in areas of language and communication. She has also consulted on communication issues in technical institutions internationally, notably at IBM and California Institute of Technology. At present, she is a senior lecturer in linguistics and semiotics at Victoria University, New Zealand. She is also the research director of the School of Linguistics and Applied Language Studies, a member of the International Association for Semiotic Studies, and a member of the Program Committee of the annual International Wiki Symposium. Marsen is author of *Communication Studies* and *Narrative Dimensions of Philosophy* (both Palgrave Macmillan, 2006).

Max More is a strategic philosopher widely recognized for his thinking on the philosophical and cultural implications of emerging technologies. More's contributions include founding the philosophy of transhumanism and cofounding Extropy Institute, an organization crucial in building the transhumanist movement since 1988. More was elected as a director of Humanity+ in 2010. More has a degree in philosophy, politics, and economics from St. Anne's College, Oxford University. His PhD is from the University of Southern California, where he studied and taught philosophy. More's research focuses on developing a highly interdisciplinary approach to making smarter decisions about advanced technologies. Drawing on philosophy, economics, cognitive and social psychology, and organizational theory, More's "proactionary principle" aims to minimize the dangers and maximize the benefits of future technologies.

Ted Peters teaches systematic theology and bioethics at Pacific Lutheran Theological Seminary and the Graduate Theological Union in Berkeley, California. He is author of *The Evolution of Terrestrial and Extraterrestrial Life* (Pandora, 2008), *The Stem Cell Debate* (Fortress, 2007), *Anticipating Omega* (Vandenhoeck & Ruprecht, 2006), *Science, Theology, and Ethics* (Ashgate, 2003), and *Playing God? Genetic Determinism and Human Freedom* (Routledge, 2002). He is coauthor of *Sacred Cells? Why Christians Should Support Stem Cell Research* (Roman and Littlefield, 2008), *Theological and Scientific Commentary on Darwin's Origin of Species* (Abingdon, 2008), and *Can You Believe in God and Evolution?* (Abingdon, 2008). He is coeditor of the journal, *Theology and Science,* published at the Center for Theology and the Natural Sciences (CTNS), and of other publications.

Andrew Pickering taught for many years at the University of Illinois at Urbana-Champaign and is now professor and chair of sociology at Exeter University, UK. He is the author of *The Mangle of Practice: Time, Agency and Science* (University of Chicago, 1995), *Constructing Quarks: A Sociological History of Particle Physics* (University of Chicago, 1999), and most recently *The Cybernetic Brain: Sketches of Another Future* (University of Chicago, 2010). He is also the editor (with Keith Guzik) of *The Mangle in Practice: Science, Society, and Becoming* (Duke University, 2008). Pickering is an internationally known leader in science and technology studies and has written on topics as diverse as post-World War II particle physics, mathematics, science, and industry in the nineteenth century, and science, technology and warfare in and since World War II.

Martine Rothblatt is an American lawyer, author, and entrepreneur. She earned her JD and MBA degrees from the UCLA Schools of Law and Management, respectively, and her PhD in medical ethics from the Royal London School of Medicine and Dentistry, University of London. Rothblatt is responsible for having created two satellite communications industries. She led the first vehicle tracking company (Geostar) and both started and led the first satellite radio companies for the U.S. (Sirius) and the developing countries (WorldSpace). In 1996 she founded United Therapeutics, the fastest-growing biotechnology company in the Washington

DC area. Rothblatt is a member of the District of Columbia Bar and is admitted to practice before the Supreme Court of the United States.

Hava Tirosh-Samuelson is director of Jewish Studies and Irving and Miriam Lowe Professor of Modern Judaism and professor of history at Arizona State University, Tempe, Arizona. She writes on Jewish intellectual history, feminist philosophy, Judaism and ecology, bioethics, and religion and science. In addition to numerous articles, book chapters, and book reviews, Tirosh-Samuelson is the author of the award-winning *The Life and Thought of Rabbi Judah Messer Leon* (1991) and of *Happiness in Premodern Judaism: Virtue, Knowledge and Well-Being* (2003) and the editor of *Judaism and Ecology: Created World and Revealed Word* (2002), *Women and Gender in Judaism* (2004), and *The Legacy of Hans Jonas: Judaism and the Phenomenon of Life* (2008).

Natasha Vita-More is a PhD researcher at the University of Plymouth, School of Art and Media. She serves on the board of directors for Humanity+ and is an advisor to Singularity University, a fellow at the Institute for Ethics and Emerging Technology, and a visiting scholar at 21st Century Medicine. She is the creator of the future human prototype Primo Posthuman and writes about the future of arts and sciences in the fields of human enhancement and life prolongation. She is published in *100 000 Ans de Beauté*, *Artifact*, and *Technoetic Arts* and has been featured in *WIRED*, *Harper's Bazaar*, *Marie Claire*, *The New York Times*, *U.S. News & World Report*, and the *Village Voice*, and in more than twenty-four televised documentaries.

Mark Walker is assistant professor of philosophy and occupies the Richard L. Hedden Endowed Chair in Advanced Philosophical Studies at New Mexico State University. His PhD is from Australian National University. He previously taught at McMaster University in the Department of Philosophy and in the Arts & Science Program. He serves on the editorial board of the *Journal of Evolution and Technology* and on the board of directors of the Institute for Ethics and Emerging Technologies. His teaching and research interests include ethics, epistemology, philosophy of law, philosophy of religion, and philosophy of science. His current primary research interest is in ethical issues arising out of emerging technologies, e.g., genetic engineering, advanced pharmacology, artificial intelligence research, and nanotechnology.

Introduction

by William Grassie and Gregory R. Hansell

"Transhumanism," writes Nick Bostrom in this volume, "is . . . an outgrowth of secular humanism and the Enlightenment. It holds that current human nature is improvable through the use of applied science and other rational methods, which may make it possible to increase human health-span, extend our intellectual and physical capacities, and give us increased control over our own mental states and moods."[1] The applied sciences involved include dramatic advancements in the neurosciences, genomics, robotics, nanotechnology, computers, and artificial intelligence. In some combination of the above bioengineering, transhumanists imagine the possibilities in the near future of dramatically enhancing human mental and physical capacities, slowing and reversing the aging process, and controlling our emotional and mental states. The imagined future is a new age in which people will be freed from mental disease and physical decrepitude, able to consciously choose their "natures" and those of their children. At first glance, it all seems like a wonderful thing, life lived more abundantly, but Francis Fukuyama calls this transhumanist vision "the most dangerous idea in the world."[2]

Humanity Plus or Minus (H±) explores this debate with sixteen essays for and against the bioengineering of an improved humanity. This book began as a special edition of Metanexus's *The Global Spiral* in June 2008. Hava Tirosh-Samuelson, an academic board member of the Metanexus Institute and a professor of history at Arizona State University, edited this special issue of *The Global Spiral*, which was uniformly critical of the transhumanist movement. Tirosh-Samuelson was also running a three-year project at ASU, funded through Metanexus on transhumanism.[3]

---

[1] See Nick Bostrom's essay in this volume.

[2] Francis Fukuyama, "Transhumanism: The World's Most Dangerous Idea," *Foreign Policy* no. 144 (2004): 42-43.

[3] See http://www.templetonresearchlectures.com/winners/asu.asp and http://transhumanism.asu.edu/.

The first set of essays went viral and provoked quite a reaction from a number of transhumanists who thought they had been misrepresented. This resulted in a second special issue of the *Spiral* guest-edited by Natasha Vita-More. In the February 2009 online journal, advocates of transhumanism presented their case, often with specific rebuttals to the earlier commentators.

In assembling this collection of essays for publication in this volume, we begin with a historical overview of transhumanism written by Hava Tirosh-Samuelson. We then give the advocates of transhumanism an opportunity to make their case and follow this with several paired essays that were written as point-counterpoint. Finally, we conclude with several essays that are critical of transhumanism. In so doing, we are partly reversing the order of the original online publications, which began with criticisms of transhumanism and then a rebuttal by advocates. Only in the point-counterpoint section is this original chronology maintained. Readers will notice references to other protagonists for and against transhumanism spread throughout this volume. That being said, we think this structure provides a more coherent exploration of human enhancement proponents and their critics.

The debate about transhumanism is an extremely fruitful field for philosophical and theological inquiry. The last hundred years of human evolution have seen remarkable scientific and technological transformations. If the pace of change continues and indeed accelerates in the twenty-first century, then in short order, we will be a much-transformed species on a much-transformed planet. The idea of some fixed human nature, a human essence from which we derive notions of humane dignities and essential human rights, no longer applies in this brave new world of free market evolution. On what basis then do we make moral judgments and pursue pragmatic ends? Should we try to limit the development of certain sciences and technologies? How would we do so? Is it even possible? Are either traditional religious or Enlightenment values adequate at a speciation horizon between humans and posthumans when nature is just not what it used to be anymore? Is the ideology of transhumanism dangerous independent of the technology? Is the ideology of the bioconservatives, those who oppose transhumanism, also dangerous and how? Are the new sciences and technologies celebrated by transhumanists realistic or just another form of wishful thinking? And which utopic and dystopic visions have the power to illuminate and motivate the future?

The collection of essays in this book presents a valuable introduction to these issues and more but offer no final resolution. You will discover much worthy of debate that will transform how you think about the world and yourself.

Special thanks to Hava Tirosh-Samuelson and Natasha Vita-More for editing the two special issues of the Metanexus online journal, from which this collection is largely derived. Thanks also to Erica Vinskie, Elizabeth Kenny, and Jonathan Camery-Hoggatt for their labors on the original publications and in assembling this volume for publication. It goes without saying that we thank each of the contributors to this volume for sharing the best of their ideas and words. In the end, we hope that this dialogue will help us to craft together a healthier and safer world for our descendants, human or otherwise, and that, in the process, we might also humanize the transhumanists and transform the humanist in each of you.

REFERENCE

Fukuyama, Francis. "Transhumanism: The World's Most Dangerous Idea." *Foreign Policy* no. 144 (2004): 42-43.

I. A Critical Historical Perspective on Transhumanism

Chapter One

Engaging Transhumanism[1]

by Hava Tirosh-Samuelson

TRANSHUMANISM IN CONTEXT

Technology is transforming human life at a faster pace than ever before. The convergence of nanotechnology, biotechnology, robotics, information and communication technology, and applied cognate science poses a new situation in which the human has become a design project. The new technologies allow for new kinds of cognitive tools that combine artificial intelligence with interface technology, molecular biology, nanotechnology, genetic enhancing of human mental and physical capacities, combating diseases and slowing down the process of aging, and exercising control over desires, moods, and mental states. Due to genetic engineering, humans are now able not only to redesign themselves, presumably in

---

[1] I am the PI of a multiyear grant from Metanexus Institute entitled "Facing the Challenges of Transhumanism: Religion, Science, and Technology," granted to ASU as part of the Templeton Lectures for Constructive Engagement of Religion and Science 2006-2009. For information about the project see www.asu.edu/transhumanism. A German version of this was published under the title "Eine Auseinandersetzung mit dem Transhumanismus aus jüdischer Perpektive," in *Die Debatte über "Human Enhnacement": historische, philosophicshe und ethische Aspekte der technologischen Verbesserung des Menschen*, ed. Christopher Coenen, Stefan Gammel, Reinhard Heil, and Andreas Woyke (Bielefeld: Transcript, 2010). Parts of the essay have been published in online journals: *The Global Spiral* 9, no. 3 (2008) and in *Religion Dispatches*. The essays by Ihde, Dupuy, Hayles, Pickering, and Peters were originally delivered at a workshop on April 24-25, 2007 and published thereafter in a special issue of *The Global Spiral* edited by me.

order to get rid of various limitations, but also to redesign future generations, thereby affecting the evolutionary process itself. As a result, a new *posthuman* phase in the evolution of the human species will emerge, in which humans will live longer, will possess new physical and cognitive abilities, and will be liberated from suffering and pain due to aging and diseases. In the posthuman age, humans will no longer be controlled by nature; instead, they will be the controllers of nature. Those who welcome the posthuman phase are known as transhumanists.

The term *transhumanism* was coined in 1957 by Julian Huxley (1887-1975),[2] the grandson of the Victorian Darwinian Thomas Henry Huxley. In his *New Bottles for New Wine* (1957), Julian Huxley advocated the fulfillment society, which will be committed to the full development of human potential and will replace the welfare society, the efficient society, or the power society. For Huxley, transhumanism was another word for his "evolutionary humanism," namely, the deliberate effort by mankind to "transcend itself—not just sporadically . . . but in its entirety, as humanity . . . Man remaining man, but transcending himself, by realizing new possibilities of and for his human nature."[3]

Huxley considered transhumanism a "key concept" of an entirely new intellectual framework, "a new ideology," or a "new system of ideas appropriate to man's new situation."[4] He considered transhumanism a "new attitude of mind" that would address the crisis of humanity by bridging science and the arts and by using science to build a better world. Similar to the Human Potential Movement associated with the psychologist Abraham Maslow,[5] Huxley believed that "the human species will be on the threshold of a new kind of existence, as different from ours as ours is from that of Peking man. It will be consciously fulfilling its real destiny."[6]

Julian Huxley was a close friend of John Burdon Sanderson Haldane (1892-1964) and John Desmond Bernal (1901-1971),[7] and these three could be

---

[2]   Julian Huxley, *New Bottles for New Wine* (London: Chatto & Windus, 1957), 17.

[3]   Ibid.

[4]   Ibid., 255.

[5]   Like his older contemporary, Julian Huxley, Abraham Maslow coined the word, "metahuman" in discussing how the self-actualizing man will be able "to go beyond the merely human" and become "divine or godlike." A. H. Maslow, *The Farther Reaches of Human Nature* (New York: Penguin, 1971), 274.

[6]   Julian Huxley, *New Bottles for New Wine*, 17.

[7]   The only biography of J. B. S. Haldane is Ronald Clark, *J. B. S.: The Life and Work of J.B.S. Haldane* (New York: Coward McMann, Inc., 1968); for a comprehensive, superb biography of J. D. Bernal see Andrew Brown, *J. D. Bernal: The Sage of Science* (Oxford: Oxford University Press, 2005). A very useful collection of essays by people who worked closely with Bernal is Brenda Swann and Francis Aprhamaian (eds.), *J. D. Bernal: A Life in Science and Politics* (London and New York: Verso, 1999).

considered the "prophets of transhumanism."[8] During the 1920s, they articulated views that would become prominent in the contemporary transhumanist movement. Thus, Huxley, an evolutionary biologist and zoologist, highlighted the evolving nature of humans and encouraged the "continuing adventure of human development" with deliberate use of eugenics, which for him meant planning and controlling human evolution. J. B. S. Haldane, whose main area of research was population genetics, disapproved of the misapplication of eugenics and scolded writers on eugenics who were not sufficiently versed in the science of heredity or who selectively manipulated scientific evidence to advance their social agenda. Yet Haldane accorded eugenics a major role in shaping the ideal future society, and he saw the "biological inventor" (today's genetic engineer) as "the most romantic figure on earth at the present time."[9] And J. D. Bernal, a specialist in crystallography and molecular biology, who like J. B. S. Haldane joined the Communist Party of Greater Britain, fantasized about the future where science would transform all aspects of social life and would replace religion as the dominant social force, primarily through the transformation of the human brain.[10]

These ideas were further developed in the 1930s, especially among the so-called Red Scientists of Cambridge University, who deeply believed in the capacity of science and technology to improve the human condition.[11] Believing in the ability of the scientifically planned welfare state to bring an end to human misery, H. G. Wells (a close friend and colleague of Julian Huxley) imagined a small group of benevolent scientist-technicians who will use science and technology to manufacture

---

[8]   For a fuller treatment of these three thinkers in light of transhumanism see Hava Tirosh-Samuelson, "The Prophets of Transhumanism: England in the 1920s," to be published in *Building Better Humans?: Refocusing the Debate on Transhumanism*," ed. Hava Tirosh-Samuelson and Kenneth L. Mossman.

[9]   J.B.S. Haldane, *Daedalus: or Science and the Future* (New York: E. P. Dutton & Co, 1924), 80.

[10]   See J.D. Bernal, *The World, The Flesh, and the Devil: An Enquiry into the Future of Three Enemies of the Rational Soul* (Bloomington and London: Indiana University Press, 1969).

[11]   For a superb reconstruction of the life and ideas of the so-called "Red Scientists" in Cambridge during the 1930s consult Gary Wersky, *The Visible College: The Collective Biography of British Scientific Socialists in the 1930s* (New York: Holt, Reinhart and Winston, 1978). Wersky focuses on J. D. Bernal, J. B.Haldane, Lancelot Hogben (1895-1975), Hyman Levi (1889-1975), and Joseph Needham (1900-1995). Since Julian Huxley was a close friend of Haldane and Bernal, he too features prominently in the narrative, although he was not formally affiliated with either the Labor Movement or the Communist Party.

a perfect future.[12] However, the Nazis' pernicious use of eugenics and the horrors of World War II invalidated the goal of creating a new and better world through a centrally imposed vision, and they also discredited the eugenics movement of the 1920s. In the 1940s, especially in England, cybernetics was developed by mathematicians and pioneering computer scientists who illustrated how cognition is possible without a subject, while problematizing the notion that the brain is an organ of representation.[13] In the 1960s, new optimistic futuristic scenarios about humanity were articulated by science fiction writers such as Arthur C. Clarke, Isaac Asimov, Robert Heinlein, Stanislaw Lem; and later Bruce Sterling, Greg Egan, and Vernor Vinge, who speculated about the new, transhuman future.[14] In the late 1960s, the futurist Fereidoun M. Esfandiary, who later changed his name to FM 2030 (the year denoting the date of his one hundredth birthday), began to identify transhumans as persons who behave in a manner conducive to a posthuman future. At that time, various organizations began to advocate life extension, cryonics, space colonization, and other scenarios; while advances in biotechnology, neuroscience, and nanotechnology began to make their mark.[15] Marvin Minsky,[16] an eminent artificial intelligence researcher, articulated many of the themes of the transhumanist vision, and he was joined by other famous scientific visionaries and technoutopians

---

[12]   See H. G. Wells, *A Modern Utopia* (London: Chapman & Hall, 1905); idem, *Men Like Gods, A Novel* (New York: Cassell, 1923). For recent critical study of H.G. Wells consult Steven McLean (ed.) *H. G. Wells: Interdisciplinary Essays* (Newcastle: Cambridge Scholars Pub., 2008).

[13]   On the history of cybernetics see Andrew Pickering, *The Mangle of Practice, Time, Agency and Science* (Chicago: University of Chicago Press, 1995); Philip Husbands, Owen Holland, and Michael Wheeler (eds.), *The Mechanical Mind in History* (Cambridge, MA: MIT Press, 2008); and David A. Mindell, *Between Human and Machine: Feedback, Control and Computing Before Cybernetics* (Baltimore, MD, and London: John Hopkins University Press, 2002).

[14]   On transhumanist themes in contemporary in science fiction see N. Katherine Hayles, *How We Became Posthuman: Cybernetics, Literature, and Informatics* (Chicago: University of Chicago, 1999) and Daniel Dinello, *Technophobia!: Science Fiction Vision of Posthuman Technology* (Austin: University of Texas Press, 2002). Both authors present science fiction as a critique of techno-optimism.

[15]   On the history of the transhumanist movement see Nick Bostrom, "Transhumanism FAQ: A General Introduction," version 2.1 (2003) available on the Web site of Nick Bostrom, http://www.nickbostrom.com. The essays on this Web site are the best gateway into transhumanist literature and issues.

[16]   See Marvin Minsky, *The Emotion Machine: Commonsense Thinking, Artificial Intelligence, and the Future of the Human Mind* (New York: Simon & Schuster, 2006); idem, *The Society of Mind* (New York: Simon and Schuster, 1986).

such as Ray Kurzweil,[17] Eric K. Drexler,[18] Frank P. Tipler,[19] and Hans Moravec.[20] These technoenthusiasts have offered an apocalyptic view in which a rupture, referred to as "the Singularity," will bring an end to human existence, ushering instead an autonomous, artificially intelligent species that will be in competition with humanity. The new species of *Robo sapiens* will supersede *Homo sapiens* as the next phase of evolution. In 1999 Hans Moravec predicted that "before the next century is over, human beings will no longer be the most intelligent or capable type of entity on the planet."[21] Due to the continued exponential growth of artificial intelligence, mind machines will become the next evolutionary step, with organic humans left behind. According to Moravec, a former director of the Mobile Robot Laboratory at Carnegie-Melon University and developer of advanced robots for the military and NASA, humans would pass their minds into artificially intelligent robots, their mechanical progeny.

In the 1980s, philosopher Max More (whose given name was Max O'Connor) formalized a transhumanist doctrine, advocating the "principles of extropy" for continuously improving the human condition.[22] According to More, humans are but a "transitional stage standing between our animal heritage and our posthuman future,"[23] which will be reached through "genetic engineering, life-extending biosciences, intelligence intensifiers, smarter interfaces to swifter computers, neural-computer integration, world-wide data networks, virtual reality, intelligent agents, swift electronic communication, artificial intelligence, neuroscience, neural

---

17   See Ray Kurzweil, *The Age of Intelligent Machines* (Cambridge, MA: MIT Press, 1990); idem, *The Age of Spiritual Machines: When Computers Exceed Human Intelligence* (New York: Viking 1999) idem, *The Singularity is Near: When Humans Transcend Biology* (New York: Viking, 2005).

18   Eric K. Drexler, *Engines of Creation* (Garden City, NY: Anchor Press/Doubleday, 1986); idem, *Nanosystems: Molecular Machinery, Manufacturing and Computation* (New York: Wiley, 1992); Erik K. Drexler and Chris Peterson *Unbounding the Future: The Nanotechnology Revolution* (New York: Morrow, 1991).

19   See Frank J. Tipler, *The Physics of Immortality: Modern Cosmology, God and the Resurrection of the Dead* (New York: Doubleday, 1994); idem, *The Physics of Christianity* (New York: Doubleday, 2007).

20   See Hans P. Moravec, *Mind Children: The Future of Robot and Human Intelligence* (Cambridge, MA: Harvard University Press, 1988); idem, *Robot: Mere Machine to Transcendent Mind* (New York: Oxford University Press, 1999).

21   Morvacec, *Robot*, 13.

22   Max More's ideas are available only on his Web site, www.extropy.org. Although he holds a PhD, he is yet to publish a book articulating his philosophy of transhumanism.

23   Max More, "Extropian Principles 3.0," http://www.maxmore.com/extprn3.htm (December 2004).

networks, artificial life, off-planet migration, and molecular nanotechnology." For More and other techno-enthusiasts genetic engineering, cloning and eugenics will reconfigure select humans into a superior transhuman species and, using robotics, bionics, and nanotechnology, will invent a new posthuman species no longer dependent on nature. Humans will thus transform themselves into posthumans, namely, "persons of unprecedented physical, intellectual and psychological capacity, self-programming, potentially immortal, unlimited individuals."

In the late 1990s, a group of transhumanist activists authored the Transhumanist Declaration, stating various ethical positions related to the use of and planning for technological advances.[24] In 1998 the World Transhumanist Association (WTA) was founded by philosophers Nick Bostrom and David Pearce, and its membership today is about five thousand people worldwide, with several geographically divided chapters and special-interest affiliates. Other contemporary organizations also play a role in the transhumanist movement for example, the Extropy Institute, the Foresight Institute, the Immortality Institute, the Institute for Ethics and Emerging Technologies, and the Singularity Institute for Artificial Intelligence.[25] These organizations and others like them were greatly helped by the communication revolution of the 1980s and 1990s, with instant communication worldwide. Indeed, cyberspace, as we shall see below, is not just a means to disseminate transhumanist ideas but part and parcel of the transhumanist eschatological and utopian vision.

Transhumanism, however, is not merely a utopian vision by techno-optimists; rather, it is a program that receives a substantial amount of funding and scientific legitimacy from the National Science Foundation, and by people such as Mihail C. Rocco and William Sims Bainbridge, who promote the transhumanist vision under the banner of "converging technologies."[26] Futuristic ideas about human physical and cognitive enhancements through human-machine fusion have been of special interest to the Defense Advanced Research Projects Agency (DARPA), which has

---

[24]   The Transhumanist Declaration is available on the Web site of the Transhumanist World Association (WTA) http://www.transhumanism.org and the Web site of Nick Bostrom. For more information about the World Transhumanist Organization (which has changed its name to Humanity +) consult the Web sites: http://www.transhumanism.org and http://humanityplus.org. In general the WTA supports a more liberal democratic agenda than other transhumanist groups. On the politics of the movement, see James J. Hughes, "The Politics of Transhumanism," http://www.changesurfer.com/Acad/TranshumPolitics.htm.

[25]   See Appendix for a list of future-oriented institutions and organizations.

[26]   See Mihail C. Roco and William Sims Bainbridge (eds.), *Converging Technologies for Improvement of Human Performance: Nanotechnology, Biotechnology, Information Technology and Cognitive Science* (Dordrecht and Boston: Kluwer Academic Publishers, 2002).

been "working on changing what it means to be human," as Joel Garreau succinctly put it.[27] The techno-enthusiasts who promote transhumanism have considerable control over deciding how to spend financial resources, and that is one reason why transhumanists deride their critics as "bio-Luddites" or "bioconservatives." After all, the conflict between transhumanists and their critics is no less about funding than about a vision for and of humanity.

By the first decade of the twenty-first century, established religions too have begun to engage transhumanism more seriously as scholars began to note that the transhumanist vision of heaven on earth followed by posthuman immortality has a strong religious dimension,[28] even though transhumanist leaders despise traditional religions or religious institutions. Indeed, for transhumanists such as Eric K. Drexler, technology itself is divine, and scientists have godlike power to structure matter and recreate nature. Whereas some Christian theologians have been very critical of transhumanism,[29] others have been more willing to accept certain aspects of the transhumanist project, for which they proceed to give theological justification.[30] Philip Hefner offers a very useful clarification about transhumanism when he distinguishes between "upper-case transhumanism" and "lower-case transhumanism." The former concerns what he considers the fantastic and rather dubious scenarios about the radical transformation of the human species, whereas the latter denotes the more ubiquitous and ambiguous use of biotechnology in everyday life. The latter is based on the belief that "it is natural and good to enhance human mental and physical abilities, and ameliorate undesirable aspects of the human condition," as well as the claim that "we need not accept as our destiny the human nature . . . with which we grew in our mother's womb."[31] In 2008 the

---

[27]   Joel Garreau, *Radical Evolution: The Promise and Peril of Enhancing our Minds, Our Bodies, and What is Means to Be Humans* (New York: Doubleday, 2004), esp. 18-44. The quote is on p. 42.

[28]   The most extensive analysis of the religious dimension of contemporary technology is offered by David F. Noble, *The Religion of Technology: The Divinity of Man and the Spirit of Invention* (New York Penguin Books, 1997).

[29]   See Brent Waters, *From Human to Posthuman: Christian Theology and Technology in a Postmodern World* (Aldershot, England and Burlington, VT: Ashgate, 2006).

[30]   See Philip Hefner, *Technology and Human Becoming* (Minneapolis: Fortress Press, 2003); Ted Peters, *Playing God? Genetic Determinism and Human Freedom* (New York: Routledge, 1997); idem, *Science, Theology and Ethics* (Aldershot, England and Burlington VT: Ashgate, 2003); idem, *For the Love of Children: Genetic Technology and the Future of the Family* (Louisville: Westminster John Knox Press, 1996).

[31]   Philip Hefner, "The Animal that Aspires to Be an Angel: The Challenge of Transhumanism," *Dialog: Journal of Technology* 48, no. 2 (2009): 164-73, quote is on p. 166. Hefner is quite supportive of enhancement technologies since medical

American Academy of Religion accorded formal status to deliberations about transhumanism, even though transhumanism does not define itself as a religion.[32] At least one established religion—The Church of Latter Day Saints—not only endorses transhumanism but also has its own transhumanist variant. In 2006 the World Transhumanist Association voted to recognize the Mormon Transhumanist Association as its first religious special-interest affiliate.

While the vision of the posthuman ideal state of affairs is generally clear, the precise meaning of the transhuman is somewhat vague. For some the term is short for *transitional human*, a phase in human evolution from the ordinary human today to the posthuman of the remote future. Thus, the transhuman is a more evolved being than an ordinary human due to the use of genetic engineering, psychopharmacology, antiaging therapies, neural interfaces, advanced information management tools, memory enhancing drugs, wearable computers, and cognitive techniques. Since the transhuman is an enhanced human, the advocates of transhumanism like to refer to their vision of humanity as H+ (that is, enhanced humanity). For others the transhuman does not denote a technologically enhanced person but an ordinary person who supports activities that promote the eventual evolvement of the posthuman. Echoing Julian Huxley, Nick Bostrom, the leading philosopher of transhumanism, defines transhumanism as follows: "a *way of thinking* about the future that is based on the premise that the human species in its current form does not represent the end of our development but rather a comparatively early phase."[33] In this definition, to be a transhumanist, one does not have to be physically enhanced by new biotechnologies but only share the outlook that affirms the possibility and desirability of fundamentally improving the human condition through the use of converging technologies.

---

advancements have made it possible for him to live an active and productive life despite the fact that he was born with *spina bifida*, a genetic defect that doomed children in previous generations to premature death.

[32] The American Academy of Religion now has special sessions, and scholars of Religious Studies have begun to engage transhumanism systematically. For example, consult Derek F. Maher and Calvin Mercer (eds.) *Religion and the Implications of Radical Life Extension* (New York: Palgrave Macmillan, 2009).

[33] Nick Bostrom, "Transhumanist FAQ: A General Introduction," version 2.1 (2003) available on the Web site of Nick Bostrom, http://www.nickbostrom.com. As mentioned in an earlier note, the essays of Nick Bostrom featured in this Web site are the best gateway into transhumanist literature and issues. A high level academic engagement with the issues involved in human enhancement is Nick Bostrom and Julian Savulescu (eds.), *Human Enhancement* (Oxford: Oxford University Press, 2009) and Julian Savulescu, R. ter Mueler, and G. Kahane (eds.), *Enhancing Human Capacities*, (Oxford: Wiley-Blackwell, 2009). Also useful is the information on the Web site of Bostrom's colleagues at Oxford, Anders Sandberg http://www.aleph.se.

Transhumanism is yet to generate systematic philosophy, although a few attempts in this direction do exist. Simon Young, for example, presents transhumanism as a unification of science and ethics and positions it as an alternative to academic postmodernism, religious theism, and radical environmentalism.[34] Against postmodernists of the academic Left, Young presents transhumanism as a critique of cognitive skepticism, social constructivism, and cultural relativism. Objective reality does exist and is independent of human perception, cognition, and apprehension; science generates knowledge about objective reality, namely, accurate and true description of reality outside the human mind that provides humans with specific courses of action, including those that change objective reality. The facts about the human condition are indeed real and painful but need not be definitive. Biology is *not* destiny because the evolutionary process has given rise to the complex human brain that now enables humans to intervene in the evolutionary process and replace it with "designer evolution," or "controlled evolution." Young argues that human consciousness is an "inevitable product of the evolutionary process"[35] and the predictable outcome of "evolutionary complexification."[36] Therefore, human beings not only can intervene and alter the biological facts through designer genes, designer drugs, and a whole range of enhancement technologies, but should also do so in order to improve the human species.

A different philosophical presentation of transhumanism is articulated by Robert Pepperell, who defines the "posthuman condition" as an "end of 'man-centered' universe," an "energetic theory of mind in which human thought, meaning and memory is understood in terms of the activity of an energy regulating system."[37] For Pepperell, transhumanism means the end of humanism, namely, the "long-held belief in the infallibility of human power and the arrogant belief in our superiority and uniqueness." Although he concedes that this belief will continue to exist well into the future, he predicts that humanism will eventually collapse because of its inherent moral weakness noted by feminism, the animal rights movement, and the antislavery movements, all of which expose the moral failings of humanism. Transhumanism moves beyond the limitations of humanism, but its evolutionary perspective is "not limited to genetics, but includes all the paraphernalia of cultural and technological existence."[38] In the posthuman future, humans will acquire machinelike enhancements and will be able to exist more effectively by recognizing "that none of us are actually distinct from

---

[34]   Simon Young, *Designer Evolution: A Transhumanist Manifesto* (Amherst, NY: Prometheus Books, 2005).

[35]   Ibid, 212.

[36]   Ibid., 209.

[37]   Robert Pepperell, *The Posthuman Condition: Consciousness beyond the Brain* (Bristol, UK: Intellect Books, 2003), 100.

[38]   Ibid., 171.

each other, or the world" and that "to harm anything is to harm oneself." Pepperell's exposition of the posthuman condition sees the biomechanical technologies that blur the distinction between humans and machines as the core of the posthuman age and its philosophical implications. Whereas "humanists saw themselves as distinct beings in an antagonistic relationship with their surroundings, posthumans regard their own being as embodied in an extended technological world."[39]

Pepperell's postmodern critique of humanism is shared by other so-called cultural posthumanists such as Neil Badmington, Elaine L. Graham, and Cary Wolfe,[40] who reflect on the interplay between scientific theorizing and cultural imagination against the background of several postmodern discourses. These cultural critics do not agree on the meaning of humanism or transhumanism. Whereas for some, *humanism* means the promulgation of secularism and scientific rationality; for others, humanism denotes a reactionary notion that "appeals (positively) to the notion of a core humanity or a common essential feature in terms of which human beings can be defined and understood."[41] It is this notion of humanity that has been under severe assault at least since the mid-nineteenth century with the critique of Karl Marx, Sigmund Freud, and Friedrich Nietzsche; and the postmodernist philosophers Jean-Francoise Lyotard, Jacques Derrida, Michel Foucault, Roland Barthes, and Jean Baudrillard, among others. As a result, in the second half of the twentieth century in literature, cinema, politics, anthropology, feminist discourse, and technology studies, the reign of universal Man has been called into question and dismantled philosophically. Searching for a new vision of humanity, the theorist Donna Haraway has issued the "Cyborg Manifesto,"[42] as a postgender, posthumanist, postmodern, postfamilial, and postnatural reality, blurring

---

[39] Ibid., 152.

[40] Neil Badmington (ed.), *Posthumanism* (New York: Palgrave, 2000); idem, "Theorizing Posthumanism," *Cultural Critique* 53 (2003): 11-27; Elaine L. Graham, *Representations of the Post/Human* (Manchester University Press, 2002); Cary Wolfe, *What is Transhumanism?* (Minneapolis: University of Minnesota, 2010). For a discussion of "cultural transhumanists," see Andy Miah, "A Critical History of Posthumanism, in *Medical Enhancement and Posthumanity*, ed. Bert Gordijn and Ruth Chadwick (Springer, 2008), 71-94, esp. pp. 77-79.

[41] Kate Soper, *Humanism and Anti-Humanism* (Chicago: Open Court Publishing Co., 1986.), 11-12; cited in Neil Badmington (ed.), *Posthumanism* (New York: Palgrave, 2000), 2.

[42] The word *cyborg*—cybernetic organism—was coined in 1960 by physiologist Manfred Clynes and psychiatrist Nathan Kline to describe a man-machine hybrid needed for a space travel. Later the term was "expanded to cover human/machine weapons systems." Currently considerable funding is given to developing brain-machine interfaces, namely, "technologies that use brain signals to control mechanical and electronic devised that can also send feedback signals to the brain." See Dinello, *Technophobia!* 115 and 118.

the traditional distinctions between humans and animals and between humans and machines.[43] Philosophical reflection about the "posthuman condition" thus takes place among literary critics, especially those who study the genre of science fiction in film, literature, television, and computer games, since the genre of science fiction serves as social criticism and popular philosophy.

The above overview of transhumanism indicates that it is not easy to engage transhumanism: transhumanists do not speak in one voice, and the movement expresses a variety of impulses, which are often at odds with each other. Nonetheless, several themes are common to transhumanist discourse: the view of evolving human nature, the focus on biotechnological enhancement that will exceed ordinary human physical and cognitive traits, a preoccupation with human happiness that can be perpetuated indefinitely, a deep concern for longevity and radical life extension, and a technoutopia of human-machine fusion that constitutes practical immortality. Each of these themes has generated considerable debates, as indicated by the essays of this volume. Drawing on the deliberations at ASU and my own work as a Jewish intellectual historian, I will engage these themes. Without trying to be exhaustive, I will illustrate that while transhumanism as a sociointellectual movement is marginal, the transhumanist discourse raises crucial issues about the meaning of being human in our contemporary technoculture.

TRANSHUMANISM AND THE MEANING OF HUMAN NATURE

At the heart of the debate on transhumanism stands the notion of evolving human nature. Julian Huxley already believed that when people come to fully appreciate the implications of the theory of evolution, they would realize "man's destiny in the world process." According to Huxley, mankind is "the dominant portion of this planet and the agent responsible for its future revolution,[44] and he urged his readers "to utilize all available knowledge in giving guidance and encouragement for the continuing adventure of human development."[45] These ideas are clearly echoed in Nick Bostrom's understanding of human nature when he states as follows:

> Transhumanists view human nature as a work-in-progress, a half baked beginning that we can learn to remold in desirable ways. Current humanity need not be the endpoint of evolution. Transhumanists hope

---

43   Donna Haraway, *Simians, Cyborgs, and Women: The Reinvention of Nature* (London: Free Association Books, 1991). The "Cyborg Manifesto" was originally published under a slightly different title in 1985.

44   Julian Huxley, "The Humanist Frame," in his *Evolutionary Humanism*, 79.

45   Julian Huxley, "Eugenics in Evolutionary Perspective," in *Evolutionary Humanism*, 287.

that by responsible use of science, technology, and other rational means, we shall eventually manage to become posthuman, beings with vastly greater capacities than present human beings have.

Bostrom's view of human nature is shared by Gregory Stock, who heads the Center for the Study of Evolution and the Origin of Life in UCLA and who similarly states that "the human species is moving out of its childhood." According to Stock,

it is time for us to acknowledge our growing powers and begin to take responsibility for them. We have little choice in this, for we have begun to play god in so many of life's intimate realms that we probably could not turn back if we tried."[46]

The transhumanist notion that human nature is malleable has generated serious criticism from political thinkers, ethicists, and theologians, including Francis Fukuyama, Ronald Cole-Turner, Leon Kass, Eric Parens, Jean Betke Elshtain, and Langdon Winner, among many others.[47] Winner, for example, has criticized Gregory Stock for equating "taking responsibility" with "recognizing the inevitability" of the development of a new species and because he advocates the use of genetic engineering to move the human organism beyond what Stock considers "its present decrepit condition."[48] A central feature of transhumanism, then, is the claim that

---

[46]   Gregory Stock, *Metaman: The Making of Humans and Machines into a Global Superorganism* (New York: Simon and Schuster, 1993), introduction; cf., *Redesigning Humans: Choosing Our Genes, Changing our Futures* (Boston and New York: Houghton Mifflin Company, 2003).

[47]   The most famous critics of transhumanism are Francis Fukuyama and Leon Kass. See Francis Fukuyma, *Our Posthuman Future: Consequences of the Biotechnology Revolution* (New York: Farrar, Strauss & Giroux, 2002); and Leon Kass, *Life, Liberty, and the Defense of Dignity: The Challenge for Bioethics* (San Francisco: Encounter Books, 2002). For a succinct summary of arguments against human enhancement consult Michael J. Sandel, *The Case against Perfection: Ethics in the Age of Genetic Engineering* (Cambridge, MA: Harvard University Press, 2007). For philosophical and religious reflections on the usefulness of the concept of "human nature," see Harold W. Baillie and Timothy K. Casey, *Is Human Nature Obsolete? Genetic, Bioengineering and the Future of the Human Condition* (Cambridge, MA, and London, England: MIT Press, 2005). The contributors to this volume represent many of the leading critics of biotechnology.

[48]   Langdon Winner, "Resistance is Futile: The Posthuman Condition and Its Advocates," in *Is Human Nature Obsolete?* 187.

human nature is not fixed and that the future of humanity is malleable because of the "dramatic progress in technological capabilities." It is technology that will enable humans to transform themselves gradually into persons whose capacities will exceed what we today recognize by the term *human*. For the advocates of transhumanism, such development is entirely welcome.

Whereas the above critics allusively referred to *human dignity* as that which distinguishes humans from all other animals, evolutionary psychologists have offered the most serious scientific defense of the notion of human nature. For evolutionary psychologists such as John Tooby, Leda Cosmides, and David Buss,[49] human nature is *not* a social construct but a reality that emerged from the long evolutionary process and that therefore should not be tinkered with technologically. Tooby and Cosmides often speak of "psychological universals that constitute human nature,"[50] and another proponent of evolutionary psychology, Steven Pinker, defines human nature as "the endowment of cognitive and emotional faculties that is universal to healthy members of the Homo sapiens."[51] According to Pinker, all human beings share a universal human nature despite differences among individuals, races, and sexes, since these differences too are also in our nature.

Cosmides and Tooby, Templeton co-fellows at ASU in 2006-2007, hold that the normal makeup of human minds is a result of evolution by natural selection.[52] Their major finding is that the human mind "has evolved a specialized machinery that is designed to carry out specific tasks."[53] For this reason, Cosmides objects to germ-line genetic engineering, which will alter "what defines a human personality . . . [because it] affects the control system of the body and alters complex, exquisitely well-designed mental mechanisms that have been engineered

---

[49] See David M. Buss, *Evolutionary Psychology: The New Science of the Mind* (Boston: Allyn and Bacon, 1999); Jerome H. Barkow, Leda Cosmides and John Tooby (eds.), *The Adapted Mind: Evolutionary Psychology and the Generation of Culture* (New York: Oxford University Press, 1992).

[50] John Tooby and Leda Cosmides, "On the University of Human Nature and the Uniqueness of the Individual: The Role of Genetics and Adaptation, *Journal of Personality* 58 (1990): 17-67; citation on p. 18.

[51] Steven Pinker, *The Blank Slate: The Modern Denial of Human Nature* (New York: Penguin Books, 2002), 142.

[52] See Jerome H. Barkow, Leda Cosmides, and John Tooby (eds.), *The Adapted Mind: Evolutionary Psychology and the Generation of Culture* (New York: Oxford University Press, 1992).

[53] For full exposition of this claim see Leda Cosmides and John Tooby, "The Modular Nature of Human Intelligence," in A. B. Scheibel and J. W. Schopf (eds.), *The Origin and Evolution of Intelligence* (Sudbury, MA: Jones and Bartlett, 1997), 71-101.

by the evolutionary process to solve problems of survival and reproduction."[54] Human intervention in the evolutionary process may produce humans with greater-than-human intelligence, but we do not know what will be the unintended consequences of such intervention.

Given this understanding of human nature, evolutionary psychologists tend to be critical of the transhumanist project. Tooby identifies two strands within transhumanism: the Enlightenment strand and the Romantic strand. The former is an extension of the eighteenth-century Enlightenment Project, and it involves the attempts by science and technology to improve the human condition. Viewed from this perspective, transhumanism is not as novel as it seems, since all of us are already augmented beings if we take into considerations the many technological advancements over the centuries that have transformed who we are. Thus, agriculture, writings, postal services, navigation, calculus, antibiotics, radio, television, photography, and computers are all technological innovations that have shaped who we are, and it is reasonable to assume that we will continue to be augmented by future technologies. So long as transhumanism simply advocates the nineteenth-century commitment to progress and alleviation of human suffering, it is hard to critique it.

However, transhumanism becomes much more problematic from an evolutionary perspective when it predicts a dramatic change in the human species due to technological enhancement. It is this claim that evolutionary psychology disputes because of the way in which the human brain has evolved to perform certain tasks, and because we are still largely ignorant about the operation of the brain. Tooby thus urges us to ask the simple but crucial question: "what is the goal of technological change?" and he correctly warns us to be careful not to confuse evolution with progress. Tooby notes that evolution is also capricious, cruel, and random; and that we are the effects of biochemical natural selection that has produced things we hate (for example, infanticide). The case of infanticide shows that human nature is real: the mind is not a blank slate but rather a computational structure that is full of mechanisms that have been selected over a long evolutionary process of adaptation. Therefore, Tooby encourages scientists to continue to map the mechanism of the adapted mind and its specific programs before we naively embrace the projects of transhumanism. At present, we do not even know what it means to have a thought, and therefore the transhumanist vision of uploading the thought content of our personality should not be taken too seriously.

Transhumanists can respond to evolutionary psychologists by saying that the field is built on a contradiction: if humanity has indeed evolved overtime, there is

---

[54]   Quoted from interview with Leda Cosmides, "Are we Already Transhuman?" in the Newsletter of the Arizona State University Center for the Study of Religion and Conflict (Spring 2007).

no reason to freeze the process and say that the way humans behave nowadays is immune to the ongoing evolutionary pressures. One can also raise doubts about the concept of universal "human nature" as understood by evolutionary psychologists and charge that it is no more than a "superstition."[55] What evolutionary psychology seems to reject, however, is not the notion that humanity can in principle be transformed over a very long period of time in response to evolutionary pressures, but rather the accelerated, humanly designed and implemented tinkering with the results of the slow evolutionary process as practiced by contemporary biotechnology and advocated by transhumanists. It is this "designer evolution," as Simon Young called it, that evolutionary psychologists consider problematic because it will tinker with the slow process of evolution.

TRANSHUMANISM AND THE CONTEMPORARY TECHNOCULTURAL MOMENT

To the extent that transhumanist ideology expresses the belief that the human condition can be improved by science and technology, transhumanism is an extension of the Enlightenment Project. Any engagement with transhumanism requires a serious reflection about technology and its role in shaping culture. The list of human technological innovations is very long indeed, including fire, the wheel, pottery, the domestication of plants and animals, metallurgy, glass, the printing press, the steam engine, the telegraph, and the personal computer, among others. Yet the word *technology* was seldom used before 1880. Leo Marx notes that "*The Oxford English Dictionary* cites R. F. Burton's use of 'technology' in 1859 to refer to 'practical arts collectively' as the earliest English instance of the inclusive modern usage."[56] It was only in the mid-nineteenth century, at the midst of the Industrial Revolution, that technology came to be used synonymously with *machine technology* and be seen as a distinguishing feature of modernity brought about by the Industrial Revolution.

---

[55]   A serious critique of evolutionary psychology is articulated by David J. Buller, *Adapting Minds: Evolutionary Psychology and the Persistent Quest for Human Nature* (Cambridge, MA, and London, England: MIT Press, 2005), esp. 419-480. Buller charges that the concept of human nature is inherently confused and that if evolutionary psychologists take evolution seriously, they must accept the notion that humans will continue to evolve. According to Buller, "there is no basis in evolutionary theory for maintaining that psychological adaptations are constitutive of human 'nature'" (ibid., 476).

[56]   Leo Marx, "The Idea of Technology and Postmodern Pessimism," in *Does Technology Drive History: The Dilemma of Technological Determinism*, ed. Merritt Roe Smith and Leo Marx (Cambridge, Mass.: MIT Press, 1994), p. 247.

The notion that science and technology are powerful agents of social change stood at the heart of the Enlightenment's idea of progress; but today, in the beginning of the twenty-first century, human beings find themselves in a totally new situation in which the intellectual assumptions of the Enlightenment are woefully inadequate, a point articulated most forcefully by Braden Allenby, a Templeton fellow at ASU in 2007-2008.[57] Today the developments in genetics, nanotechnology, and robotics seem to generate a new human condition in which the Enlightenment separation between observer and observed, subjective and objective, knower and known no longer applies. The new genetics enables us to enhance our biological state; nanotechnology enables us to manipulate materials on an atomic scale; and robotics not only replaces the human brain with nonbiological computing power, which will exceed the human brain, but also facilitates the integration of biological and information technology.

These new technologies carry broad cultural implications because technological evolution can destabilize clusters and create conditions leading to the evolution of new ones; technology is the means by which humans have expressed their will to power, and the rate of technological change is accelerating dramatically and extends the gaps between elites and those who have no access to technological advances. The current technological revolution challenges the Enlightenment paradigm and relates to the postmodern fragmentation of time, space, and culture. Transhumanism can be viewed as the expression of a broad technological wave, which challenges mental models, cultural constructs, institutional systems and human relationships with them all. Allenby convincingly holds that to address these challenges we need a new intellectual paradigm that genuinely embraces the complexity and uncertainty of the contemporary human condition.

Transhumanism indeed provokes engagement with all the ambiguity and ambivalence of technological progress, but only time will tell if a comprehensive intellectual paradigm will emerge to address the new technoculture. As we grapple with these issues, we need to maintain the appropriate perspective from which to assess the current technocultural moment. Daniel Sarewitz, the Templeton co-fellow of Braden Allenby at ASU in 2007-2008, [58] has noted that, in a world saturated

---

[57] See Braden Allenby, "The Industrial Ecology of Emerging Technologies: Complexity and the Reconstruction of the World," *Journal of Industrial Ecology* 13, no. 2 (2009): 168-183. Allenby developed this point in his Templeton Lecture, "From Human to Transhuman: Technology and the Reconstruction of the World," delivered at ASU on October 23, 2007, as part of the project "Facing the Challenges of Transhumanism." He continues to elaborate these ideas in his forthcoming book, coauthored with Daniel Sarewitz, *The Techno-Human Condition* (Cambridge, Mass.: The MIT Press, 2010).

[58] Daniel Sarewitz, "Technology and the Culture of Progress," Lecture delivered at ASU on April 24, 2008. His ideas are expressed in fuller version in the book he coauthored by Braden Allenby cited in the preceding note.

with technology, we make decisions about new technologies on the basis of what actually works and does not work, and there is no way to determine in advance which technologies will actually evolve. However, the assessment of technological innovation is always relative to a certain current technological state rather than relative to some pretechnological or nontechnological state. Technology should also be linked to human will rather than to human rationality, since it enables us to accomplish what we want to do. Any given technology is thus always part of some systematic complexity that embodies some irrationality and dysfunction, and all technologies have a likelihood of unintended consequences. Since many technologies attempt to create a human ability to do something better than could be done without that technology, it is important to reflect on the claims of transhumanism in favor of human enhancement.

What exactly does it mean for people to be "enhanced"? In light of the works of Jacques Ellul, Langdon Winner, and Lewis Mumford,[59] Sarewitz suggests that we need to bring technological systems that we create under our more direct, effective, and democratic control. He soberly argues that "in reality there is no easy path to addressing fundamental challenges, but technologies can sometimes help find a shortcut to dealing with some of the particular consequences of these challenges." It is thus wrong for transhumanists to pose a chasm between two technological futures, one utopian, the other dystopian. Rather, we need to realize that "there is a scale of experience where one does not have to give up one's sophistication about the complexity of the world to accept the possibility of modest yet encouraging technological progress." Humans as a species have an innate capacity to technologically innovate: we perceive difficulties, and we employ physical artifacts to get around these difficulties. But as we solve a particular problem, we also give rise to new types of problems. The challenge to human beings is to be continually attentive and to realize that human inventiveness through technology does not offer a cure to political problems and vice versa. Politics is never the cure for technology; they need each other. The essays in this volume, presented originally at a workshop at ASU, offer deep reflections on transhumanism and technoculture.

TRANSHUMANISM AND THE PURSUIT OF HAPPINESS

To engage transhumanism from a religious perspective is challenging because transhumanism is an outgrowth of modern humanism. As such, transhumanism is secular, rationalist, individualistic, and concerned with the attainment of individual

---

[59]   Jacques Ellul, *The Technological Society* (New York: Vintage Books, 1964); Langdon Winner, *Autonomous Technology: Technics-out-of-Control as a Theme in Political Thought* (Cambridge, MA: MIT Press, 1977); and Mumford Lewis, *Technics and Civilization*, 2nd ed. (New York: Harcourt, Brace & World, 1963).

happiness. The pursuit of happiness, of course, has been a major concern of humanity and a major feature of western thought, at least since ancient Greek philosophy.[60] Happiness, or human well-being and flourishing, was understood by Greek and Hellenistic philosophers to be an objective standard that organizes all human activities into a meaningful pattern for the duration of one's life. According to Aristotle, the first to offer systematic analysis of the concept of happiness (in Greek, *eudaimonia*), happiness is not an affect or a subjective feeling but an *objective state* that expresses human nature, and to be happy means to flourish and experience well-being in accord with the nature of the human species.[61] Aristotle regarded reason as the distinguishing marks of humanity and concluded that to be happy, or to flourish as a human being, necessitates the actualization of the human potential to know abstract, necessary, and eternal truths. The highest kind of reasoning, according to Aristotle, is the kind of reasoning that belongs to God, a thought thinking itself eternally.

When Greek and Hellenistic reflections on happiness were integrated into monotheistic religions—first Judaism, later Islam, and finally Christianity—the pursuit of happiness was given a decidedly religious interpretation even when analyzed philosophically, illustrating the integration of science and religion characteristic of the premodern era.[62] In the modern period, however, the secularization of the Christian West and the scientific revolution gave rise to materialism and naturalism and the dissociation of science and religion. In the seventeenth and eighteenth centuries, happiness came to be identified with

---

[60] For an overview of the discourse on happiness in western culture see Darrin MacMahon, *Happiness: A History* (New York: Atlantic Monthly Press, 2006). In the past decade a new academic discipline emerged known as Happiness Studies. The discipline combines Positive Psychology, Social Psychology, and Cognitive Science. Main contributors to the discipline include: Ruut Veenhoven. *Conditions of Happiness* (Dordrecht: Reidel, 1984); Michael Eysenck, *Happiness: Facts and Myths* (London: Lawrence Erlbauum, 1990); Ed Diener and E. M. Suh (eds.), *Culture and Subjective Well-Being* (Cambridge MA: MIT Press, 1998); Michael Argyle, *The Psychology of Happiness* (New York: Taylor and Francis, 2001); and Martin Seligman, *Authentic Happiness* (New York: Simon and Schuster, 2002).

[61] The secondary literature on Aristotle's analysis of happiness is too large to be cited here. Most useful are Richard Kraut, *Aristotle on the Human Good* (Princeton: Princeton University Press, 1989); John M. Cooper, *Reason and Human Good in Aristotle* (Indianapolis: Hackett Publishing, 1986); Sarah Broadie, *Ethics with Aristotle* (New York: Oxford University Press, 1991).

[62] For analysis of this process, consult Hava Tirosh-Samuelson, *Happiness in Premodern Judaism: Virtue, Knowledge and Well-Being* (Cincinnati: Hebrew Union College Press, 2003).

well-being. By the nineteenth century, this idea would give rise to utilitarianism and its calculus of happiness as a balance between pleasure and pain for the greatest number of people. Moving away from the eudaimonistic conception of happiness, the utilitarians defined happiness subjectively. For Jeremy Bentham, for example, pleasure is the only good and pain is the only evil; pleasure and pain determine what we do, and it is only the scientific analysis of the balance between them that leads to happiness, requiring no recourse to religious belief. Occasionally, Bentham used the phrase "the greatest happiness of the greatest number," but he explicitly corrected this, saying that he meant the greatest total sum of happiness.[63]

As science and religion were gradually pulled apart from each other during the nineteenth century, a strictly materialistic and hedonic notion of happiness prevailed: happiness is a subjective, mental state of individuals closely akin to joy and inherently associated with a range of pleasures. In a capitalistic setting, the hedonic notion of happiness means that happiness was reduced increasingly to possession of material goods or the instant gratification of bodily cravings. The discoveries of chemical substances (legal or illegal) that control moods and mental states further trivialized the pursuit of happiness. As neuroscientists have unraveled the chemical processes of the brain, they have enabled the pharmaceutical industry to produce chemical substances that control, alleviate, or change moods and emotions. Under the impact of the brain sciences, both happiness and unhappiness are now viewed strictly in materialist terms: a pill presumably makes one attain happiness or alleviate unhappiness. By the beginning of the twenty-first century, a strict materialist approach to happiness prevails.

The Transhumanist Declaration does not discuss "happiness" directly, but if one peruses the literature generated by Max More, the founder of the Extropy Institute, one can immediately detect how this conception of happiness undergirds the entire project. Max More defines *extropy* as "the extent of a living or organizational system's intelligence, functional order, vitality, and capacity and drive for improvement" and *extropic* are the "actions, qualities, or outcomes that embody or further extropy." According to More, extropy "is not a real entity or force, but only metaphor representing all that contributes to our flourishing," in other words, happiness. The principles of extropy enumerated by More include: "perpetual progress, self transformation, practical optimism, intelligent technology, open society in terms of information and democracy, self-direction, and rational thinking."[64] Like other promoters of transhumanism, Max More emphasizes how the pace of change—technological, cultural, and economic—continues to accelerate and to reach deeper. For him advances in technologies (including "social

---

[63]   Jeremy Bentham, *An Introduction to the Principles of Morals and Legislation* (1789), ed. J. H. Burns and H. L. A. Hart (Oxford: Clarendon Press, 1996).

[64]   Cited on the Web site of the Extropy Institute.

technologies" of knowledge management, learning, and decision making) will enable us to change human nature itself in its physical, emotional, and intellectual aspects. More predicts that, with better knowledge and decision making, humans could live far longer in better than "perfect" health, improve their self-knowledge and awareness of interpersonal dynamics; overcome cultural, psychological, and mimetic biases in thinking; enhance intelligence in all its various forms; and learn to thrive on change and growth. In short, humans will finally be happy.

The transhumanist approach to the pursuit of happiness is problematic for the following reasons. First, the transhumanist notion is an extension of the hedonic understanding of happiness characteristic of nineteenth-century utilitarianism. Focusing on self-fulfillment, transhumanists do not take seriously the connection between happiness and virtue, which was central to the premodern analysis of human happiness.

Virtue is a character trait that humans must cultivate in order to flourish as human beings. The transhumanist discourse has no use for the concept of virtue and the ethos of self-control and character formation that accompany it because it takes happiness to be a product of engineering. Transhumanists talk a lot about life satisfaction, self-fulfillment, and self-realization, but they have not provided an analysis of the relationship between the subjective and objective aspects of happiness. A more rigorous analysis of the meaning of happiness that lies at the foundation of the transhumanist project is needed. When that is undertaken, the shallowness of the technoparadise of heaven on earth will become clear.

Beyond the lack of clarity, the hedonic understanding of happiness is problematic on scientific grounds because it is materialistic and reductionistic. Reducing mind to brain functions, transhumanists use the metaphor of the computer to explain how the mind works, but as Pinker has already argued persuasively, this metaphor has serious shortcomings. The human brain is much more than a computational machine; it is part of a highly complex and integrated organism that takes into account not only the nervous system but also the immune system, as well as the sociocultural context in which we are embedded. If happiness concerns the flourishing of the individual as a whole, happiness cannot be reduced just to the functioning of the body as we encounter it in transhumanist literature. Nor can we reduce the human self just to brain functions of neurons that communicate using chemical messengers, neurotransmitters, and neuromodulators via synaptic transmission. We need a more holistic understanding of the human self than the one presupposed by transhumanism.

But the most troubling aspect of the transhumanist approach to happiness is the notion that technology will allow us to produce pleasant sensations all the time. The ability to manipulate the molecules and electrical impulses in the brain is reaching a new, sophisticated level due to precise brain scanning, and soon neural implants, which are now treating people with Parkinson's disease, will someday jolt regions of the brain to induce or suppress specific emotions. It is this specter of transhumanism which makes me most uneasy because it ignores the value of insecurity, anxiety, and uncertainty, which are very much part of being human. Human culture (especially art and philosophy) could not have been possible without these allegedly negative aspects of being human. But if chemicals root out these human abilities, what will be the source of creativity? Hedonic engineering is not a prescription for cultural depth and creativity; it is a prescription for childish shallowness that regards having fun and feeling good above all other values. That transhumanism perpetuates the youth culture that has prevailed in America becomes more evident once we examine the third main concern of transhumanism, namely, radical life extension.

TRANSHUMANISM AND RADICAL LIFE EXTENSION

Extending human life and postponing death is a prominent goal of the transhumanist movement. Anti-aging medicine is now the fastest-growing medical specialty in the United States.[65] This reflects the enormous scientific advances that have been made in understanding the causes of aging in which genetic, environmental, and lifestyle factors contribute to the symptoms of aging, such as loss of strength and mobility, decreased cognitive ability, decreased energy and vitality, decreased sexual response, joint pain, skin aging, weight gain, and other diseases such as heart disease, diabetes, cancer, etc. The goal of the anti-aging program is to grow older without becoming aged. There are many theories about the process of aging, and since I am a nonspecialist in the field of gerontology, I cannot judge the validity of the various scientific claims in this field. I focus on Aubrey de Grey's *Ending Aging: The Rejuvenation Breakthroughs That Could Reverse Human Aging in Our Lifetime* (2007) because he is a leading transhumanist who promotes radical life extension.

De Grey sees aging as a "humanitarian crisis" (36). He defines aging as a "deadly pandemic disease" (78) and calls us all to declare a "war on aging" (312), analogous to the "war on cancer" declared in 1970. For de Grey, aging is "an enemy" because "it saps our strength and ability to enjoy life, [it] cripples us, and eventually kills us," as de Grey's website puts it. Seeing himself as a "crusader" against aging, De Grey frames the problem of aging as an engineer and even calls himself "anti-aging engineer" (250). De Grey predicts that main breakthroughs will come from biomedical gerontological research, which he conducts under the title of Strategies for Engineered Negligible Senescence (SENS).

---

[65]　A typical example of this literature is Philip Lee Miller and the Life Extension Foundation with Monica Reinagel, *Life Extension Revolution: The New Science of Growing Older without Aging* (New York: Bantam Books, 2005). For a critical overview of this industry, see Stephen S. Hall, *Merchants of Immortality: Chasing the Dream of Human Life Extension* (Boston and New York: Houghton Mifflin Company, 2003).

For de Grey the problem of aging lies in mitochondrial mutations caused by free radicals. Articulating "a complete, detailed and consistent scenario to explain the link between mitochondrial free radicals and the increase in oxidative stress throughout the body with aging," (74) he explains how the cell is taken over by defective mitochondria and proposes the postponement of aging by the following strategies: First, he focuses on eliminating the telomere-related mechanisms that lead to cancer by selectively modifying our telomere elongation genes by tissue type using targeted gene therapies. Second, the program is interested in the mitochondrial DNA outside the cellular nucleus, which accumulates damage with age and thus impairs its critical function. De Grey suggests using gene therapy to copy mitochondrial DNA in the cellular nucleus and other strategies for manipulating and remapping mitochondrial DNA in situ. This is the most innovative part of de Grey's program because it promises "to put these mutations 'beyond use' of harm." He writes, "This could be accomplished by putting *backup copies* of the genes that are currently housed in the mitochondria in the safe haven of the cell's nucleus, far from the constant bombardment of free radicals from the mitochondrion itself" (83). With a nuclear backup copy of these genes, any such mutation would be rendered functionally irrelevant because the cell would be able to keep producing the proteins that the knocked-out genes in the mitochondrion had previously encoded. A third aspect of the aging process is the protein outside our cells such as those vital to artery walls and skin elasticity. Research is now underway for suitable enzymes or compounds to break down problem proteins that the body cannot handle. A fourth area of research focuses on certain classes of senescent cells that accumulate where they are not wanted, for example, in the joints. De Grey proposes to use immune therapies to tailor our immune systems to destroy cells as they become senescent and thus prevent any related problems. Further research into the biochemistry of "junk material" that accumulates outside the cells will facilitate immune therapies (vaccines). De Grey and other scientists also envision searching for suitable nontoxic microbial enzymes in soil bacteria that could be safely introduced into human cells.

I find de Grey's vision of radical life extension problematic for the following reasons. First, it is important to note that although de Grey defines aging as a disease and considers it a humanitarian crisis, he approaches the problem not as a physician interested in healing but as an engineer who is interested in fixing a mechanical problem. Not coincidentally, the dominant metaphor of de Grey's program is the vintage car: as much as a vintage car can continue to run many years beyond the initial design of the car, provided the car undergoes periodic, expensive maintenance, so can the human being postpone death indefinitely by undergoing periodic regenerations. Viewing the human body as a "resilient machine" that requires long-term care is problematic because human beings are not just machines, although some aspects of human somatic operation bear some resemblance to them. The car metaphor indicates that, for de Grey and other transhumanists, humans are no more than a sum of their physiological processes, which are entirely mechanistic, knowable, and controllable. At some point, de Grey actually admits that there is much about the human body that we still do not know, but he is convinced that, in principle, with future research we will be able to know all we need to perpetuate life indefinitely. Through periodic gene therapy, we will be able to grow old without aging, actualizing the dream of remaining young forever. This for de Grey is a compelling vision of humanity that justifies putting all our resources into the "war on aging."

Second, I am not convinced that aging per se should be viewed as a disease that kills us, even though it is true that, as we age, we become more susceptible to diseases. Since the human is an *organism* rather than a mechanical device, human beings undergo the cycle of birth, maturation, aging, and death, which exemplifies the rhythm of creation and the gift of life. All organisms experience aging and death precisely because they are alive, and the gift of life is not less precious because it is finite but more so. Moreover, the process of aging does not merely have negative but also positive aspects, since we gain wisdom with age as we encounter the challenges of growing frail and losing vigor. With aging comes the wisdom of compassion, acceptance, and forgiveness that are hard to attain when the good life is defined in terms of having fun or feeling perpetual pleasure. Life is lived more deeply and richly if we are aware of our mortality and finitude; we make decisions differently, and we live less wantonly and superficially with the awareness of death than without it.

But more poignantly, it is not clear to me what exactly will be the purpose of indefinite postponement of death. What will people live for if they live indefinitely? What is human life going to be about for the extended duration of 150 or 500 years? Will human life consist of more consumerist activities, more entertainment, more "fun," more wars, more destruction of the natural environment, and more boredom? I wonder. Needless to say, to the extent that longevity research promotes ways to alleviate the suffering caused by debilitating diseases such as Alzheimer's and Parkinson's, they are all very beneficial. However, I also believe that all programs about extension of human life cannot be divorced from deeper reflection on the *purpose* of human life. Such reflection seems to be missing from the transhumanist literature, although in recent years, some of the promoters of transhumanism have paid attention to issues of human rights to give the transhumanist movement a strong democratic commitment. One could object and say that human life should *not* have a purpose, since mere living is itself a blessing that does not require further justification. This point is well taken, but I would suggest that it is precisely because so many people today (especially in Western, post-industrialized nations) live without a sense of purpose or commitment to a task that can ennoble life as a whole that so many experience boredom, emptiness, and meaninglessness, which generate destructive behavior toward self and others. The specter of perpetuating the current anomie indefinitely through periodic genetic engineering seems to be a very undesirable outcome for humanity.

From the vantage point of the Jewish tradition at least, the ideal of indefinite postponement of death is the highest form of human hubris, one more example of human rebellion against God who created humans as finite beings whose life narrative has a beginning, a middle, and an end. Instead of extending our physical lives forever, it will be more beneficial if we make sure that our life stories have meaning and that they are instructive to others. These life stories include emotional, social, aesthetic, and spiritual dimensions that prove we are more than "resilient machines." It is this allusive and ineffable "more" that we must honor and dignify, not because it belongs to a disembodied substance called "soul," but because this "more" is inseparable from our being created as finite, embodied human beings who are extended in space while having a unique capacity to transcend their embodied, spatial temporality and feel concerned about future generations. It is this embodiment that transhumanism seeks to transcend in its most radical program of cyberimmortality.

TRANSHUMANISM AS AN ESCHATOLOGICAL VISION

The most radical aspect of transhumanism is the scenario that humans will be able to transport the content of their brains, their minds, to a nonbiological entity and thereby achieve immortality. Kurzweil and other transhumanist visionaries imagine a "brain-porting scenario" that will involve "scanning a human brain capturing all of the *salient details.*" This will entail reinstantiating the brain's state in a different—most likely much more powerful—computational substrate. According to Kurzweil this will be a feasible procedure and will happen most likely around the late 2030s.[66] In this scenario "we will continue to have human bodies, but they will become *morphable projections of our intelligence.* Such "software-based humans," he predicts, "will be vastly extended beyond the severe limitations of humans as we know them today. They will live out on the Web, projecting bodies whenever they need or want them, including virtual bodies in diverse realms of virtual reality, holographically projected bodies, foglet-projected bodies, and physical bodies comprising nanobot swarms and other forms of nanotechnology."[67] For Kurzweil, this is a form of immortality, although he concedes that the data and information do not last forever; the longevity of information depends on its relevance, utility, and accessibility.

According to Kurzweil, here lies the meaning of transcendence, which he takes literally to mean "to go beyond," that is, "to go beyond the ordinary powers of the material world through the power of patterns."[68] Yes, the body, the hardware

---

[66]   Raymond Kurzweil, *The Singularity Is Near* (New York: Viking, 2005), 324.

[67]   Ibid., 325.

[68]   Ibid., 388.

of the human computer, will die; but the software of our lives, our personal "mind file" will continue to live on the Web in the posthuman futures where holographic avatars will interact with others without bodies. For Kurzweil, uploading ourselves to a human-made machine is spiritual because it will exhibit complexity, elegance, knowledge, intelligence, beauty, creativity, and levels of subtle attributes such as love. While Kurzweil is reluctant to talk about his own personal belief in God, he does assert that "evolution moves inexorably toward this conception of God, although never quite reaching this ideal."[69]

How do we make sense of the transhumanist vision of the eschatological future? Should we simply dismiss this vision, or should we engage it historically, philosophically, and ethically? I recommend that we do the latter. Historically speaking, the vision of the eschatological end as immortality of the intellect is not new; it was articulated already in the Middle Ages by Muslim and Jewish thinkers, most notably by Ibn Rushd (d. 1198) and by Maimonides (d. 1204), who followed Aristotle's conception of God as a mind that thinks itself eternally. Following Aristotle, these thinkers indeed understood God as a thought that thinks itself eternally and envisioned that very developed human minds (the minds of outstanding philosopher-prophets) will reach such perfect knowledge, and such minds will experience the bliss of immortality, an infinite intellectual activity unencumbered by the corporeal body.

Does that mean that Maimonides was the first transhumanist? Not really. Yes, Maimonides did believe that it is possible for some humans to be outstanding in knowledge and understanding of the structure of reality, and he clearly believed that the prophet Moses was such an individual.[70] However, Maimonides did not think that Moses was God, nor did he identify Moses with the separate intellects, the philosophic version of the traditional beliefs in angels. Moses was in a class of his own among humans, but he was neither an angel nor God; Moses remained human and was able to translate his profound understanding into laws that guide human action. In other words, even in regard to Moses, Maimonides was clear not to erase the boundaries between the human and the divine, and to acknowledge the humanity of Moses. But it is precisely the boundary between the human and the divine that transhumanism, in its hubris, seeks to erase as it imagines the fusion between human and intelligent machines.

What is problematic about this vision of technologically-based immortality? First, it is quite problematic to talk about humans as "software-based" entities. While Kurzweil and others think about humans in terms of patterns, human identity and idiosyncratic personalities cannot be reduced to these patterns of information,

---

[69]   Ibid., 389.

[70]   For a full discussion of Maimonides's view of happiness, see Hava Tirosh-Samuelson, *Happiness in Premodern Judaism*, 192-245.

because each one of us is distinctive and unique, an Other who cannot be reduced to sameness. This point was raised already in the thirteenth century during the debate about Maimonides's legacy, and it has been developed philosophically in a profound manner by Emmanuel Levinas.[71] Andy Miah has used Levinas to buttress the notion that "the histories of posthumanism consist in an ongoing undecidability over the values of transgressing boundaries, in some cases as they relate to biological change."[72] But such appropriation of Levinas is misleading since it is precisely the *face* of the Other, the source of moral obligation, according to Levinas, that contemporary technological culture threatens to efface.

Several Christian theologians have critiqued the transhumanist vision of cybernetic immortality as a return to premodern substance dualism. The notion that information patterns can exist as disembodied intelligent entities is but another name to the premodern notion of the disembodied soul. But this notion is problematic both scientifically and theologically, as Ted Peters has already noted.[73] Scientifically is it problematic because "the brains and hence minds are embodied, perhaps even communal," and theologically it is problematic because transhumanism presupposes a dualistic view of the human, which denigrates the human body, considering it as an evil that should be combated and fixed by use of technology. The vision of cybernetic immortality, advanced by Kurzweil or Frank Tipler, fails to appreciate the wisdom of our finite, created body and the implications of theology of createdness. Even if uploading our personality to a machine were possible, which is highly doubtful, is it the spiritual vision we want to promote? Isn't this spiritual vision rather impoverished precisely because the machine is but a human product? As Noreen Herzfeld has observed, the transcendence depicted by transhumanists is no more than prolongation of a materially based human product. In the transhumanist vision of cybernetic immortality, eternity simply means a "very long time," rather than a fundamentally different kind of existence.[74]

More troubling is the notion that humans can actually achieve the eschatological ideal. Here I am speaking as a Jew who is committed to the pursuit of the ideal rather than to its realization. The pursuit of the ideal endows life with meaning and gives life direction, but when the prescription is taken as a description of a state of affairs, disasters lurk. The description of the eschatological end as envisioned by transhumanism fills me not with beauty and elegance but with horror and disgust.

---

[71]   Levinas and an explanation of the word *facing* in the title of the project.

[72]   Andy Miha, "A Critical History of Posthumanism," in *Medical Enhancement and Posthumanity*, ed. Bert Gordijn and Ruth Chadwick (Springer, 2009), 71-94; citation is on p. 88.

[73]   Ted Peters, *Anticipating Omega: Science, Faith and Our Ultimate Future* (Göttingen: Vandenhoeck & Ruprecht, 2006), 119.

[74]   Cited in Peters, *Anticipating Omega*, 124.

Perhaps, this reaction indicates a failure of the imagination, but it can also be that my reluctance to endorse the transhumanist future is based on a historical awareness of the destructive powers of utopian thinking. No one understood this point better than Hans Jonas,[75] the German Jewish philosopher and early critic of modern technology and its utopian visions of enhanced humans.

It is befitting to remind ourselves of Jonas's profound reservations about biotechnology as we assess transhumanism. In terms of life expansion, Jonas suggested that mortality is not just a curse or a burden; it is also a blessing. It is a burden insofar that we organic beings must wrest our being from the continuous threat of nonbeing. But it is a blessing insofar as our wresting is the very condition for any affirmation of being at all, so that "mortality is the narrow gate through which alone value—the addressee of a yes—could enter the otherwise indifferent universe."[76] For Jonas, the effort to forestall death or overcome mortality is a fundamental denial of what makes us human. The process of life requires mortality as the counterpart of the natality that alone can supply the novelty and creativity that enrich human life and express freedom. Freedom is imperiled when it ignores necessity. (In terms of genetic engineering, Jonas considered many ends of genetic engineering to be frivolous). Genetic enhancement for the sake of improving one's look or one's chances of social success falls in that category.

As for germ-line intervention, without which the transhumanist vision is not possible, Jonas appealed exclusively to consequences: the irreversibility of germ-line interventions, the range of their effects, the impossibility of drawing a line in practice between therapy and enhancement of traits or of prohibiting the outright invention of new human forms that isolate the ontological states of human nature.[77] In terms of human improvement, or eugenics, Jonas distinguished between *negative eugenics* (namely, developing diagnostic tools to identify genetic diseases and then manipulating the genetic code to eliminate bad genes) and *positive eugenics* (namely, manipulating genes so as to enhance human performance). In regard to both programs, he reminds us that an ambitious eugenics violates the normative status of nature, but that we do not have criteria or standard to determine what is normal and what is pathogenic. Finally, as for the elimination of "bad genes" from the population, Jonas held that any effort to eliminate undesirable genes from the gene pool altogether threatens the biological necessity of a varied gene pool and

---

[75] See Christian Wiese, *The Life and Thought of Hans Jonas: Jewish Dimensions* (Hanover and London: University Press of New England, 2007).

[76] Hans Jonas, *The Phenomenon of Life: Toward a Philosophical Biology* (New York: Harper & Row, 1966), 36.

[77] For a comprehensive view of Jonas, see Hava Tirosh-Samuelson and Christian Wiese, *The Legacy of Hans Jonas: Judaism and the Phenomenon of Life* (Boston and Leiden: Brill Academic Press, 2008).

encounters our ignorance about the role apparently useless genes may play in human adaptability. Jonas argued against positive eugenics on the same ground: the lack of criteria and standards for intervention; positive eugenics aims at a qualitative improvement over nature, and therefore it cannot claim the sanction of nature. Although technology has advanced well beyond what Jonas reflected about, his reservations about biotechnology, in which the human becomes a design object, deeply resonate with me.

CONCLUDING PERSONAL REFLECTIONS

Modern technology has indeed transformed and will continue to transform our lives in numerous and yet unforeseeable ways. We should not categorically reject these advances because many of them do and will alleviate human suffering and misery. However, we should not naively endorse all technologies, nor should we let scientists alone determine our technological future. Rather, we must involve theologians, philosophers, ethicists, historians, sociologists, and political scientists in the conversation about technology and not be afraid of robust debate. Indeed, the Jewish tradition deeply respects debate and intellectual probing as an expression of our spirituality and commitment to the pursuit of truth.

The transhumanist project is misguided because of its mechanistic engineering-driven approach to being human, its obsession with perfection understood in terms of performance and accomplishments rather than moral integrity, and its disrespect for the unknown future. Transhumanism is a utopian vision that, like all utopias, has gone awry because it mistakenly believes that the ideal is realizable in the present instead of remaining just a beacon for the future. Instead of the transhumanist fixation on either postponing death or transcending death, I think it is more appropriate for humans to accept the reality of death as part of the very fabric of human life and to dignify how we live, how we age, and how we die.

To live with dignity, we need to strengthen our failing social fabric and enable human beings to have dignified family lives, dignified work, and dignified public space. We need to do whatever necessary to put an end to exploitation, poverty, violence, and corruption, and revive human creativity, which has been often numbed by technology. We need to ensure that our children and youth grow to behave with dignity toward others—be they parents, siblings, peers, relatives, coworkers, strangers, and even enemies—and we inculcate in youth the virtues that make such dignified interaction possible, chief among them, the virtue of humility. Our youth will be able to treat others with dignity if we teach them to take the imperative of responsibility seriously and to act accordingly, so that they care not just about themselves but also about others, including humans of future generations and nonhuman others.

As for aging with dignity, I for one believe that we should not put our efforts into reengineering cell biology so as to postpone aging indefinitely; rather, we should recognize the beauty of the life processes and the cycle of birth, maturation, aging, and death. Understanding the rhythm of human life, living with this and not against it is a source of wisdom that many ancient thinkers, beginning with Ecclesiastes, already taught us. In order to age well and become sages, we need to pay attention to the wisdom of the ancients in all traditions and in all societies, and we need to reject the cult of foolish youth; being young has its own merits, but these do not exhaust the meaning of being human. If we focus on aging with dignity, we will pay attention not merely to weight control, physical exercise, and supplements, but also to the arts, wisdom, traditions, and religions that provide us with insights into the purpose of human life and its inherent value. If we make aging with dignity our goal, we will not allow our healthcare to be driven solely by financial considerations of insurance companies, and we will create caring facilities in which the full person, not just the material body, is taken into consideration.

Finally, since death is part of the cycle of life characteristic of finite creatures, we will need to concern ourselves with dignified death, a process that the Bible describes as "being gathered into one's kin." Yes, dying is not pretty but a process suffused with pain, anguish, and suffering that can be alleviated through palliative care. But the dying process need not be humiliating or dehumanizing; if done properly, as the hospice movement has shown to us, the dying process itself can be dignified by remembering that we are dealing with persons whose life narratives in community are imbued with meaning, and that meaning does not disappear when bodily functions decline or finally cease. It is the concern with meaning that will shift the focus of end-of-life decisions, which are always difficult and never straightforward. The concern with meaning entails that framing human embodiments cannot and should not be left only to engineers or scientists; it must encompass other perspectives that go beyond science, technology, and engineering. Contemporary science and technology have indeed changed our ethical situation forever, challenging human dignity. With further deliberation on transhumanism, we will articulate new insights into the meaning of being human in the twenty-first century.

REFERENCES

Allenby, Braden. "The Industrial Ecology of Emerging Technologies: Complexity and the Reconstruction of the World, *Journal of Industrial Ecology* 13, no. 2 (2009): 168-183.

Allenby, Braden and Daniel Sarewitz. *The Techno-Human Condition*. Cambridge, Mass.: The MIT Press, 2010.

Argyle, Michael. *The Psychology of Happiness*. New York: Taylor and Francis, 2001.

Badmington, Neil (ed.). *Posthumanism.* New York: Palgrave, 2000.

Badmington, Neil. "Theorizing Posthumanism," *Cultural Critique* 53 (2003): 11-27.

Baillie, Harold W. and Timothy K. Casey. *Is Human Nature Obsolete? Genetic, Bioengineering and the Future of the Human Condition.* Cambridge, Mass. and London: MIT Press, 2005.

Barkow, Jerome H., Leda Cosmides and John Tooby, eds. *The Adapted Mind: Evolutionary Psychology and the Generation of Culture.* New York: Oxford University Press, 1992.

Bentham, Jeremy. *An Introduction to the Principles of Morals and Legislation* (1789), ed. J. H. Burns and H. L. A. Hart. Oxford: Clarendon Press, 1996.

Bernal, J. D. *The World, The Flesh, and the Devil: An Enquiry into the Future of Three Enemies of the Rational Soul.* Bloomington and London: Indiana University Press, 1969.

Bostrom, Nick. "Transhumanism FAQ: A General Introduction," version 2.1 (2003) available on the Web site of Nick Bostrom, www.nickbostrom.com.

Bostrom, Nick and Julian Savulescu, eds. *Human Enhancement.* Oxford: Oxford University Press, 2009.

Broadie, Sarah. *Ethics with Aristotle.* New York: Oxford University Press, 1991.

Brown, Andrew. *J. D. Bernal: The Sage of Science.* Oxford: Oxford University Press, 2005.

Buller, David J. *Adapting Minds: Evolutionary Psychology and the Persistent Quest for Human Nature.* Cambridge, Mass. and London: MIT Press, 2005.

Buss, David M. *Evolutionary Psychology: The New Science of the Mind.* Boston: Allyn and Bacon, 1999.

Clark, Ronald. *J. B. S.: The Life and Work of J.B. S. Haldane.* New York: Coward McMann, Inc., 1968.

Cooper, John M. *Reason and Human Good in Aristotle.* Indianapolis: Hackett Publishing, 1986.

Diener, Ed, and E.M. Suh, eds. *Culture and Subjective Well-Being.* Cambridge, Mass.: MIT Press, 1998.

Dinello, Daniel. *Technophobia! Science Fiction Vision of Posthuman Technology.* Austin: University of Texas Press, 2002.

Drexler, Eric K. *Engines of Creation.* Garden City, NY: Anchor Press/Doubleday, 1986.

_____. *Nanosystems: Molecular Machinery, Manufacturing and Computation.* New York: Wiley, 1992.

_____. and Chris Peterson. *Unbounding the Future: The Nanotechnology Revolution.* New York: Morrow, 1991.

Ellul, Jacques. *The Technological Society.* New York: Vintage Books, 1964.

Eysenck, Michael. *Happiness: Facts and Myths.* London: Lawrence Erlbauum, 1990.

Fukuyama, Francis. *Our Posthuman Future: Consequences of the Biotechnology Revolution.* New York: Farrar, Strauss & Giroux, 2002.

Garreau, Joel. *Radical Evolution: The Promise and Peril of Enhancing our Minds, Our Bodies, and What is Means to Be Humans.* New York: Doubleday, 2004.

Graham, Elaine L. *Representations of the Post/Human.* Manchester University Press, 2002.

Haldane, J. B. S. *Daedalus: or Science and the Future.* New York: E. P. Dutton & Co, 1924.

Hall, Stephen S. *Merchants of Immortality: Chasing the Dream of Human Life Extension.* Boston and New York: Houghton Mifflin Company, 2003.

Haraway, Donna. *Simians, Cyborgs, and Women: The Reinvention of Nature.* London: Free Association Books, 1991.

Hayles, N. Katherine. *How We Became Posthuman: Cybernetics, Literature, and Informatics.* Chicago: University of Chicago, 1999.

Hefner, Philip. *Technology and Human Becoming.* Minneapolis: Fortress Press, 2003.

Hefner, Philip. "The Animal that Aspires to Be an Angel: The Challenge of Transhumanism." *Dialog: Journal of Technology* 48, no. 2 (2009): 164-73.

Hughes, James J. "The Politics of Transhumanism." http://www.changesurfer.com/Acad/TranshumPolitics.htm.

Husbands, Philip, Owen Holland, and Michael Wheeler, eds. *The Mechanical Mind in History.* Cambridge, Mass.: MIT Press, 2008.

Huxley, Julian. *New Bottles for New Wine.* London: Chatto & Windus, 1957.

Jonas, Hans. *The Phenomenon of Life: Toward a Philosophical Biology.* New York: Harper & Row, 1966.

Kass, Leon. *Life, Liberty, and the Defense of Dignity: The Challenge for Bioethics.* San Francisco: Encounter Books, 2002.

Kraut, Richard. *Aristotle on the Human Good.* Princeton: Princeton University Press, 1989.

Kurzweil, Ray. *The Age of Intelligent Machines.* Cambridge, Mass.: MIT Press, 1990.

———. *The Age of Spiritual Machines: When Computers Exceed Human Intelligence.* New York: Viking 1999.

———. *The Singularity is Near: When Humans Transcend Biology.* New York: Viking, 2005.

Lewis, Mumford. *Technics and Civilization* 2nd ed. New York: Harcourt, Brace & World, 1963.

MacMahon, Darrin. *Happiness: A History.* New York: Atlantic Monthly Press, 2006.

Maher, Derek F. and Calvin Mercer, eds. *Religion and the Implications of Radical Life Extension.* New York: Palgrave Macmillan, 2009.

Marx, Leo. "The Idea of Technology and Postmodern Pessimism." In *Does Technology Drive History: The Dilemma of Technological Determinism*, ed. by Merritt Roe Smith and Leo Marx Cambridge, Mass.: MIT Press, 1994.

Maslow, A. H. *The Farther Reaches of Human Nature*. New York: Penguin, 1971.

McLean, Steven, ed. *H.G. Wells: Interdisciplinary Essays*. Newcastle: Cambridge Scholars Pub., 2008.

Miah, Andy. "A Critical History of Posthumanism." In *Medical Enhancement and Posthumanity*, ed. by Bert Gordijn and Ruth Chadwick, 71-94. Springer, 2008.

Miller, Philip Lee and the Life Extension Foundation with Monica Reinagel. *Life Extension Revolution: The New Science of Growing Older without Aging*. New York: Bantam Books, 2005.

Mindell, David A. *Between Human and Machine: Feedback, Control and Computing Before Cybernetics*. Baltimore, MD, and London: John Hopkins University Press, 2002.

Minsky, Marvin. *The Emotion Machine: Commonsense Thinking, Artificial Intelligence, and the Future of the Human Mind*. New York: Simon & Schuster, 2006.

Minsky, Marvin. *The Society of Mind*. New York: Simon and Schuster, 1986.

Moravec, Hans P. *Mind Children: The Future of Robot and Human Intelligence*. Cambridge, Mass.: Harvard University Press, 1988.

Moravec, Hans P. *Robot: Mere Machine to Transcendent Mind*. New York: Oxford University Press, 1999.

More, Max. "Extropian Principles 3.0." http://www.maxmore.com/extprn3.htm.

Noble, David F. *The Religion of Technology: The Divinity of Man and the Spirit of Invention*. New York Penguin Books, 1997.

Pepperell, Robert. *The Posthuman Condition: Consciousness beyond the Brain*. Bristol, UK: Intellect Books, 2003.

Peters, Ted. *Anticipating Omega: Science, Faith and Our Ultimate Future*. Göttingen: Vandenhoeck & Ruprecht, 2006.

———. *For the Love of Children: Genetic Technology and the Future of the Family*. Louisville: Westminster John Knox Press, 1996.

———. *Playing God? Genetic Determinism and Human Freedom*. New York: Routledge, 1997.

———. *Science, Theology and Ethics*. Aldershot, England and Burlington VT: Ashgate, 2003.

Pickering, Andrew. *The Mangle of Practice, Time, Agency and Science*. Chicago: University of Chicago Press, 1995.

Pinker, Steven. *The Blank Slate: The Modern Denial of Human Nature*. New York: Penguin Books, 2002.

Roco, Mihail C. and William Sims Bainbridge, eds. *Converging Technologies for Improvement of Human Performance: Nanotechnology, Biotechnology, Information Technology and Cognitive Science*. Dordrecht and Boston: Kluwer Academic Publishers, 2002.

Sandel, Michael J. *The Case against Perfection: Ethics in the Age of Genetic Engineering.* Cambridge, Mass.: Harvard University Press, 2007.

Sarewitz, Daniel. "Technology and the Culture of Progress." Lecture delivered at ASU on April 24, 2008.

Savulescu, Julian, R. ter Mueler, and G. Kahane, eds. *Enhancing Human Capacities.* Oxford: Wiley-Blackwell, 2009.

Seligman, Martin. *Authentic Happiness.* New York: Simon and Schuster, 2002.

Soper, Kate. *Humanism and Anti-Humanism.* Chicago: Open Court Publishing Co., 1986.

Stock, Gregory. *Metaman: The Making of Humans and Machines into a Global Superorganism.* New York: Simon and Schuster, 1993.

Stock, Gregory. *Redesigning Humans: Choosing Our Genes, Changing our Futures.* Boston and New York: Houghton Mifflin Company, 2003.

Swann, Brenda and Francis Aprhamaian, eds. *J. D. Bernal: A Life in Science and Politics.* London and New York: Verso, 1999.

Tipler, Frank J. *The Physics of Immortality: Modern Cosmology, God and the Resurrection of the Dead.* New York: Doubleday, 1994.

Tipler, Frank J. *The Physics of Christianity.* New York: Doubleday, 2007.

Tirosh-Samuelson, Hava. *Happiness in Premodern Judaism: Virtue, Knowledge and Well-Being.* Cincinnati: Hebrew Union College Press, 2003.

Tirosh-Samuelson, Hava and Christian Wiese. *The Legacy of Hans Jonas: Judaism and the Phenomenon of Life.* Boston and Leiden: Brill Academic Press, 2008.

Tooby, John and Leda Cosmides. "On the University of Human Nature and the Uniqueness of the Individual: The Role of Genetics and Adaptation." *Journal of Personality* 58 (1990): 17-67.

Transhumanist World Association (WTA). "Transhumanist Declaration." http://www.transhumanism.org.

Veenhoven, Ruut. *Conditions of Happiness.* Dordrecht: Reidel, 1984.

Waters, Brent. *From Human to Posthuman: Christian Theology and Technology in a Postmodern World.* Aldershot, England and Burlington, VT: Ashgate, 2006.

Wells, H.G. *A Modern Utopia.* London: Chapman & Hall, 1905.

Wersky, Gary. *The Visible College: The Collective Biography of British Scientific Socialists in the 1930s.* New York: Holt, Reinhart and Winston, 1978.

Wersky, Gary. *Men Like Gods, A Novel.* New York: Cassell, 1923.

Wiese, Christian. *The Life and Thought of Hans Jonas: Jewish Dimensions.* Hanover and London: University Press of New England, 2007.

Winner, Langdon. *Autonomous Technology: Technics-out-of-Control as a Theme in Political Thought.* Cambridge: MIT Press, 1977.

Wolfe, Cary. *What is Transhumanism?* Minneapolis: University of Minnesota, 2010.

Young, Simon. *Designer Evolution: A Transhumanist Manifesto.* Amherst, NY: Prometheus Books, 2005).

Appendix: List of Organizations That Support the Transhumanist Vision

Accelerating Future: http://www.acceleratingfuture.com
Alcor Life Extension Foundation: http://www.alcor.org
Anders Transhuman Resources: http://www.aleph.se.Trans
Applied Foresight Network: http://www.appliedforesight.org
Artificial General Intelligence Research Institute: http://www.agiri.org
Betterhumans: http://www.betterhumans.com
BrainMeta: http://www.brainmeta.com
Cryonics Institute: http://www.cryonics.org
Cryostasis: http://www.cryostais.com
Eudoxa: http://www.eudoxa.se
Extropy Institute: http://www.extropy.org
Future Human Evolution Gateway: http://www.human-evolution.org
Genetics & Public Policy Center: http://www.dnapolicy.org
Immortality Institute: http://www.imminist.org
Institute for Ethics and Emerging Technologies: http://www.ieet.org
Institute for the Study of Accelerating Change: http://www.accelerating.org
Journal of Evolution and Technology: http://www.jetpress.org
Mormon Transhuman Association: http://www.transfigurism.org
Omega Point Institute: http://www.ometapoint.org
Posthuman Manifesto: http://www.stem-arts.com/Poshuman.cont.htm
Singularity for Artificial Intelligence: http://www.singinst.org
Transhuman Culture InfoMark: http://www.transhuman.org
Transhumanism Search: http://www.transhumanismsearch.net
Transhumanist Arts & Culture: http://www.transhumanist.biz
Trans-Spirit: http://groups.yahoo.com/troup/Trans-Spirit
Upwingers: http://smi21e-upwinger/blogspot.com

II. H+ Proponents of Transhumanism

Chapter Two

In Defense of Posthuman Dignity[1]

by Nick Bostrom

TRANSHUMANISTS VERSUS BIOCONSERVATIVES

Transhumanism is a loosely defined movement that has developed gradually over the past two decades and can be viewed as an outgrowth of secular humanism and the Enlightenment. It holds that current human nature is improvable through the use of applied science and other rational methods, which may make it possible to increase human health span, extend our intellectual and physical capacities, and give us increased control over our own mental states and moods.[2] Technologies of concern include not only current ones, like genetic engineering and information technology, but also anticipated future developments such as fully immersive virtual reality, machine-phase nanotechnology, and artificial intelligence.

Transhumanists promote the view that human enhancement technologies should be made widely available and that individuals should have broad discretion over which of these technologies to apply to themselves (morphological freedom),[3] and that parents should normally get to decide which reproductive technologies to

---

[1] N. Bostrom, "In Defense of Posthuman Dignity," *Bioethics* 19, no. 3 (2005). This paper has been chosen for inclusion in a special anthology of the best papers published in the journal *Bioethics* in the past two decades.

[2] N. Bostrom et al., *The Transhumanist FAQ: A General Introduction*, 2.1, 2003, World Transhumanist Association, Available:http://www.transhumanism.org/resources/faq. html.

[3] Max More, "Technological Self-Transformation: Expanding Personal Extropy," *Extropy* 10.Winter/Spring (1993).

use when having children (reproductive freedom).[4] Transhumanists believe that, while there are hazards that need to be identified and avoided, human enhancement technologies will offer enormous potential for deeply valuable and humanly beneficial uses. Ultimately, it is possible that such enhancements may make us, or our descendants, "posthuman" beings who may have indefinite health spans, much greater intellectual faculties than any current human being—and perhaps entirely new sensibilities or modalities—as well as the ability to control their own emotions. The wisest approach vis-à-vis these prospects, argue transhumanists, is to embrace technological progress while strongly defending human rights and individual choice, and taking action specifically against concrete threats, such as military or terrorist abuse of bioweapons, and against unwanted environmental or social side effects.

In opposition to this transhumanist view stands a bioconservative camp that argues against the use of technology to modify human nature. Prominent bioconservative writers include Leon Kass, Francis Fukuyama, George Annas, Wesley Smith, Jeremy Rifkin, and Bill McKibben. One of the central concerns of the bioconservatives is that human enhancement technologies might be "dehumanizing." The worry, which has been variously expressed, is that these technologies might undermine our human dignity or inadvertently erode something that is deeply valuable about being human, but that is difficult to put into words or to factor into a cost-benefit analysis. In some cases (e.g., Leon Kass), the unease seems to derive from religious or cryptoreligious sentiments whereas for others, (e.g., Francis Fukuyama) it stems from secular grounds. The best approach, these bioconservatives argue, is to implement global bans on swathes of promising human enhancement technologies to forestall a slide down a slippery slope toward an ultimately debased posthuman state.

While any brief description necessarily skirts significant nuances that differentiate writers within the two camps, I believe the above characterization nevertheless highlights a principal fault line in one of the great debates of our times: how we should look at the future of humankind and whether we should attempt to use technology to make ourselves "more than human." This paper will distinguish two common fears about the posthuman and argue that they are partly unfounded, and that, to the extent that they correspond to real risks, there are better responses than trying to implement broad bans on technology. I will make some remarks on the concept of dignity, which bioconservatives believe to be imperiled by coming human enhancement technologies, and suggest that we need to recognize that not only humans in their current form but posthumans too could have dignity.

---

4   Nick Bostrom, "Human Genetic Enhancements: A Transhumanist Perspective," *Journal of Value Inquiry* 37, no. 4 (2003).

Two Fears about the Posthuman

The prospect of posthumanity is feared for at least two reasons. One is that the state of being posthuman might in itself be degrading, so that by becoming posthuman, we might be harming ourselves. Another is that posthumans might pose a threat to "ordinary" humans. (I shall set aside a third possible reason, that the development of posthumans might offend some supernatural being.). The most prominent bioethicist to focus on the first fear is Leon Kass.

> Most of the given bestowals of nature have their given species-specified natures: they are each and all of a given *sort*. Cockroaches and humans are equally bestowed but differently natured. To turn a man into a cockroach—as we don't need Kafka to show us—would be dehumanizing. To try to turn a man into more than a man might be so as well. We need more than generalized appreciation for nature's gifts. We need a particular regard and respect for the special gift that is our own given nature.[5]

Transhumanists counter that nature's gifts are sometimes poisoned and should not always be accepted. Cancer, malaria, dementia, aging, starvation, unnecessary suffering, and cognitive shortcomings are all among the presents that we wisely refuse. Our own species-specified natures are a rich source of much of the thoroughly unrespectable and unacceptable—susceptibility for disease, murder, rape, genocide, cheating, torture, racism. The horrors of nature in general and of our own nature in particular are so well documented,[6] that it is astonishing that somebody as distinguished as Leon Kass should still, in this day and age, be tempted to rely on the natural as a guide to what is desirable or normatively right. We should be grateful that our ancestors were not swept away by the Kassian sentiment, or we would still be picking lice off each other's backs. Rather than deferring to the natural order, transhumanists maintain that we can legitimately reform ourselves and our natures in accordance with humane values and personal aspirations.

If one rejects nature as a general criterion of the good, as most thoughtful people nowadays do, one can of course still acknowledge that particular ways of modifying human nature would be debasing. Not all change is progress. Not even all well-intended technological interventions in human nature would be on balance beneficial. Kass goes far beyond these truisms, however, when he declares that

---

[5]   L. R. Kass, "Ageless Bodies, Happy Souls," *The New Atlantis* 1 (2003): 9-28.

[6]   Jonathan Glover, *Humanity: A Moral History of the Twentieth Century*, (New Haven, CT: Yale University Press, 2001).

utter dehumanization lies in store for us as the inevitable result of our obtaining technical mastery over our own nature.

> The final technical conquest of his own nature would almost certainly leave mankind utterly enfeebled. This form of mastery would be identical with utter dehumanization. Read Huxley's *Brave New World*, read C. S. Lewis's *Abolition of Man*, read Nietzsche's account of the last man, and then read the newspapers. Homogenization, mediocrity, pacification, drug-induced contentment, debasement of taste, souls without loves and longings—these are the inevitable results of making the essence of human nature the last project of technical mastery. In his moment of triumph, Promethean man will become a contented cow.[7]

The fictional inhabitants of *Brave New World*, to pick the best-known of Kass's examples, are admittedly short on dignity (in at least one sense of the word). But the claim that this is the *inevitable* consequence of our obtaining technological mastery over human nature is exceedingly pessimistic—and unsupported—if understood as a futuristic prediction, and false if construed as a claim about metaphysical necessity.

There are many things wrong with the fictional society that Huxley described. It is static, totalitarian, and caste-bound; its culture is a wasteland. The brave new worlders themselves are a dehumanized and undignified lot. Yet posthumans they are not. Their capacities are not superhuman but in many respects substantially inferior to our own. Their life expectancy and physique are quite normal; but their intellectual, emotional, moral, and spiritual faculties are stunted. The majority of the brave new worlders have various degrees of engineered mental retardation. And everyone, save the ten world controllers (along with a miscellany of primitives and social outcasts who are confined to fenced preservations or isolated islands), are barred or discouraged from developing individuality, independent thinking, and initiative, and are conditioned not to desire these traits in the first place. *Brave New World* is not a tale of human enhancement gone amok, but a tragedy of technology and social engineering being used to deliberately cripple moral and intellectual capacities—the exact antithesis of the transhumanist proposal.

Transhumanists argue that the best way to avoid a "brave new world" is by vigorously defending morphological and reproductive freedoms against any would-be world controllers. History has shown the dangers in letting governments curtail these freedoms. The last century's government-sponsored coercive eugenics programs, once favored by both the left and the right, have been thoroughly

---

[7] Leon Kass, *Life, Liberty, and the Defense of Dignity: The Challenge for Bioethics*, 1st ed. (San Francisco: Encounter Books, 2002), 48.

discredited. Because people are likely to differ profoundly in their attitudes toward human enhancement technologies, it is crucial that no one solution be imposed on everyone from above, but that individuals get to consult their own consciences as to what is right for themselves and their families. Information, public debate, and education are the appropriate means by which to encourage others to make wise choices, not a global ban on a broad range of potentially beneficial medical and other enhancement options.

The second fear is that there might be an eruption of violence between unaugmented humans and posthumans. George Annas, Lori Andrews, and Rosario Isasi have argued that we should view human cloning and all inheritable genetic modifications as "crimes against humanity" in order to reduce the probability that posthuman species will arise, on grounds that such a species would pose an existential threat to the old human species.

> The new species, or "posthuman," will likely view the old "normal" humans as inferior, even savages, and fit for slavery or slaughter. The normals, on the other hand, may see the posthumans as a threat and if they can, may engage in a preemptive strike by killing the posthumans before they themselves are killed or enslaved by them. It is ultimately this predictable potential for genocide that makes species-altering experiments potential weapons of mass destruction, and makes the unaccountable genetic engineer a potential bioterrorist.[8]

There is no denying that bioterrorism and unaccountable genetic engineers developing increasingly potent weapons of mass destruction pose a serious threat to our civilization. But using the rhetoric of bioterrorism and weapons of mass destruction to cast aspersions on therapeutic uses of biotechnology to improve health, longevity, and other human capacities is unhelpful. The issues are quite distinct. Reasonable people can be in favor of strict regulation of bioweapons while promoting beneficial medical uses of genetics and other human enhancement technologies, including inheritable and "species-altering" modifications.

Human society is always at risk of some group deciding to view another group of humans as fit for slavery or slaughter. To counteract such tendencies, modern societies have created laws and institutions, and endowed them with powers of enforcement, that act to prevent groups of citizens from enslaving or slaughtering one another. The efficacy of these institutions does not depend on all citizens having equal capacities. Modern, peaceful societies can have large numbers of

---

8   G. J. Annas, L. B. Andrews and R. M. Isasi, "Protecting the Endangered Human: Toward an International Treaty Prohibiting Cloning and Inheritable Alterations," *Am J Law Med* 28, nos. 2-3 (2002): 162.

people with diminished physical or mental capacities along with many other people who may be exceptionally physically strong or healthy or intellectually talented in various ways. Adding people with technologically enhanced capacities to this already broad distribution of ability would not need to rip society apart or trigger genocide or enslavement.

The assumption that inheritable genetic modifications or other human enhancement technologies would lead to two distinct and separate species should also be questioned. It seems much more likely that there would be a continuum of differently modified or enhanced individuals, which would overlap with the continuum of as-yet unenhanced humans. The scenario in which "the enhanced" form a pact and then attack "the naturals" makes for exciting science fiction, but it is not necessarily the most plausible outcome. Even today, the segment containing the tallest 90 percent of the population could, in principle, get together and kill or enslave the shorter decile. That this does not happen suggests that a well-organized society can hold together even if it contains many possible coalitions of people sharing some attribute such that, if they ganged up, they would be capable of exterminating the rest.

To note that the extreme case of a war between humans and posthumans is not the most likely scenario is not to say that there are no legitimate social concerns about the steps that may take us closer to posthumanity. Inequity, discrimination, and stigmatization—against, or on behalf of, modified people—could become serious issues. Transhumanists would argue that these (potential) social problems call for social remedies. One example of how contemporary technology can change important aspects of someone's identity is sex reassignment. The experiences of transsexuals show that Western culture still has work to do in becoming more accepting of diversity. This is a task that we can begin to tackle today by fostering a climate of tolerance and acceptance toward those who are different from ourselves. Painting alarmist pictures of the threat from future technologically modified people, or hurling preemptive condemnations of their necessarily debased nature, is not the best way to go about it.

What about the hypothetical case in which someone intends to create, or turn themselves into, a being of so radically enhanced capacities that a single one or a small group of such individuals would be capable of taking over the planet? This is clearly not a situation that is likely to arise in the imminent future, but one can imagine that, perhaps in a few decades, the prospective creation of super-intelligent machines could raise this kind of concern. The would-be creator of a new life form with such surpassing capabilities would have an obligation to ensure that the proposed being is free from psychopathic tendencies and, more generally, that it has humane inclinations. For example, a future artificial intelligence programmer should be required to make a strong case that launching a purportedly human-friendly super-intelligence would be safer than the alternative. Again, however, this (currently) science fiction scenario must be clearly distinguished from our present situation and our more immediate concern with taking effective steps toward incrementally improving human capacities and health span.

Is Human Dignity Incompatible with Posthuman Dignity?

Human dignity is sometimes invoked as a polemical substitute for clear ideas. This is not to say that there are no important moral issues relating to dignity, but it does mean that there is a need to define what one has in mind when one uses the term. Here, we shall consider two different senses of dignity:

1. Dignity as moral status, in particular the inalienable right to be treated with a basic level of respect.
2. Dignity as the quality of being worthy or honorable; worthiness, worth, nobleness, excellence.[9]

On both these definitions, dignity is something that a posthuman could possess. Francis Fukuyama, however, seems to deny this and warns that giving up on the idea that dignity is unique to human beings—defined as those possessing a mysterious essential human quality he calls "Factor X"[10]—would invite disaster.

> Denial of the concept of human dignity—that is, of the idea that there is something unique about the human race that entitles every member of the species to a higher moral status than the rest of the natural world—leads us down a very perilous path. We may be compelled ultimately to take this path, but we should do so only with our eyes open. Nietzsche is a much better guide to what lies down that road than the legions of bioethicists and casual academic Darwinians that today are prone to give us moral advice on this subject.[11]

What appears to worry Fukuyama is that introducing new kinds of enhanced person into the world might cause some individuals (perhaps infants, or the mentally handicapped, or unenhanced humans in general) to lose some of the moral status that

---

[9]   J. A. Simpson, E. S. C. Weiner and Oxford University Press., *The Oxford English Dictionary*, 2nd ed., 20 vols. (Oxford & New York: Clarendon Press; Oxford University Press, 1989).

[10]   Francis Fukuyama, *Our Posthuman Future: Consequences of the Biotechnology Revolution* (New York: Farrar Straus & Giroux, 2002), 149.

[11]   Fukuyama, *Our Posthuman Future: Consequences of the Biotechnology Revolution*, 160.

they currently possess, and that a fundamental precondition of liberal democracy, the principle of equal dignity for all, would be destroyed.

The underlying intuition seems to be that instead of the famed "expanding moral circle," what we have is more like an oval, whose shape we can change but whose area must remain constant. Thankfully, this purported conservation law of moral recognition lacks empirical support. The set of individuals accorded full moral status by Western societies has actually increased, to include men without property or noble decent, women, and nonwhite peoples. It would seem feasible to extend this set further to include future posthumans, or, for that matter, some of the higher primates or human-animal chimaeras should such be created—and to do so without causing any compensating shrinkage in another direction. (The moral status of problematic borderline cases, such as fetuses or late-stage Alzheimer patients, or the brain dead, should perhaps be decided separately from the issue of technologically modified humans or novel artificial life forms.) Our own role in this process need not be that of passive bystanders. We can work to create more inclusive social structures that accord appropriate moral recognition and legal rights to all who need them, be they male or female, black or white, flesh or silicon.

Dignity in the second sense, as referring to a special excellence or moral worthiness, is something that current human beings possess to widely differing degrees. Some excel far more than others do. Some are morally admirable; others are base and vicious. There is no reason for supposing that posthuman beings could not also have dignity in this second sense. They may even be able to attain higher levels of moral and other excellence than any of us humans may. The fictional brave new worlders, who were subhuman rather than posthuman, would have scored low on this kind of dignity, and partly for that reason they would be awful role models for us to emulate. But surely we can create more uplifting and appealing visions of what we may aspire to become. There may be some who would transform themselves into degraded posthumans—but then some people today do not live very worthy human lives. This is regrettable, but the fact that some people make bad choices is not generally a sufficient ground for rescinding people's right to choose. And legitimate countermeasures are available: education, encouragement, persuasion, social and cultural reform. These, not a blanket prohibition of all posthuman ways of being, are the measures to which those bothered by the prospect of debased posthumans should resort. A liberal democracy should normally permit incursions into morphological and reproductive freedoms only in cases where somebody is abusing these freedoms to harm another person.

The principle that parents should have broad discretion to decide on genetic enhancements for their children has been attacked on grounds that this form of reproductive freedom would constitute a kind of parental tyranny that would undermine the child's dignity and capacity for autonomous choice; for instance, by Hans Jonas:

Technologically mastered nature now again includes man who (up to now) had, in technology, set himself against it as its master . . . But whose power is this—and over whom or over what? Obviously the power of those living today over those coming after them, who will be the defenseless other side of prior choices made by the planners of today. The other side of the power of today is the future bondage of the living to the dead.[12]

Jonas is relying on the assumption that our descendants, who will presumably be far more technologically advanced than we are, would nevertheless be defenseless against our machinations to expand their capacities. This is almost certainly incorrect. If, for some inscrutable reason, they decided that they would prefer to be less intelligent, less healthy, and lead shorter lives, they would not lack the means to achieve these objectives and frustrate our designs.

In any case, if the alternative to parental choice in determining the basic capacities of new people is entrusting the child's welfare to nature, that is, blind chance, then the decision should be easy. Had Mother Nature been a real parent, she would have been in jail for child abuse and murder. And transhumanists can accept, of course, that just as society may in exceptional circumstances override parental autonomy, such as in cases of neglect or abuse, so do too may society-imposed regulations to protect the child-to-be from genuinely harmful genetic interventions—but not because they represent choice rather than chance.

Jürgen Habermas, in a recent work, echoes Jonas's concern and worries that even the mere *knowledge* of having been intentionally made by another could have ruinous consequences: "We cannot rule out that knowledge of one's own hereditary features as programmed may prove to restrict the choice of an individual's life, and to undermine the essentially symmetrical relations between free and equal human beings."[13]

A transhumanist could reply that it would be a mistake for an individual to believe that she has no choice over her own life just because some (or all) of her genes were selected by her parents. She would, in fact, have as much choice as if her genetic constitution had been selected by chance. It could even be that she would enjoy significantly *more* choice and autonomy in her life if the modifications were such as to expand her basic capability set. Being healthy, smarter, having a wide range of talents, or possessing greater powers of self-control are blessings that tend to open more life paths than they block.

---

[12] Hans Jonas, *Technik, Medizin Und Ethik: Zur Praxis Des Prinzips Verantwortung*, 2. Aufl. ed. (Frankfurt am Main: Insel, 1987).

[13] Jürgen Habermas, *The Future of Human Nature* (Cambridge, UK, and Malden, MA: Polity; Distributed in the USA by Blackwell Pub., 2003), 23.

Even if there were a possibility that some genetically modified individuals might fail to grasp these points and thus might feel oppressed by their knowledge of their origin, that would be a risk to be weighed against the risks incurred by having an unmodified genome, risks that can be extremely grave. If safe and effective alternatives were available, it would be irresponsible to risk starting someone off in life with the misfortune of congenitally diminished basic capacities or an elevated susceptibility to disease.

WHY WE NEED POSTHUMAN DIGNITY

Similarly ominous forecasts were made in the seventies about the severe psychological damage that children conceived through in vitro fertilization would suffer upon learning that they originated from a test tube—a prediction that turned out to be entirely false. It is hard to avoid the impression that some bias or philosophical prejudice is responsible for the readiness with which many bioconservatives seize on even the flimsiest of empirical justifications for banning human enhancement technologies of certain types but not others.

Suppose it turned out that playing Mozart to pregnant mothers improved the child's subsequent musical talent. Nobody would argue for a ban on Mozart-in-the-womb on grounds that we could not rule out that some psychological woe might befall the child once she discovered that her facility with the violin had been prenatally programmed by her parents. Yet when it comes to, genetic enhancements, for example, arguments which are not so very different from this parody are often put forward as weighty if not conclusive objections by eminent bioconservative writers. To transhumanists, this looks like doublethink. How can it be that, to bioconservatives, almost any anticipated downside, predicted perhaps on the basis of the shakiest pop psychological theory, so readily achieves that status of deep philosophical insight and knockdown objection against the transhumanist project?

Perhaps a part of the answer can be found in the different attitudes that transhumanists and bioconservatives have toward posthuman dignity. Bioconservatives tend to deny posthuman dignity and view posthumanity as a threat to human dignity. They are therefore tempted to look for ways to denigrate interventions that are thought to be pointing in the direction of more radical future modifications that may eventually lead to the emergence of those detestable posthumans. But unless this fundamental opposition to the posthuman is openly declared as a premise of their argument, this then forces them to use a double standard of assessment whenever particular cases are considered in isolation: for example, one standard for germ-line genetic interventions and another for improvements in maternal nutrition (an intervention presumably not seen as heralding a posthuman era).

Transhumanists, by contrast, see human and posthuman dignity as compatible and complementary. They insist that dignity, in its modern sense, consists in what we are and what we have the potential to become, not in our pedigree or our causal origin. What we are is not a function solely of our DNA but also of our technological and social context. Human nature in this broader sense is dynamic, partially human-made, and improvable. Our current extended phenotypes (and the lives that we lead) are markedly different from those of our hunter-gatherer ancestors. We read and write; we wear clothes; we live in cities; we earn money and buy food from the supermarket; we call people on the telephone, watch television, read newspapers, drive cars, file taxes, vote in national elections; women give birth in hospitals; life expectancy is three times longer than in the Pleistocene; we know that Earth is round and that stars are large gas clouds lit from inside by nuclear fusion, and that the universe is approximately 13.7 billion years old and enormously big. In the eyes of a hunter-gatherer, we might already appear "posthuman." Yet these radical extensions of human capabilities—some of them biological, others external—have not divested us of moral status or dehumanized us in the sense of making us generally unworthy and base. Similarly, should we or our descendants one day succeed in becoming what relative to current standards we may refer to as posthuman, this need not entail a loss of dignity either.

From the transhumanist standpoint, there is no need to behave as if there were a deep moral difference between technological and other means of enhancing human lives. By defending posthuman dignity, we promote a more inclusive and humane ethics, one that will embrace future technologically modified people, as well as humans of the contemporary kind. We also remove a distorting double standard from the field of our moral vision, allowing us to perceive more clearly the opportunities that exist for further human progress.[14]

REFERENCES

Annas, G. J., L. B. Andrews, and R. M. Isasi. "Protecting the Endangered Human: Toward an International Treaty Prohibiting Cloning and Inheritable Alterations." *Am J Law Med* 28 2-3 (2002): 151-78.

---

[14]   For their comments I am grateful to Heather Bradshaw, John Brooke, Aubrey de Grey, Robin Hanson, Matthew Liao, Julian Savulescu, Eliezer Yudkowsky, Nick Zangwill, and to the audiences at the Ian Ramsey Center seminar of June 6 in Oxford, the Transvision 2003 conference at Yale, and the 2003 European Science Foundation Workshop on Science and Human Values, where earlier versions of this paper were presented, and to two anonymous referees.

Bostrom, N. "In Defense of Posthuman Dignity." *Bioethics* 19, no. 3 (2005): 202-14.

Bostrom, N. et. al. "The Transhumanist Faq: A General Introduction." 2003. 2.1: World Transhumanist Association. http://www.transhumanism.org/resources/faq.html.

Bostrom, Nick. "Human Genetic Enhancements: A Transhumanist Perspective." *Journal of Value Inquiry* 37, no. 4 (2003): 493.

Fukuyama, Francis. *Our Posthuman Future: Consequences of the Biotechnology Revolution*. New York: Farrar Straus & Giroux, 2002.

Glover, Jonathan. *Humanity: A Moral History of the Twentieth Century*. New Haven, CT: Yale University Press, 2001.

Habermas, Jürgen. *The Future of Human Nature*. Cambridge, UK and Malden, Mass.: Polity; Distributed in the USA by Blackwell Pub., 2003.

Jonas, Hans. *Technik, Medizin Und Ethik: Zur Praxis Des Prinzips Verantwortung*. 2. Aufl. ed. Frankfurt am Main: Insel, 1987.

Kass, Leon. "Ageless Bodies, Happy Souls." *The New Atlantis* 1 (2003): 9-28.

Kass, Leon. *Life, Liberty, and the Defense of Dignity: The Challenge for Bioethics*. 1st ed. San Francisco: Encounter Books, 2002.

More, Max. "Technological Self-Transformation: Expanding Personal Extropy." *Extropy* 10 Winter/Spring (1993).

Simpson, J. A., E. S. C. Weiner, and Oxford University Press. *The Oxford English Dictionary*. 2nd ed. 20 vols. Oxford & New York: Clarendon Press; Oxford University Press, 1989.

Chapter Three

SENS Statement of Principle

by Aubrey de Grey

STATEMENT OF PRINCIPLES

Two thirds of all deaths worldwide, and about 90 percent of all deaths in the developed world, are from causes that only rarely kill young adults. These causes include Alzheimer's, cardiovascular disease, type 2 diabetes, and most cancers. They are age-related because they are expressions of the later stages of aging, occurring when the molecular and cellular damage that has accumulated in the body throughout life exceeds the level that metabolism can tolerate. Moreover, before it kills them, aging imposes on most elderly people a long period of debilitation and disease. For these reasons, aging is inarguably the most prevalent medically relevant phenomenon in the modern world, and the primary ultimate target of biomedical research.

Regenerative medicine can be defined as the restoration of an individual's molecular, cellular and/or tissue structure to broadly the state it was in before it experienced damage or degeneration. Aging is a degenerative process, so in theory it can be treated by regenerative medicine, thereby postponing the entire spectrum of age-related frailty and disease. But in practice, could regenerative medicine substantially postpone aging any time soon? If so, it will do so via the combined application of many distinct regenerative therapies since aging affects the body in so many ways. Recent biotechnological progress indicates that many aspects of aging may indeed be effectively treatable by regenerative medicine in the foreseeable future. We cannot yet know whether all aspects will be, but extensive scrutiny has failed to identify any definite exceptions. Therefore, at this point, there is a significant chance that such therapies would postpone age-related decline by several years, if not more, which constitutes a clear case for allocating significant resources to the attempt to develop those therapies.

Unfortunately, the regenerative medicine approach to combating aging is not yet being adequately pursued by major funding bodies: only a small number of laboratories worldwide are funded (either publicly or privately) to develop therapies that could rejuvenate aged but otherwise undamaged tissues. The SENS Foundation has risen to the challenge of filling this void in the biomedical research-funding arena. Research is chosen for funding by the foundation on the basis of the following major criteria:

- It is demonstrably relevant to the development of regenerative medicine targeting some aspect of aging.
- It is poorly funded by other sources.
- Funding from other sources seems unlikely to be forthcoming in the near future.

As and when it is developed, this panel of therapies may provide many years, even decades, of additional youthful life to countless millions of people. Those extra years will be free of all age-related diseases, as well as the frailty and susceptibility to infections and falls that the elderly also experience. The alleviation of suffering that will result, and the resulting economic benefits of maintained productivity of the population, are almost incalculable. In our capacity as the overseers of the SENS Foundation's research strategy, we urge you to do all you can to help the SENS Foundation carry out this mission with maximum speed.[1]

∞

This statement of principle has been endorsed by the SENS Foundation's research advisory board. The members of the research advisory board are:

- Pedro Alvarez, PhD, George R. Brown Professor of Engineering, Rice University
- Anthony Atala, MD, professor and director of the Wake Forest Institute for Regenerative Medicine
- María A. Blasco, PhD, group leader, Telomeres and Telomerase Group, Spanish National Cancer Centre (CNIO)
- Judith Campisi, PhD, senior scientist, Cell and Molecular Biology, Lawrence Berkeley National Laboratory, and Buck Institute for Age Research

---

[1]   SENS Foundation is located at http://www.sens.org/.

- Irina Conboy, PhD, assistant professor, Department of Bioengineering, UC Berkeley, and Berkeley Stem Cell Center
- Marisol Corral-Debrinski, PhD, Institut de la Vision, Université Pierre et Marie Curie-Paris 6
- Leonid Gavrilov, PhD, Center on Aging, NORC at the University of Chicago
- William Haseltine, chair, Haseltine Global Health
- Janko Nikolich-Zugich, MD, PhD, head, Department of Immunobiology and codirector of the Arizona Center on Aging
- Graham Pawelec, PhD, Tübingen University Aging and Tumor Immunology Group
- Bruce Rittman, PhD, director, Institute for Environmental Biotechnology in the Biodesign Institute at Arizona State University
- Jerry W. Shay, PhD, codirector, Shay/Wright Laboratory, University of Texas Southwestern
- Vladimir P. Skulachev, ScD, head, Department of Bioenergetics, A. N. Belozersky Institute of Physico-Chemical Biology
- Fyodor Urnov, PhD, team leader, Advanced Genomics Technologies, Sangamo Biosciences
- Jan Vijg, PhD, chair, Department of Genetics, Albert Einstein College of Medicine

Chapter Four

Bringing Arts/Design into the Discussion of Transhumanism

by Natasha Vita-More

The current discussion of transhumanism focuses on human enhancement. Questions relating to the sciences and technologies of enhancement include social impacts of nanotechnology, biotechnology, information technology, and cognitive sciences (NBIC).[1] Of interest and debate is the ethical practice of whether to develop biosynthetic structures and, if so, how will these structures be integrated with human physiology for the purpose of eradicating disease and radically extending human life. Because the practice and theory of human enhancement is multidisciplinary, there is growing interest in biosynthetic and virtual bodies within the fields of media arts and design.

Why would artists and designers be compelled to enhance human physiology—both cognitive and somatic? Historically, artists and designers have been altering the human form—perceptually, conceptually, and in actuality—from existing states to envisioned, preferred states. The perception of an ideal human is evident in the classical construction of statuesque sculptures. The conception of an enhanced human is more recently evident in imagined mechanism in providing electronic senses and robotic extensions.

The central issue now is that the opponents and the advocates of transhumanism have realized that altering the human form is practicable, that duplicating the mind is probable, and that extending life is feasible.

---

[1]   M. C. Roco and W. S. Bainbridge, "Converging Technologies for Improving Human Performance: Integrating from the Nanoscale," *Journal of Nanoparticle Research* 4, no. 4 (2002).

THE FORM

The human form continues to be one of the predominant themes in the arts. Its image symbolizes the core of human nature. Michelangelo's *David* and da Vinci's *Mona Lisa* reflect the deep-rooted sentiment of Pico della Mirandola when he said, "There is nothing to be seen more wonderful than the image of man."[2]

The late Archaic, early classical period's *Kritios Boy* was sculpted with a perceived ideality of physical proportion and muscular strength. Varied representations of the human form continued into the Golden Age's melding of chiaroscuro and what Rembrandt called "beweechgelickhijt."[3] Proportion and physical strength evolved into impressionism's ease of interpretation and spontaneity through visual experience and effects of light. In contrast, the human form was pulled apart and broken down in cubism's reassembled pieces. Communicating directly to popular culture, pop art's larger than life portraits from Mao to Monroe turned the human idealized form into perceived icons. Removing the icon from popularity and rendering the banal, Fluxus blurred the interpretational form with performative art itself. New media's electronically extended platforms augment the human with robotic machines, as with the Internet performance of Ping Body.[4] Transbio design's conceptual representation of the human form syncretizes technology and biology, as with Primo Posthuman.[5]

In *Art of the Electronic Age*, Frank Popper constructs a timeline of works framing advances in electronic practices, which cover the telematic, interactive, immersive, sensorial, and performative spheres in intimately connecting the machine and man. As Popper writes, "although technological art is clearly the art form most representative of our Electronic Age, its full implications lie in the future. The artists share an exploration into a vast spectrum of aesthetics with the various electronic technologies."[6] Popper evidences the relationship between technology and artist in works that visibly reflect the time frame in which they are constructed and in epitomizing reciprocity where both artist and viewer benefit from the bioelectronic exchange.

---

[2] William Fleming, *Arts and Ideas*, Rev. ed. (New York: Holt, 1963), 284.

[3] *Rembrandt Harmenszoon Van Rijn*, Available: http://www.francescorizzi.com/version_EN/Links/Rembrandt.html2010. Seymour Slive, "Art Historians and Art Critics—Il Huygens on Rembrandt," *The Burlington Magazine* 94, no. 594,1 (1952): 260-264.

[4] Stelarc, *Parasite: Event for Invaded and Involuntary Body,* a performance at the 1997 Ars Electronica Festival in Linz, Austria. Available: http://www.stelarc.va.com.au/.

[5] Natasha Vita-More, Primo Posthuman—Future Human Body Prototype, 1999, Available: http://www.natasha.cc/primo.htm.

[6] Frank Popper, *Art of the Electronic Age* (New York: Harry N. Abrams, 1993).

The aggregate of practices that share creative uses of electronics and computers also seek to augment the sensorial experience and reality—including the artist, the viewer, and the works themselves. Sensory expansions affect the viewer's reality through uses of light and space in impacting perceptions, as in Turrell's architectural illusion of *Skyscape*.[7] Altered reality in the medium of video offers a different sensorial exchange by evoking emotional narratives through the sheer magnitude of the figures, their movements, and gestures, as in Viola's *The Greeting*.[8] Presence and realness of connectivity between computer and corporeal interaction brings the virtual and real into a shared, augmented space as in Ascott's *Aspects of Gaia: Digital Pathways Across the Whole Earth*.[9]

Human augmentation may influence and impact traditional notions of classical style as contextualized by history in experiencing, examining, and understanding works of art. Merleau-Ponty's phenomenological theory suggests that human perception stylizes what it perceives "because it cannot help but to constitute and express a point of view."[10] An individual's frame of reference may be typical or vastly atypical depending on his sensory and cognitive augmented attributes and capabilities, suggesting a richer sensorial and cognitive reaction to style. Virtually enhanced head displays, such as *Eyetap*,[11] enable augmented visual attributes by replacing the field of vision of one eye with a camera and computer that manipulate the real-time images with preferential, stylized images. In a cognitively enhanced environment, reality turns the viewer into a participator by providing the tools to build her own personalized reality firsthand.[12]

Assessing the technologies and sciences available to us today, we can identify ancient myths and project future trends that reflect and affect our ever-changing nature. The stylized cyborg combines the ideal of perfection with the machine, as a primary human mythic archetype, comprised of robotics and electronics, as the cyborg "will not only make a significant step forward in man's scientific progress, but may well provide a new and larger dimension for man's spirit as well."[13] The

---

[7]   James Turrell, *Skyscape* (Pomona University), 2008, Available: http://www.arcspace. com/exhibitions/turrell/turrell.html.

[8]   Bill Viola, *The Greeting*, 1995, Available: http://www.medienkunstnetz.de/works/the-greeting/.

[9]   Roy Ascott, *Aspects of Gaia: Digital Pathways across the Whole Earth*, an installation for the 1989 Ars Electronica Festival in Linz, Austria.

[10] Maurice Merleau-Ponty and Claude Lefort, *The Visible and the Invisible; Followed by Working Notes*, Northwestern University Studies in Phenomenology & Existential Philosophy (Evanston [Ill.]: Northwestern University Press, 1968).

[11] Steve Mann, *The Eyetop Lab*, 1998, Available: http://www.eyetap.org.

[12] Damien Broderick, *The White Abacus* (New York: Avon Books, 1997).

[13] Manfred E. Clynes and Nathan S. Kline, "Cyborgs and Space," *Astronautics* (1960): 33.

cybernetic posthuman combines the alchemic past and a future noosphere by inferring the immateriality of consciousness.

Yet the transhumanist view of the human form is not differentiated by association with a metal cyborg or disembodied human, as Katherine Hayles,[14] in her contribution to *The Global Spiral*, suggests, but as a synergistic being, comprising a fluid continuity of self[15] over time and suggesting distributed identity over disembodiment. Therefore, the continuation of personal existence is instrumental to radical life extension, which is the core of transhumanism. When I designed the future human prototype, Primo Posthuman,[16] my aim was to combine design with proposed use of nanotech and biotech. Unlike the classical human form, this prototype takes the ideal of "man" and incorporates the transhumanist value of improving the human condition (in particular, the limited life span). Unlike the cyborg, the prototype's unfolding nature is based on expanding choices. Unlike the disembodied entity discussed by Hayles, the prototype suggests a distributed entity. Rather than an erasure of the human form, the prototype suggests a transbiological form and the continuation of personal existence as "a living organism is an open system in which matter and energy are exchanged within the environment,"[17] and for the human system, consciousness is intrinsic and instrumental. However, for the purposes of transhumanism, "the environment" is understood as "an environment" to clarify that there may be a number of environments where living organisms could exchange matter and energy.

Further, the idea of matter is not limited to biological matter, but different types of substrates, which could contain a living presence or process of life in nonbiological systems and on nonbiological platforms. Here, the transformative human disposition emphasizes regenerative existence as a primary aim, and the construction of its mass, or body, whether semibiological or synthetic, as a secondary aim.

THE CONCEPT

Design is the "process of taking something from its existing state and moving it to a preferred state."[18] This is why design aptly relates to transhumanism. It

---

[14] N. Katherine Hayles, "Wrestling with Transhumanism," *The Global Spiral* 9, no. 3 (2008), http://www.metanexus.net/magazine/tabid/68/id/10543/default.aspx.

[15] Max More, "The Diachronic Self: Identity, Continuity, Transformation," Thesis (PhD), University of Southern California, 1995.

[16] Natasha Vita-More, "Radical Body Design," Available: http://www.kurzweilai.net/meme/frame.html?m=5.

[17] I. Prigogine and Isabelle Stengers, *Order out of Chaos: Man's New Dialogue with Nature* (New York: Bantam Books, 1984).

[18] *Carnegie Mellon Design*, Carnegie Mellon University, Available: http://design.cmu.edu/index.php.

also relates to the adaptive processes of the human species. In *The Human Use of Human Beings*, Norbert Wiener states, "The human species is strong only insofar as it takes advantage of the innate, adaptive, learning faculties that its physiological structure makes possible."[19] This view of cybernetics contrasts with Jean-Pierre Dupuy's assertion in *The Global Spiral* when he writes, "Cybernetics is meant to signify control, mastery, governance . . ."[20]—over mankind.

According to Alfred North Whitehead, organisms anticipate the future, choose routes to take, and then adjust their behavior accordingly, as "every organism exhibits some degree of aim or purpose,"[21] thereby becoming a model. Such a model can be seen in what Whitehead provides as a philosophical vision of behavior. Also, such a model can be recognized in Wiener's scientific framework of cybernetics and the potential for organisms to be viewed as formations in assessing technological advancements. Notably, "a living organism is no longer seen as a permanent form but rather as a network of activity. With this new definition of life, the philosophy of becoming supersedes the philosophy of being . . ."[22] and life becomes a process bound to a notion of change.

THE ADAPTATION

In May 2007, MIT Media Lab held a symposium to explore how technology is merging with humans and to define the emerging science of human adaptability.

> The story of civilization is the story of humans and their tools. Use of tools has changed the human mind, altered the human body, and fundamentally reshaped human identity . . . . A science is emerging that combines a new understanding of how humans work to usher in a new generation of machines that mimic or aid human physical and mental capabilities . . . . Given all or even most of this population a quality of life beyond mere survival is both the scientific challenge

---

[19] Norbert Wiener, *The Human Use of Human Beings: Cybernetics and Society* (Boston: Houghton Mifflin, 1954) 58.

[20] Jean-Pierre Dupuy, "Cybernetics Is an Antihumanism: Advanced Technologies and the Rebellion against the Human Condition," *The Global Spiral* 9, no. 3 (2008), http://www.metanexus.net/magazine/tabid/68/id/10544/Default.aspx.

[21] Alfred North Whitehead, David Ray Griffin and Donald W. Sherburne, *Process and Reality: An Essay in Cosmology*, Gifford Lectures [Delivered at the University of Edinburgh], Corrected ed. (New York: Free Press, 1978).

[22] *H2.0 - New Minds, New Bodies, New Identities: Ushering a New Era for Human Capability*, 2007, MIT Media Lab, Available: http://h20.media.mit.edu/about.html.

of the epoch and the basis for a coming resolution over what it means to be human.[23]

Design and Process. Human beings demand change as a result of evolutionary cravings for stimuli. But how will our senses be satisfied in the future? A group of designers at ID Fuel agree that "it could be argued that the reason humans have come so far so fast where technology is concerned, is that we've never been satisfied with our own physical abilities. Our arms weren't fast enough to catch fish, so we whittled fishhooks. Our feet got cut when we worked tending crops, so we covered them with shoes. Our eyes went blind in the glaring snow, so we carved slitted goggles from wood to protect them. And, as our command of tools continues to improve, so do the items we develop to augment ourselves."[24]

State of the Art Human Futures. Consider a field of human biosculpture, where the human body, mind, and identity are modified by the user. If design is a social process, then the art of human enhancement can be viewed as a process of adaptation. For artists and designers in the biological arts, the idea of molding or sculpting the human form has enormous potential. For media artists in interactive, immersive environments, the idea of virtuality as a constructed identity has continuing value regardless of its creator. Tom Ray, creator of the Tierra artificial life simulation, suggests that "the idea of creating life is exciting but extending life of humans for the purposes of continued and regenerative existence may not be realized as a mode of aesthetic creation in traditional works of art."[25]

Even if we accept the 2,480-year-old *Kritios Boy* as a traditional aesthetic creation, over time it broke down and was restructured—its body in 1965 and its head in 1988. Like the metamorphic rock, humans are made of atoms, which systems deconstruct over time. We too need to be restructured when our parts break down. Outside the sphere of what Ray identifies as traditionalized art comes the NBIC quartet as the probable tools for aesthetic creations of continued and regenerative existence.

THE DEATH

Atoms make up molecules, and molecules make up cells. Cells organize to make up systems, and the systems (organs) make up an organism. Atoms are, for the most part, indestructible and, thereby, immortal. However, the most stable state for

---

[23] *H2.0: New Minds, New Bodies, New Identities; Ushering a New Era for Human Capability.*

[24] *Humansys: Further Human Enhancement,* Available: http://www.idfuel.com/index.ph p?blog=2&p=451&more=1&c=1&tb=1&pb=1.

[25] Tom Ray, e-mail message to author, March 2007.

the atoms of living systems is as molecules, not as isolated atoms. Atoms are more stable when joined together than when isolated, so you will never see degradation of living systems all the way down to the atomic level.

The death of cells is known as apoptosis—and it is theorized that every cell is programmed to die. Each cell contains genetic information related to its life span, and this span is different for cells in different organs. The triggering of cell death is considered to be a protection against mutation of offspring cells, which are more exposed to risk than the parent stem cells. According to Grey Fahy of 21st Century Medicine cryobiology laboratory:

> The molecular components of living cells are constantly being broken down and built back up again. Molecular modules will last until (a) they are hydrolyzed by direct, spontaneous reaction with water, (b) they are transformed into something else by extraneous reactions such as oxidation or other forms of random damage, or (c) they are absorbed by a living entity and rebuilt into that entity.[26]

Personalizing Death. The human form continues to be one of the predominant themes in the narrative arts, reminding us of human-perceived ideals and of human misfortune. Denigrating human biology is not the telos of life for transhumanists. Rather, it is the perceived ideal of a "continuation" over time and the ability to endure—that even if we age and fall apart, we can reconstruct and continue to live on.

I turn to Derek Parfit on personal identity and continuity: "What matters to me in ordinary survival is not identity over time, but something else. Further, since the only thing of significance in common between fission and ordinary survival is the psychological connectedness/continuity . . ."[27] Parfit suggests that persons are themselves separate and distinct from their bodies, but those persons' existence is, in fact, nothing other than the existence of a brain and a body, the foundation of Parfit's constitutive reductionism. An analogy applied to this understanding is suggested by Carsten Korfmacher:

> Cellini's *Venus* is made of bronze. Although the lump of bronze and the statue itself surely exist, these objects have different persistence conditions: if melted down, *Venus* ceases to exist while the lump of bronze does not. Therefore, they are not identical; rather, so the suggestion, the lump of bronze constitutes the statue. The same is true of persons, who are constituted by, but not identical with, a physiology,

---

26   Greg Fahy, e-mail message to author, March 2007.
27   Derek Parfit, "Personal Identity," *The Philosophical Review* 80, no. 1 (1971).

a psychology, and the occurrence of an interrelated series of causal and cognitive relations.[28]

I do not intend this to be a diversion, but more an insight into a growing concern about personalizing death. A person might have a biological death but continue, immediately or sequentially, in another platform. This might be looked at as a transformative or transitional stage but not an irreversible death. It also bears on the notion of an optional and temporary death—one could decide to cease to exist in one platform for a period of time but continue in a different medium, or cease to exist in any platform until a later date.

THE ISSUE

According to Popper, the full implications of technology's use lie in the future. Popper suggests that those who create share a "preoccupation with exploiting a vast spectrum of aesthetic categories" with advanced technologies and an "awareness of the extent of social and cultural change produced by the latest technological developments . . . to bring about a significant relationship between basic human experiences . . . and the radical and global intrusion into them of the new technologies, in all walks of life, with all the beneficial effects, potential hazards and immense possibilities they offer."[29]

I recognize the many questions and concerns about whether or not modifying or enhancing the human is advantageous, and there is deep interest in the ratio of positive versus negative outcomes of human enhancement. Nevertheless, most of the relevant literature reports a consensus of opinion that NBIC technologies—separately or together—will inevitably affect human biology and increase human life spans. What might those working within the exploratory sciences, especially biology and life extension (gerontology), grasp from this opinion? Neither over-enthusiasm nor overwhelming negativity offers a solution because both options lack the transdisciplinary rigor necessary for strategizing the future, and because both are sorely outdated by pigeonholing the potential of creative possibilities into one or the other. This offers little option other than to choose between them. We must develop a field that addresses human futures and the transformative human by engaging more inclusive discussion and encouraging deeper research and study.

---

28   Carsten Korfmacher, "Personal Identity," *The Internet Encyclopedia of Philosophy* (2006), June 2, 2009 <http://www.iep.utm.edu/person-i/>.

29   Popper, *Art of the Electronic Age.*

Hayles claims that "there is little discussion of how access to advanced technologies would be regulated or of the social and economic inequalities entwined with the questions of access."[30] The issue of distribution is one of the most often-discussed transhumanist topics, as evidenced by the numerous transhumanist venues expressly developed for this purpose. Hayles continues with "or at least that transhumanist individuals will be among the privileged elite that can afford the advantages advanced technologies will offer."[31] While I have admiration and respect for Hayles's scholarship on many topics, this is one where she is uninformed. My televised cable program *Transcentury Update*, which aired in Los Angeles and Telluride from 1986 through 1993, broadcast numerous segments on the political and ethical issues of technology and segments on building scenarios for the global distribution of technology (green energy, etc.), the latter largely based on Buckminster Fuller's distribution plan.[32] Far more recently, the Extropy Institute discussed these issues at its 2004 Vital Progress Summit,[33] whose press release stated "[n]o organization, no policy, no person should have the absolute power and authority to hinder scientific and medical advances that can and do help millions of people throughout the world."[34] And more recently still, the Institute for Ethics and Emerging Technologies addresses these issues as fundamental to our future.

THE FIELD

Over the past five or more decades, artists have developed a variety of descriptive entities—the cyborg, transhuman, prosthetic being, posthuman, avatar, and upload—all as a result of artistic works that aim to extend cognition, mobility, and the senses. Artists have also developed alternative environments to exist within, such as the virtual atmosphere of the gaming, interactivity, the Metaverse, and new environments not yet realized—that of enhanced reality and telepresence. Artists have also developed corresponding theoretical views such as telematics and technoethics, and philosophical worldviews such as transhumanism. These efforts reflect an anticipated awareness of the sciences and technologies of biological and artificial modification, and issues of consciousness and identity.

Computer-generated works, including robotics, AI, and virtuality, as well as biological arts in altering cell structures, signify the developing artistic field of human enhancement. In introducing NBIC sciences and technologies as potential media, artistic options will

---

[30] Hayles, "Wrestling with Transhumanism."

[31] Hayles, "Wrestling with Transhumanism."

[32] R. Buckminster Fuller, *Critical Path*, 1st ed. (New York: St. Martin's Press, 1981).

[33] *About the Vital Progress ("Vp") Summit 2004*: Austin, TX.

[34] *About the Vital Progress ("Vp") Summit 2004.*

expand in creating new practices for designing of biosynthetic bodies, sensorial extension, cognitive enrichment, gender diversity, identity transfer, and radical life extension.

The exploratory experimentation and manipulation of biological life systems, from single cells to organisms, increases the transdisciplinarity of the arts and sciences. As noted, some practices have reached far into the uncomfortable zone of bioengineering and genetics, where science and medicine reside, in aptly creating bioexperiments and offering opinions on the meaning of life. On another side of the creative spectrum, exploratory creations with nanotechnological particles have become a molecular vehicle for establishing artistic practice and theory. The transformative human arises when we combine biodesign and nanodesign, along with information technology and cognitive/neuroscience. The practice and theory concerning the scope of human enhancement is, I suggest, located at the transformative human. This becomes a projected field concerning human futures, especially for the purpose of radical life extension.

In one sentence: the required tools are found in the coming together of nanotechnology, biotechnology, information technology, and the neurological and cognitive sciences provide the transdisciplinary media for investigating the continuation of life by enhancing, extending, and regenerating life in biological, synthetic and cybernetic forms.

While Dupuy suggests that NBIC are dehumanizing humanity, I see it quite differently. He states, "They quarrel with the very fact that we are born."[35] To the contrary, I thank my mother very dearly that she birthed me and wish that when I was pregnant that I had the good health and the medical advances to have carried my pregnancy to term as well.

THE STUDY

Lowry Burgess of Carnegie Mellon's "Studio for Creative Inquiry," offers a pedagogical approach to the future. The program's mission elegantly states, "interdisciplinary projects bring together the arts, sciences, technology, and the humanities, and impact local and global communities."[36] It seems that a wide-open view of the arts and personal responsibility ties in nicely to the field of future studies.

Cultivating observational "polis pods" for discourse on the future, including transhumanism, is timely. The impacts of change affect everyone, regardless of what domain the changes originally occur in and where the impacts are first felt.

---

[35]   Dupuy, "Cybernetics Is an Antihumanism: Advanced Technologies and the Rebellion against the Human Condition."

[36]   *Fellowships*, Carnegie Mellon College of Fine Arts, Available: http://www.cmu.edu/studio/fellowships/index.html.

Considering the evolving human form as a research objective is imperative because of the intersection of human enhancement and the future, as well as academic discourse pertaining to theories concerning this intersection. For the past twenty years, I have engaged in the fields of media arts and the social science of futurology concerning human enhancement technologies. Through this immersion, my insights have developed beyond the biotechnological attributes, toward ideological viewpoints and the worldview of transhumanism, including the body biopolitic and personal biofreedom of human enhancements. Of course this is directly affected by issues of when life begins and ends, identity in simulated environments, the conjectured transhuman and posthuman. I have come to understand that a developed approach to human enhancement reaches beyond electronic media, bioart, and immersive design. I propose that what is needed is a field focusing on radical life extension, especially at the convergence of NBIC technologies. These technologies and the supporting science relate to the push beyond limited life span, senescence, and apoptosis, toward regenerative existence and optional death. To balance out the discussion between disenchanted spectators and transhumanism, we need more creative inquiry. Let's adjust our caps at a slight tilt and engage with more information and constructive creative thinking, for "ideas evolve just as do living things."[37]

THE CONCLUSION

Bringing arts/sciences and design into the contemporary discussion of transhumanism reflects the idea of the human as a form which transforms. Over time, the inventive approach has been to augment, extend, modify, and enhance our communication, our mobility, and our experiences of the world around us. Often when our passions are the driving force of change, they are discounted or misconceived. To sum up this sentiment, I refer to a misconception about *Brave New World*.

Brave New World represents the fears of society toward the possible negative outcomes of emerging technologies. This is a regretful paradox because Aldous Huxley borrowed the phrase from Shakespeare, where it occurs in Miranda's inspiring soliloquy in *The Tempest:*

> *O Wonder!*
> *How many goodly creatures there are here!*
> *How beauteous mankind is! O brave new world*
> *That has such people in 't!*

---

[37]   Jonas Salk, *Man Unfolding*, World Perspectives, 1st ed. (New York: Harper & Row, 1972), 77-78.

"Shakespeare's words originally meant something far different"[38] than what Huxley intended in his famed story *Brave New World*. Huxley's satirical piece is fiction, not scientific prophecy. "Though Huxley's vision seems, to the cynic or to the defeatist, to have prevailed in this strange age, it is Shakespeare's insightful vision that resonates more strongly in its deep perception, in its profundity, and in its power to inspire."[39] Perhaps future discussions will inject a little more Shakespeare and a little less Huxley fear.

What is not science fiction is the fact that our species's biology is fragile. This fragility is recognized in diseases such as brain trauma, spinal injury, cell degeneration, and apoptosis. The slowing down, malfunction, and loss of physiological performance erase the precious moments of existence we experience in giving meaning to our lives. The sustainability of existence is at the crux of human enhancement futures, whereby a person could extend existence past the fixed biological time frame.

From the perspective of the last decades, the vast potential of technological art lies in the future. That future is now, and one set of multimedia is NBIC. It is from this vantage that I introduce the cybernetic transformative aesthetics for conceptualizing the future human, whether cyborg, transhuman, prosthetic being, or posthuman as they relate to human enhancement.

The field of human enhancement is linked to cyborg theory, which illustrates man and machine as a primary human mythic archetype, comprised of robotics and electronics. Human enhancement is linked to the theoretical view of distributed identity rather than the disembodied posthuman. Human enhancement combines the philosophical poiesis with techne by coalescing the psychological behaviors of intuition—heightened awareness of the world around us—with an artistic/design-based intention and anticipated outcome.

As art technology historian Frank Popper observed, artists share a preoccupation with exploiting a vast spectrum of aesthetic categories in works of art with numerous advanced technologies and an

> . . . awareness of the extent of social and cultural change produced by the latest technological developments . . . to bring about a significant relationship between basic human experiences . . . and the radical and global intrusion into them of the new technologies, in all walks of life, with all the beneficial effects, potential hazards and immense possibilities they offer.[40]

---

38   Eileen M. Ciesla, "Miranda's Invitation," <http://jollyroger.com/miranda/invitation.html>.
39   Ciesla, "Miranda's Invitation."
40   Popper, *Art of the Electronic Age,* 181.

REFERENCES

About the Vital Progress ("Vp") Summit 2004. Vital Progress Sumit 2004. Austin, TX.

"Carnegie Mellon Design." Carnegie Mellon University. http://design.cmu.edu/index.php.

"Fellowships." *Studio for Creative Inquiry.* Carnegie Mellon College of Fine Arts. http://www.cmu.edu/studio/fellowships/index.html.

"H2.0: New Minds, New Bodies, New Identities; Ushering a New Era for Human Capability." 2007. *h2.0* MIT Media Lab. http://h20.media.mit.edu/about.html.

"Humansys: Further Human Enhancement." *ID Fuel.* http://www.idfuel.com/index.php?blog=2&p=451&more=1&c=1&tb=1&pb=1.

"Radical Body Design by Natasha Vita-More." *KurzweilAI.net.* http://www.kurzweilai.net/meme/frame.html?m=5.

"Rembrandt Harmenszoon Van Rijn." *Francesco Rizzi Art.* 2010. http://www.francescorizzi.com/version_EN/Links/Rembrandt.html.

Ascott, Roy. *Aspects of Gaia: Digital Pathways across the Whole Earth.* An installation at the 1989 Ars Electronica Festival in Linz, Austria.

Broderick, Damien. *The White Abacus.* New York: Avon Books, 1997.

Ciesla, Eileen M. "Miranda's Invitation." http://jollyroger.com/miranda/invitation.html.

Clynes, Manfred E., and Nathan S. Kline. "Cyborgs and Space." *Astronautics* (1960): 29-33.

Dupuy, Jean-Pierre. "Cybernetics Is an Antihumanism: Advanced Technologies and the Rebellion against the Human Condition." *The Global Spiral* 9, no. 3 (2008). http://www.metanexus.net/magazine/tabid/68/id/10544/Default.aspx.

Fleming, William. *Arts and Ideas.* Rev. ed. New York: Holt, 1963. Print.

Fuller, R. Buckminster. *Critical Path.* 1st ed. New York: St. Martin's Press, 1981. Print.

Hayles, N. Katherine. "Wrestling with Transhumanism." *The Global Spiral* 9, no. 3 (2008). http://www.metanexus.net/magazine/tabid/68/id/10543/default.aspx.

Korfmacher, Carsten. "Personal Identity." *The Internet Encyclopedia of Philosophy* (2006). June 2, 2009. http://www.iep.utm.edu/person-i/.

Mann, Steve. "The Eyetop Lab." 1998. http://www.eyetap.org.

Merleau-Ponty, Maurice, and Claude Lefort. *The Visible and the Invisible; Followed by Working Notes.* Northwestern University Studies in Phenomenology & Existential Philosophy. Evanston [Ill.]: Northwestern University Press, 1968.

More, Max. "The Diachronic Self: Identity, Continuity, Transformation." Thesis (PhD). University of Southern California, 1995.

Parfit, Derek. "Personal Identity." *The Philosophical Review* 80, no. 1 (1971): 3-27.

Popper, Frank. *Art of the Electronic Age.* New York: Harry N. Abrams, 1993.

Prigogine, I., and Isabelle Stengers. *Order out of Chaos: Man's New Dialogue with Nature.* New York: Bantam Books, 1984.

Roco, M. C., and W. S. Bainbridge. "Converging Technologies for Improving Human Performance: Integrating from the Nanoscale." *Journal of Nanoparticle Research* 4, no. 4 (2002): 281-95.

Salk, Jonas. *Man Unfolding*. World Perspectives, 1st ed. New York: Harper & Row, 1972.

Slive, Seymour. "Art Historians and Art Critics-II: Huygens on Rembrandt." *The Burlington Magazine* 94, no. 594 (1952): 261-64.

Stelarc. *Parasite: Event for Invaded and Involuntary Body*. An performance at the 1997 Ars Electronica Festival in Linz, Austria. http://www.stelarc.va.com.au/.

Turrell, James. "Skyscape (Pomona University)." 2008. *arcspace.com*. http://www.arcspace.com/exhibitions/turrell/turrell.html.

Viola, Bill. "The Greeting." 1995. *Media Art Net*. http://www.medienkunstnetz.de/works/the-greeting/.

Vita-More, Natasha. "Primo Posthuman—Future Human Body Prototype." 1999. *Future Body 2006*. http://www.natasha.cc/primo.htm.

Whitehead, Alfred North, David Ray Griffin, and Donald W. Sherburne. *Process and Reality: An Essay in Cosmology*. Gifford Lectures [Delivered at the University of Edinburgh]. Corrected ed. New York: Free Press, 1978.

Wiener, Norbert. *The Human Use of Human Beings: Cybernetics and Society*. Boston: Houghton Mifflin, 1954.

Chapter Five

Playing by the Rules—or Not? Constructions of Identity in a Posthuman Future

by Sky Marsen

Scientific developments and changes in how humans define themselves, and in how they live and interact, often go hand in hand. Throughout history, progress in science and technology has allowed humans to overcome physical constraints and to increase choice and opportunity. At the same time, it has created new power relations and generated a host of new existential questions. In discourses and debates about human existence, technology tends to play a contrastive role: it is seen either as an aid to a fulfilling existence or as an enemy to social cohesion and the preservation of the status quo. Adopting a transhumanist perspective, this essay briefly discusses some effects of science and technology on the human quest for personal meaning, individual freedom, and happiness. In particular, the essay examines how transhumanist ideas contribute to attempts to reconceptualize the notion of personal identity in light of technological developments. The essay is divided into two main parts. The first part of the paper discusses transhumanism in relation to the interplay between identity and technology. The second part presents an analysis, inspired by transhumanist ideas, of the science fiction film *Gattaca*.

SCIENCE, TRANSHUMANISM, AND EXISTENCE

Science and technology can modify human physical constitution in a way that redefines agency and identity, and allows individuals to lead personally meaningful lives. Such changes, however, have far-reaching consequences on social values and accepted norms and are not embraced without trepidation. Two examples from the first decade of the twenty-first century, chosen at random, illustrate clearly the ambivalent attitudes toward technologically produced modifications, as well as the reactions of the popular media that such modifications attract.

On January 16, 2005, Adriana Iliescu, aged sixty-six, gave birth to a baby girl conceived through in vitro fertilization and donor eggs, making her the oldest known woman to give birth at that time.[1] As is the case with stories of postmenopausal women and procreation, this event attracted popular media attention and a host of controversy. Public response included praise for the technology that enabled this to happen as well as criticisms concerning Iliescu's ability to raise a child after she had passed the socially prescribed stage of motherhood.[2]

In 2008, British military paratrooper Ian Hamilton underwent a series of surgical procedures to change his sex from male to female. His decision had serious repercussions on his military career, with a series of hostile exchanges between Hamilton and the British Army. It was also detrimental to his family life, with his parents disowning him.[3] The controversy that unfolded in the popular media surrounding this sex change seems to have been compounded by Hamilton's military profession, with its connotations of masculinity and conservatism. This was a good example of how popular culture conflates psychological disposition, social status, and physical appearance.

Examples such as these illustrate at best, the controversy, at worst, the resistance that deliberate changes to socially prescribed identity attract from a society that sees these changes as serious offenses to its myths of linearity, continuity, and essence. Indeed, the ambivalent role of technology and science (and indeed of any form of knowledge) can be found in social debates since ancient times. However, the historical situation in the early twenty-first century has certain peculiarities. We live in an era where significant advances are made in information technology, imaging technology, nanotechnology, and genetics—advances that give us access to areas of human physiology previously hidden from view (such as the functions of different parts of the brain) and that promise to give more control over natural processes previously thought of as unchangeable (such as genetically inherited traits). In this context, we need a conceptual framework in which we can theorize and speculate on these advances, both anticipating and suggesting their possible uses, benefits, risks, and consequences. In other words, we need intellectual and cultural perspectives from where we can observe, think, and talk about these advances. Science fiction is one such forum where technology is conceptualized in cultural terms. The group of futurist discourses grouped under the term *transhumanism* is another.

---

[1] Kristen Philipkoski, "No Magic for Older Moms," *Wired*, January 19, 2005.

[2] The popular British newspaper *The Telegraph* set up an online forum eliciting public responses on Iliescu's status as a postmenopausal mother, www.telegraph.co.uk.

[3] See Jane Preston's Channel Four documentary, *Sex Change Soldier*, first aired on British television, Channel Four, 20 March 2008.

Transhumanism is a set of dynamic and diverse approaches to the relationship between technology, self, and society. Since transhumanism is not a crystallized and static doctrine, my use of the term in this essay requires definition. The working definition that informs the subsequent discussion is this: transhumanism is a general term designating a set of approaches that hold an optimistic view of technology as having the potential to assist humans in building more equitable and happier societies mainly by modifying individual physical characteristics. Such modifications include cognitive enhancements to increase mental abilities and genetic interventions to eliminate disease and prolong life. Some branches of transhumanism also research methods to transfer consciousness from its physical embodiment to cybernetic forms and so elude death altogether.

A defining characteristic of transhumanism is that it proposes an "alternative" interpretation and evaluation of science while maintaining and supporting "mainstream" principles and methods of scientific research. In this respect, it differs from nontechnophile New Age philosophies because it embraces scientific, or rational, principles. These include the tenets that not all phenomena can be reduced to absolute causes, that randomness is a law of the universe, and that big effects may have much smaller causes. This way, transhumanism retains scientific methods of falsifiability, precision, and objectivity, while investigating how they can be put at the service of the human goals of social justice and individual fulfillment.

Those attracted to the transhumanist movement (which consists largely of a network of individuals meeting mostly in online fora and some conferences) tend to share an interest in science fiction and in the philosophy of science, as well as a belief that human design contains flaws that can and should be corrected if we are to create an enlightened society that caters both for the common good and for individual happiness.

Some argue that transhumanism idealizes technology and overlooks its limitations and the dangerous consequences it may have.[4] Yet debates on possible effects of scientific developments and on the equitable social regulation of technology proliferate in transhumanist circles. In fact, the concern with implications and effects is evident in Nick Bostrom's description of transhumanism as "the study of the ramifications, promises and potential dangers of the use of science, technology, creativity, and other means to overcome fundamental human limitations."[5]

Indisputably, science and technology do not offer absolute answers to existential questions. One reason for this is that personal meaning comes from an experience of one's subjectivity in interaction with the objective world. It is therefore not

---

[4]   See for example, Ted Peters's essay in this volume "Transhumanism and the Posthuman Future: Will Technological Progress Get Us There?"

[5]   *The Transhumanist Frequently Asked Questions*, section 1.1. Available at http://www. transhumanism.org/resources/FAQv21.pdf.

assessable in quantifiable terms. Science deals with probabilities and statistical averages. This makes many scientific tenets and declarations irrelevant when applied to individual everyday experiences. In other words, the truth of science not only does not answer the question "what is it to me?" It can also be dismissive of the self-focus that such a question implies. As proponent of positive psychology, Mihaliy Csikzentmihalyi says, "science can promise truth, but its version of truth is as often harsh as it is soothing."[6] Thus, for example, biology can tell me what the odds are that I will exhibit a certain trait, but it cannot tell me if and how this trait will manifest, or what meaning I will attribute to it—whether I will be proud of it, merely accept it, or be ashamed of it. In the final analysis, how I, and others, experience my genetic trait depends on cultural and individual values, social opportunities, and that archenemy of control seekers—chance.

At the same time, however, technological developments can change drastically the human experience of life and the personal meanings and subjectivities that go with this, both by modifying the material world (not many would dispute that living in a modern house is more comfortable than living in a cave) and by adapting human faculties for better performance and resilience in living in this world. In the past two hundred years, human societies have been radically altered by scientific developments, which are now so pervasive they are almost transparent. To mention just a few examples, the contraceptive pill has liberated women from the demands of reproduction and changed the structure of the workforce, making possible living arrangements and experiences that were previously so impractical they were almost unimaginable; antibiotics have radically changed attitudes toward disease and have contributed to extending life spans; and aviation technology has enabled rapid global travel, facilitating access to different parts of the world and, therefore, to different experiences. Such developments are not just add-ons to an unchanging human "essence." They lay the groundwork for the creation of different metaphors, discourses, and representations, and they change the ways in which identities and relationships are perceived and enacted.[7]

This situation motivates an interplay between personal identity and technology that can be constructed and represented in different ways. The texts and narratives that emerge in this context often stage the dilemmas, freedoms,

---

[6]   M. Csikszentmihalyi: *Good Business: Leadership, Flow and the Making of Meaning* (London: Hodder and Stoughton, 2003), 8.

[7]   For a discussion on metaphors of technology in describing human activity, see, for example, George Lakoff's classic text, *Women, Fire and Dangerous Things: What Categories Reveal About the Mind* (Chicago: University of Chicago Press, 1990); and Ulrike Schultze and Wanda Orlikowski's article on organizational discourse, "Metaphors of Virtuality: Shaping an Emergent Reality," in *Information and Organization* 11, no. 1 (2001): 45-77.

and conflicts of individuals in a technologized society. So returning to the example of global travel, although from one perspective the technologies involved can be seen as breakthroughs that enable freedom of movement, trade possibilities, and easy international communications, from another perspective such a development is devoid of value per se and can only be evaluated through the lens of the individual experiences that it grounds. So global relocation can signify freedom from confining social situations, persecution, or poverty, and possibilities for career and educational development for some, but it can also signify the centralization of capitalist globalization, separation from loved ones, exile, culture shock, alienation, and tourist pollution for others (as well as, of course, a combination of these). Thus, the scientific development, as a social artifact, becomes meaningful only in relation to the individual performances that it underpins and, to use an existentialist term, to the "states of being" that these performances generate.

When thinking about matters such as these, we have a choice: we can focus on the negative consequences of technology and lament the mindless arrogance of people who allowed them to develop (as much dystopian science fiction as well as technophobic, or "bioconservative," discourses do), or we can attempt to trace and analyze the elements that produce positive effects and speculate on ways to maximize these—which is what many transhumanist texts do.

Transhumanism has two distinctive features that are pertinent here. First, it begins with human experience and then looks to science (as a body of knowledge based on rational discovery) to find how it can be used by humans to affect this experience. In fact, many transhumanist writers emphasize that the ultimate goal of technology is to enhance the well-being of all humans—and, indeed, of all sentient creatures. As the Transhumanist Declaration states,[8]

> It is not our human shape or the details of our current human biology that define what is valuable about us, but rather our aspirations and ideals, our experiences and the kinds of lives we live. To a transhumanist, progress is when more people become more able to deliberately shape themselves, their lives, and the ways they relate to others, in accordance with their own deepest values.[9]

---

[8]   Principle 7 of the Transhumanist Declaration states: "Transhumanism advocates the well-being of all sentience (whether in artificial intellects, humans, posthumans, or non-human animals) . . . " Available at, http://www.transhumanism.org/index.php/WTA/declaration/.

[9]   *The Transhumanist Frequently Asked Questions* section 1.1. Available at http://www.transhumanism.org/resources/FAQv21.pdf.

Second, it complements approaches that examine the social causes of human suffering and injustice because it focuses on the physical limitations of the "human" itself. For transhumanism, a benevolent welfare society coupled with individual will power and discipline are not enough to guarantee realization of potential, fulfillment, fairness, and diversity. More is required for substantive change than good intentions. Incidentally, this situation in which well-being is mistakenly equated with goodwill is satirized in fictional texts. For example, in Rob Grant's humorous novel *Incompetence*,[10] set in a "politically correct" future society, equal opportunity is the highest value. In this society, policy dictates that no one can be refused a job regardless of the person's qualifications and ability. Inevitable results of this misplaced benevolence include airline pilots who suffer from vertigo, doctors with a blood phobia, and blind security officers. The human agents in this world are hampered by their own physical constitution rather than by laws or prejudices. This underlines that, besides social revisions, we also require modifications to human biology to allow different possibilities of perception, thought, and action to emerge. As Patrick Hopkins explains:

> The first element of a transhumanist moral vision is that the effort to address the human condition requires that we change the physical facts that in part generate the human condition. Curing the human condition requires altering the "human" part of the equation.[11]

In her article "Wrestling with Transhumanism,"[12] N. Katherine Hayles claims that transhumanist texts "perform decontextualizing moves that over-simplify the situation," and offers science fiction as a contextualizing forum. I concede that a significant part of transhumanist discourse constructs reductive and technical models of analysis that could be interpreted as favoring a minimalist version of the human. However, this could also be seen as a reflection of the rhetorical structures used in the communities of many transhumanist writers (who have educational backgrounds in science). As the transhumanist movement grows, it is likely that it will benefit from a wider diversity of supporters and a proportional increase in the kinds of discourses used. In the meantime, motivated by Hayles's claim, I will attempt a transhumanist reading of the film *Gattaca*, directed by Andrew Niccol in 1998.[13]

---

10   Rob Grant, *Incompetence* (London: Orion, 2003).
11   Patrick Hopkins, "A Moral Vision for Transhumanism," in *Journal of Evolution and Technology* 19, no. 1 (2008): 4. Available at http://jetpress.org/v19/hopkins.pdf.
12   Katherine Hayles, "Wrestling with Transhumanism," in this volume.
13   For a more detailed analysis of this film, see Sky Marsen, "Against Heritage: Invented Identities in Science Fiction Film," *Semiotica* 2004, no.152-1/4 (2004): 141-157.

ANALYSIS OF *GATTACA*

Gattaca contextualizes the interface between the freedoms and constraints of a technological society and the personal motivations of the individual. To do this, it creates its story around speculation on the possible effects of human genetic engineering. Developments in genome research suggest that, when the genome is fully decoded, an individual's genetic constitution will become a blueprint of the biological qualities that make this individual unique and motivate his/her behavior and physiopsychological condition. As with other scientific developments, one can expect this to have both positive and negative consequences. For example, it could allow for the customized treatment of diseases for each individual, thereby minimizing adverse side effects. It could also enable the modification of specific genes to prevent diseases or physical weaknesses from being passed on to future generations. At the same time, it could "brand" individuals as specific types, which is very likely to lead to the phenomena of exclusion and scapegoating that most often accompany the creation of stereotypes. This is the situation that *Gattaca* thematizes.

Described briefly, the story is set in a society where power and authority rest with those citizens who are born through genetic engineering ("GATTACA" being the transcription for human DNA). These privileged citizens have been engineered to possess skills that enable them to work in specific professions. In this context, social mobility is a predetermined system with fixed criteria: job interviews, for example, are based solely on DNA sampling and have no personalized or negotiable aspect. Those unfortunate to have been born through natural means form an underclass of outcasts, restricted by their inherited weaknesses and confined to menial tasks. The film presents a social setting where identity is defined in terms of social functionality, as this is perceived to be determined by genetics.

The main character, Vincent Freeman (the name itself signifying "winning" and "freedom"), a natural-born with inherited defects, such as a weak heart and bad eyesight, finds his desired socioprofessional status to be unattainable, as he is forbidden to pursue the aeronautic career that he values. However, every time a rule is created, the means to break this rule also emerges. *Gattaca's* society includes "identity brokers" who help the so-called invalids to construct a new and more successful identity by finding socially acceptable individuals who are willing to trade their identities with the genetically less fortunate. In order to realize his dream, Vincent finds just such an accomplice, Jerome Morrow, and he gradually assumes his identity. In the technological society of *Gattaca*, where citizens are repeatedly blood and urine-tested to confirm their genetic identities, this exchange of identities entails much more than a forging of documents. Vincent has to carry samples of Jerome's blood, urine, nails, skin, and hair for the daily DNA tests.

Although at first sight this may seem like a standard dystopian story, a closer look at the construction of the main character supports a different interpretation.

First, Vincent is not the usual dystopian hero whose actions are directed at finding his "true" self or at discovering an "original" identity that was stolen from him by a society that uses technology to manipulate and control its citizens. Rather, he is a transformational agent, whose actions are directed at dismantling an enforced, inherited identity and creating one that is more amenable to his desired existence. He is happy to shed his identity (quite literally in this case, since he scrubs off the outer layer of his skin every day) if this identity is an obstacle to obtaining the experiences that he desires. Second, Vincent does not intend to destroy or change his technological society for a more "natural" existence but wants to renegotiate his position in it. Also, he relies on the technology of the system to fulfill his aspirations. His transformation itself is aided by technology (he has surgery to become taller, wears contact lenses to correct vision and change the color of his eyes, etc.), and his ideal career is in the high-tech profession of interstellar navigation.

By presenting the main character this way, the film's ideology stands in contrast to the ideology widespread in much popular culture, which espouses that the be-all and end-all of the quest for personhood is to achieve an integrated and unified identity, usually by accepting some limitation or by finding a hidden, true self. Instead, the main criterion by which to evaluate personal identity becomes here the criterion of happiness. Since Vincent's socially defined identity constrains him, the narrative allows him to use technological means to shed it like discarded skin. This alone, I contend, would qualify him as a transhumanist hero.

Vincent challenges the system by exploiting its weaknesses. So what then are these weaknesses, and what do they show about the possible dangers of technological advancement? I distinguish two in the story: the unchecked existence of human prejudice, and the coexistence of conflicting and anachronistic conceptual systems.

Arguably, the most prominent danger exposed by the film is human prejudice. Vincent suffers not because of his actual physical constitution but because of others' attitudes toward stereotypes, which he has to endure. His society has laws against "genoism," but as Vincent points out, "no one takes the law seriously." This parallels the situation in our present early twenty-first century society (not to say in all known societies), where legislation does not reflect social attitudes and where change can only occur in any substantial sense when new meanings, and not just new laws, are created.

Interestingly, although the society of *Gattaca* is focused on matching abilities with social function, the abilities of impartial judgment and empathy (which could counteract prejudice) are not evoked in any of the social roles presented in the story. For example, the director of the aeronautic institute declares that if someone succeeds in tasks for which he or she was considered incapable, this does not mean that this individual exceeded his or her potential: "no one exceeds his potential; it would mean that we didn't accurately gauge his potential in the first place." However, no mention is made of the processes used to assess abilities and match them with actions, or of the reasoning and ideologies that underlie these processes. Therefore, a transhumanist moral of this story is that understanding human prejudice and the forms it can take should be part of the program to reinvent identity in the future.

The second danger, closely related to the first, is anachronistic concepts and definitions. The film shows what might happen with technological advancement if other factors (especially conceptual factors, such as dominant metaphors) are not updated to keep up with this advancement. It does this through the textual strategy of constructing a society where genetic engineering has progressed considerably since the late twentieth century, but where everything else seems to be lagging. For example, the definition of *physically fit* remains exactly the same as the one used in the late twentieth and early twenty-first centuries. Vincent is barred from his desired profession because he is deemed to be not physically fit. Yet, after a while, one begins to wonder why he needs perfect vision and a strong heart for the kinds of tasks his job requires. The fact that he succeeds in them despite his "defects" shows that the definition of the agent does not match the actions or abilities of the agent. It is also interesting that "keeping fit" is still imaged as running on a treadmill, which suggests that concepts and metaphors of physicality have not changed. So another moral of the story lies in the importance of how people think and talk about things (as manifest in concepts, definitions, metaphors, and other discursive strategies) in enabling new forms of identity to emerge.

In this essay, I briefly overviewed transhumanist approaches to the creation of personal identity in a technological society. At the very least, I hope to have shown that transhumanist ideas expand the scope of discussions on social and personal implications of technology by suggesting two questions: "What narratives would we get if we cast technology in a helper's role?" and "What do these narratives show about our (human) hopes, aspirations, and fears?"

REFERENCES

Csikszentmihalyi, M. *Good Business: Leadership, Flow and the Making of Meaning.* London: Hodder and Stoughton, 2003.

Grant, Rob. *Incompetence.* London: Orion, 2003.

Hayles, Katherine. "Wrestling with Transhumanism."

Hopkins, Patrick. "A Moral Vision for Transhumanism." *Journal of Evolution and Technology* 19, no. 1 (2008): 4. http://jetpress.org/v19/hopkins.pdf

Lakoff, George. *Women, Fire and Dangerous Things: What Categories Reveal About the Mind.* Chicago: University of Chicago Press, 1990.

Marsen, Sky. "Against Heritage: Invented Identities in Science Fiction Film." *Semiotica* 2004, no.152-1/4 (2004): 141-157.

Peters, Ted. "Transhumanism and the Posthuman Future: Will Technological Progress Get Us There?"

Schultze, Ulrike and Wanda Orlikowski. "Metaphors of Virtuality: Shaping an Emergent Reality." *Information and Organization* 11, no. 1 (2001): 45-77.

Transhumanist World Association (WTA). "Transhumanist Declaration." http://www.transhumanism.org.

Chapter Six

Ship of Fools: Why Transhumanism Is the Best Bet to Prevent the Extinction of Civilization

by Mark Walker

WHAT DOES TRANSHUMANISM MEAN?

Transhumanism is the thesis that we can and ought to use technology to alter and improve human biology. Some likely targets for the technological makeover of human nature include making ourselves smarter, happier, longer-living, and more virtuous. The operative assumption here of course is that intelligence, moods, longevity, and virtues each have deep roots in our biology. By altering biology, transhumanists propose to improve human nature to the point of creating a new genus: posthumans. Perhaps the most powerful means to adequately conceptualize what is at stake is in terms of a phylogenetic analogy: posthumans will stand to us in moral and intellectual virtues as we stand to chimps. The phylogenetic analogy underscores the importance of biology in making humans what we are: it is not prejudice or cultural differences that prevent chimps from integrating into our society, but differences in human and chimp nature. Chimps have congenital limitations that prevent them from understanding much of what we know and doing much of what we do. The confirming experiment is easy enough to run: send any chimp to the best private school in the world. The chimp is not going to succeed academically as well as an average human toddler, no matter how many years of intensive one-on-one tutoring it receives. Accepting the phylogenetic analogy means that we will be similarly intellectually challenged compared with posthumans.

The same point applies to moral virtues: apes stand to us in moral virtues as we may stand to posthumans.[1] Here it may be objected that chimps do not possess even rudimentary moral virtues. Yet, even granting this, we can simply switch to the ontogenetic analogy: children are not as morally developed as adults are. It is not merely their lack of experience but their biologically immature brains that prohibit them from being full-fledged moral agents. Consider that often developmentally challenged adults are not held morally culpable precisely because their cognitive capacity is said to be childlike in certain respects. Posthumans may stand to us morally as we stand to children.

The phylogenetic analogy suggests further that not only might posthumans excel beyond us in ways that we highly value, e.g., in terms of our intellectual and moral virtues, etc., but also in ways that we have failed to develop. Consider that quantum physics is not merely unknown to apes; quantum physics is unknowable to even the brightest ape. We have access to whole worlds that chimps fail to comprehend: philosophy, science, literature, art are forever closed to them.[2] Unless we assume that we are the crowning development of intellect, it seems quite likely that there are whole universes of value from which we are congenitally cut off, just as apes are congenitally cut off from many areas of our culture.

Notice that transhumanism encompasses a moral thesis. Transhumanism does not say that we will create posthumans; rather, it makes a moral claim: we ought to create posthumans.[3] The hint of an argument based on the accrual of moral benefits is perhaps obvious from what has been said: to the extent that we value the development of intellectual, emotional, and moral virtue, becoming posthuman is imperative. I won't pursue this line of argument here directly. Rather, I want to explore the objection that transhumanism is an ill-advised experiment because it puts us at unnecessary risk. My reply will be that creating posthumans is our best bet for avoiding harm. In a nutshell, the argument is that, even though creating posthumans may be a very dangerous social experiment, it is even more dangerous not to attempt it: technological advances mean that there is a high probability that a human-only future will end in extinction.

WHAT IS A SOCIAL EXPERIMENT?

Social experiments, in the very broad sense I have in mind, involve observing the results of changing a norm of society. A few examples may help clarify. In

---

[1]   Mark Walker, "Genetic Virtue," 2009.

     http://www.nmsu.edu/~philos/documents/sept-2008-genetic-virtue-august-revised.doc.

[2]   Mark Walker, "Prolegomena to Any Future Philosophy," *Journal of Evolution and Technology* 10 (2002).

[3]   Ibid.

many western countries, women were not granted the vote until the early part of the twentieth century. The battle to change the norm opposing women's suffrage was often met with predictions of dire consequences. The most over-the-top of these predicted women's participation in politics would lead to the collapse of civil society because it would lead to the corruption of "womanly nature." Others predicted that women would simply vote as their husbands or fathers instructed them to. Obviously, these and other outlandish prognostications turned out to be false. The more general point, conceded by many on both sides, was that granting women suffrage was an experiment: no one knew for certain the outcome prior to its implementation. This experiment is of course a resounding success, but not all social experiments turn out so well. Consider the prohibition social experiment in the early part of the twentieth century in the U.S. The norm that permitted the sale of alcohol was changed by constitutional amendment in 1919. This social experiment ran until 1933 (when the amendment was repealed) and was generally seen as a failure. The experiment failed for any number of reasons, not the least of which was the relative ease in which persons could make their own alcohol; for example, home beer brewing and small moonshine distilleries made the enforcement of the norm extremely difficult.

Macro social experiments include the adoption of agriculture, the alphabet, and the industrial and computer revolutions. Each of these has had a profound impact on our world and our lives; for example, our human population of nearly seven billion is not sustainable without agriculture. If we were forced to return to hunter-gatherer forms of obtaining food, billions would die in short order. The alphabet is critical to literacy and thus to philosophy, science, and other intellectual endeavors. It is impossible to imagine any of these without the development of the alphabet.[4] Agriculture, the alphabet, and the industrial and computer revolutions required the experimental adoption of norms. We can easily imagine that our ancestors might have banned such activities: social conservatives or Luddites amongst hunter-gatherers might have prohibited agriculture, and the same for the alphabet and industrial and computer technology.

THE TRANSHUMANIST EXPERIMENT

If initiated, transhumanism promises to eclipse all previous experiments combined. In part, this is because all social experiments hitherto attempted have been intraspecies experiments. We remained *Homo sapiens* in the transition from preindustrial to industrialized society. We remained *Homo sapiens* in the

---

[4]   Eric A. Havelock, *Preface to Plato*, (Cambridge, Mass.: Harvard University Press, 1963).

transition to women's emancipation. For the first time in history, technology has advanced sufficiently to allow an interspecies experiment: one species conducts the experiment to create a new species.

But it is not merely the creation of a new species that makes the experiment so unique. For imagine, contrary to fact, that *Homo erectus* had conducted an experiment to create *Homo sapiens*. (Suppose they had initiated the norm to select for breeding only those members with the largest brains and other features that differentiate the two species). This still would not rank with the creation of posthumans. This is because the posthuman social experiment promises that rapid cultural evolution will be married for the first time with rapid biological evolution. Let me explain. By *culture* here, I mean something very general: nongenetic means of transmission of information between generations, as opposed to biological information that is almost exclusively passed through DNA to succeeding generations.[5] When *Homo sapiens* evolved from *Homo erectus*, there was no rapid cultural evolution. *Homo sapiens* walked this earth for at least 100,000 years before the advent of rapid cultural evolution. It is only in the last 20,000 years or so (with the invention of agriculture) that there has been rapid cultural evolution.

The posthuman experiment promises to unite cultural and biological evolution. With changes in biology, more intelligent posthumans will likely be able to accelerate cultural evolution, and cultural evolution should enhance posthuman ability to create new species. For example, if we create a new species, *Homo bigheadus*, a genetically modified descendent with a larger brain, they should be able to leverage their intelligence to improve technology to permit the creation of *Homo biggerheadus*, and they in turn create *Homo evenbiggerheadus*, and so on. In other words, there may be a feedback loop between cultural and biological evolution.

WHY CRITICS SEE THE TRANSHUMANIST EXPERIMENT AS A BAD BET

So what reasons are there for attempting the superlative social experiment called transhumanism? The mere fact that we have attempted many experiments in the past is hardly sufficient reason. As we have said, some of these experiments have been dismal failures. We mentioned prohibition; we could add countless others: the Soviet experiment under Stalin, European colonialism, Jim Crow laws, etc. On the other hand, so much of what we enjoy today is the result of previous successful social experiments. Knowing that social experiments may go well or

---

[5]   J. T. Bonner, *The Evolution of Culture in Animals* (Princeton: Princeton University Press, 1984).

poorly suggests that, at minimum, we need some assessment of what benefits or harms might come from the posthuman experiment.

To simplify, let us think in terms of two stark and simplified alternatives: the optimistic and pessimistic scenarios. The optimistic scenario sees us creating posthumans that are indeed smarter, happier, longer-lived, and more virtuous. Most of us value intelligence, happiness, long life, and virtue; and so it seems our descendants would be better off to the extent that they would enjoy more of each. After all, who doesn't wish for their children wisdom, happiness, long life, and virtue? If *Homo erectus* had any say in the matter, surely it would have been the morally correct decision for them to wish that their children would evolve into humans so that their descendants would have more of these goods. With better minds, posthumans should be able to solve many of the intellectual and practical problems that stymie us. With longer lives, posthumans will have a chance to have more of what is to be valued in life. With greater emotional well-being and with greater virtue, we must imagine that fewer of them would die at the hands of one another (in comparison with humans). On the optimistic scenario, those that become posthumans lend a helping hand to the other species on this planet, including those who choose to remain human. The age of posthumanity ushers in a paradise of biblical proportions.

The pessimistic scenario sees posthumans creating a hell on earth. Let us imagine that they first destroy their human progenitors. Next they turn on one another in a war using weapons that are as powerful in comparison to contemporary human weapons as contemporary human weapons are to the sticks used by chimps. All posthumans die, and the environment is completely destroyed. The earth lays a barren wasteland—even cockroaches don't survive.

Of course these alternatives are purposely stark. In reality, we could probably imagine any number of gradations between posthuman heaven and hell on earth. But the point remains that creating posthumans is a social experiment, so we cannot be certain where between these two poles we will end if we adopt a norm that permits (or obligates) the creation of posthumans.

The wisest counsel seems to be that we should not attempt the posthuman social experiment. For as tempting as the positive scenario may sound (at least for some), it entails risking the possibility of the pessimistic scenario. It seems that only a gambler's mentality would make us want to risk so much. That is, the negative scenario is so bad that no amount of possible good would make this a prudent bet.

The idea that transhumanism is a bad bet is one frequently made by critics. Perhaps most prominent amongst them is Francis Fukuyama. Fukuyama concedes at least the temptation of transhumanism for moral good:

> The human race, after all, is a pretty sorry mess, with our stubborn
> diseases, physical limitations and short lives. Throw in humanity's

jealousness, violence and constant anxieties, and the transhumanist project begins to look downright reasonable.[6]

The problem with the transhumanist project, says Fukuyama, comes when we think seriously about what characteristics to change:

> Our good characteristics are intimately connected to our bad ones: If we weren't violent and aggressive, we wouldn't be able to defend ourselves; if we didn't have feelings of exclusivity, we wouldn't be loyal to those close to us; if we never felt jealousy, we would never feel love. Even morality plays a critical function in allowing our species as a whole to survive and adapt . . . Modifying any one of our key characteristics inevitably entails modifying a complex, interlinked package of traits, and we will never be able to anticipate the ultimate outcome.[7]

So, although Fukuyama sees the pull of transhumanism, how it might look "downright reasonable," the fact that traits we might hope to modify are interconnected means that "we will never be able to anticipate the ultimate outcome." The task is so complex that the transhumanist project is a bad bet.

Probably, much to the ire of some of the more Panglossian transhumanists, I confess I have some sympathy with the bad bet argument. Indeed, I would be sorely tempted by an offer from the good fairy to wave a magic wand that would promise us safe passage through the next thousand years in exchange for a moratorium on the transhumanist project. A pause such as this would allow us to fully understand and appreciate the consequences (as best we can) of the transhumanist experiment.

In absence of any such good fairy, the reason I oppose a moratorium for the next thousand years is precisely because there is no guarantee for our safety. My main concern is that the very same technologies that could enable the transhumanist project are also the ones that could lead to our demise.

TWENTY-FIRST-CENTURY TECHNOLOGIES

Three of the most commonly discussed twenty-first-century technologies in transhumanist circles are nanotechnology, advanced computer technology, and

---

[6] Francis Fukuyama, *Our Posthuman Future: Consequences of the Biotechnology Revolution* (New York: Farrar, Straus, and Giroux, 2002), 42.

[7] Ibid, 43.

genetic engineering. For the sake of brevity, I will discuss only the most mature of these—genetic engineering. Suppose one wanted to go about creating the aforementioned *Homo bigheadus*; how might one proceed? Perhaps the simplest method would be to genetically alter at the zygote stage human homeobox genes. Homeobox genes are responsible for many large-scale features of organisms. For example, a single mutation of a homeobox gene on a fruit fly can lead to a complete extra set of wings or an extra pair of legs. The relative size of brains in invertebrates appears to be controlled by homeobox genes. By altering the homeobox genes responsible for brain growth, we have the technology today to attempt to genetically alter a human zygote to create a being with a brain twice the size of an average human; that is, we could attempt to create *Homo bigheadus* today!

I cannot defend in depth the claim that it is possible to create *Homo bigheadus* today,[8] but let me address an obvious criticism, as well as add a clarifying remark. The objection is that the argument that we could attempt to create *Homo bigheadus* today overestimates the current state of technological development. Genetic engineering is still pretty crude. The most advanced uses include making transgenic crops, but even here there are far more failures than successes. Experimenters attempting to insert foreign genes in crop plants have to contend with the fact that many fail to germinate, and many of those that do germinate are deformed or fail to have an active form of the inserted gene, etc. Genetic engineering is still hit and miss, with many more misses than hits.

The problem with this objection is not that what it claims is false, for indeed genetic engineering is still very crude. Rather, the objection is beside the point. The fact that there are many more failures than successes does not show that we could not attempt to create *Homo bigheadus*—only that if we do so, there will likely be many failures. Imagine lining up 10,000 human embryos in test tubes on a (very) large lab bench and inserting extra copies of homeobox genes associated with brain size. If 1.0 percent of the insertions worked, then this means that the experiment would lead to the creation of 100 *Homo bigheadus*—if only 0.1 percent, then a mere 10 *Homo bigheadus*.

What stops us from performing such an experiment is not technology but ethics: clearly, it would be unethical to perform the experiment at this stage, but it is technically possible to perform it. And the only point I am trying to make at this

---

[8]   See Walker (2002 and 2004) for further evidence that it is possible to conduct this experiment using extant knowledge and technology. In a latter paper (2008), I discuss an in vivo experiment to create posthumans that could be conducted today and is, I believe, ethically permissible.

stage is about how far we have come with technology and science, not whether we ought to use it today.

Dual Use

One of the complications in thinking about twenty-first-century technologies is what is known as "dual use." Technologies designed for one purpose may be appropriated for an entirely different purpose. Ostensibly, the purpose of a car is to transport us from A to B, but it has the dual use of being a very deadly weapon in the hands of a jealous spouse. Screwdrivers have the purpose of tightening or loosening screws, but they have dual use potential. They too can be used as a weapon to stab an assailant, and as many a frustrated homeowner may attest, they will also serve as a hammer in a pinch.

To see the relevance, it will be helpful to contrast world engineering and person engineering. *Person engineering* refers to remaking of the biology of persons, which, for our purposes here, we may think of as coextensive with the use of technology to remake human biology. *World engineering* refers to any nonperson engineering use of twenty-first-century technologies. Thus, the aforementioned experiment to create *Homo bigheadus* is an example of person engineering, whereas the use of genetic engineering for the modification of crops and the application of nanotechnology to create inexpensive solar cells are examples of world engineering.

It is no secret that there is massive funding and interest in biotechnologies and nanotechnologies, but it is equally obvious that the primary driver is the desire for world engineering applications. One dual use problem is that the very same technology developed for world engineering purposes may easily lend itself to person engineering. Although there is a huge moral difference between genetically modifying cows to produce more milk and genetically modifying human zygotes for larger brains, there is little difference at the technology level. The dual use point then is that technology developed for world engineering purposes can easily be reapplied for person engineering. For example, there is little technical difference between the experiment carried out almost a decade ago that resulted in a jellyfish gene being inserted in a rhesus monkey and the technical challenges of genetically altering humans.[9] A second dual use problem stems from the fact that the same technology developed for benign world engineering purposes can be easily reapplied to more destructive ends. To this frightening prospect we now turn.

---

[9]   W. S. Chan et al., "Foreign DNA Transmission by ICSI: Injection of Spermatozoa Bound with Exogenous DNA Results in Embryonic GFP Expression and Live Rhesus Monkey Births," *Molecular Human Reproduction* 6, no. 1 (2000): 26-33.

UNPRECEDENTED DANGERS OF
TWENTY-FIRST-CENTURY TECHNOLOGIES

In the widely read piece "Why the Future Doesn't Need Us," Bill Joy argues that one of the main differences between previous technology and twenty-first-century technology is the possibility of self-replication.[10] Genetically modified organisms can create copies of themselves using the very same processes that life now uses for replication: a genetically modified crop may create seeds that contain the same mutation. A genetically modified virus can replicate in the usual manner of viruses, and *Homo bigheadus* can replicate through the usual method of sexual reproduction.

One of the powerful and frightening aspects of self-replication is the possibility of "exponential explosion." The point can be illustrated by a simple example. There is going to be a battle between warlords in a month as soon as the rainy season ends. The evil fairy allows Warlord A the choice between 100,000 riffles or one rifle that can create a copy of itself once a day. Naturally, having skipped math class, warlord A chooses 100,000 riffles. Warlord B gets the self-replicating rifle. Since the rifle is self-replicating, it means that all the copies of itself it builds are also self-replicating. So at the end of the first day there are 2 self-replicating rifles, the following day 4, then 8, then 16, and so on. After one month there are 1,073,741,824 self-replicating rifles. The example illustrates the well-known exponential explosion associated with biological reproduction. The frightening relevance of this is how quickly pathogens might reproduce and spread through the human population. Fears here are only compounded by the fact that most pathogens have an incubation time longer than even the longest international flight times. This means that attempts to isolate outbreaks may prove futile or, at best, relatively ineffectual.

The other aspect of twenty-first-century technologies that is relevant is the fact that they require very little industrial footprint. It is reasonably easy to monitor which countries are part of the nuclear club with the aid of spy satellites. The size of the industrial infrastructure necessary to make nuclear bombs is such that a country has to go to extraordinary lengths to hide their activities should they wish to keep a nuclear development program secret.

Not so with genetic technologies. True, it helps to have millions of dollars in equipment and a well-trained research team to conduct genetic experiments, but it is not necessary. Even as I write this, private citizens are using genetic technologies in their basements and their garages with no government oversight. This burgeoning movement is referred to as *biohacking*. For a few thousand dollars and a small room to work, one can become a biohacker. A recent article in the *Boston Globe* explains:

---

[10]   Bill Joy, "Why the Future Doesn't Need Us," *Wired*, April 2000. http://www.wired.com/wired/archive/8.04/joy.html.

The movement is getting much of its steam from synthetic biology, a field of science that seeks to make working with cells and genes more like building circuits by creating standardized biological parts. The dream, already playing out in the annual International Genetically Engineered Machine competition at MIT, is that biology novices could browse a catalog of ready-made biological parts and use them to create customized organisms. Technological advances have made it quite simple to insert genes into bacteria to give them the ability to, for example, detect arsenic or produce vitamins.[11]

In some ways, this is a feel-good story in that it promises the democratization of science. Just as computer do-it-yourselfers started to democratize the computer industry in the 1970s, so too will genetic do-it-yourselfers democratize the biological sciences. However, the potential downside is noted in the same article: "But the work also raises fears that people could create a deadly microbe on purpose, just as computer hackers have unleashed crippling viruses or broken into government websites." Worries here are fueled by the fact the information about how to construct novel pathogens in animal models is openly published. Little original insight would be needed to apply the same strategies to constructing novel human pathogens.[12]

The analogy with computer hacking is in some ways apt. We are all familiar with computer hackers taking down our favorite Web sites or having a virus-infected computer slow to a crawl. On the other hand, the analogy seems to fail to illuminate the magnitude of the risk biological viruses designed by biohackers present. I can live without my computer or my favorite Web site (at least for a while, and I wouldn't be very happy), but a biohacker who creates a pathogen or a series of pathogens may wipe out human civilization.

Sometimes it is suggested that there are always survivors when a virus or some other pathogen attacks a population, and so even the worst form of bioterrorism will not kill off the human species. In response, it should be pointed out that it is simply empirically false that there is no evidence that pathogens can cause the extinction of a species.[13] A biomisanthropist who was worried that a virus was not virulent enough to wipe out the entire human population might be well advised to

---

[11] Carolyn Y. Johnson, "Accessible Science: Hackers Aim to Make Biology Household Practice," *Boston Globe*, September 15, 2008. http://www.boston.com/news/science/articles/2008/09/15/accessible_science/.

[12] Christopher F. Chyba and Alexander L. Greninger, "Biotechnology and Bioterrorism: An Unprecedented World," *Survival* 24, no. 2 (2004): 143-162.

[13] K. B. Wyatt et al., "Historical Mammal Extinction on Christmas Island (Indian Ocean) Correlates with Introduced Infectious Disease," PLoS ONE 3, no. 11 (2008): e3602 doi:10.1371/journal.pone.0003602.

create two or more viruses and release them simultaneously. Furthermore, it is not clear that one would need to kill every last human to effectively bring civilization to a halt for the foreseeable future.[14]

INTELLECTUAL AND MORAL FOIBLES

Fortunately, we are short on examples of biohackers, terrorist organizations, or states creating pathogens that destroy human civilization. To illustrate the general points I want to make, a somewhat analogous case involving a naturally occurring rabbit virus will have to serve. Reasoning that it would be nice to have some rabbits to hunt, in 1859 Thomas Austin released twenty-four rabbits into the wild in Australia. The old adage "be careful what you wish for" seems apropos, for by 1900 there were over two million rabbits in Australia. Through competition, this invasive species is estimated to have caused the extinction of about 12 percent of all Australian mammals. The massive rabbit population has also had a continuing and significant impact on Australian agriculture. To combat the rabbit problem, in 1989 scientists in Australia imported a sample of a deadly virus, rabbit calicivirus (RCD), from China. A number of biological technologies were used during intense clinical testing of RCD on rabbits and other species in the early 1990s. Results from this research showed that there was no indication of transmission to other species. So in 1994 a high-security test site for field trials of RCD was established on Wardang Island, off the coast of Southern Australia. As expected, the test rabbits in the quarantine area quickly became infected with the disease, and so this part of the field trial was a success. However, in October 1995, unexpectedly the virus broke the containment area on Wardang Island and infected the island's entire rabbit population beyond the test site. On October 10, 1995, the Australian government's premier scientific agency, the CSIRO, issued the following communiqué concerning RCD: "Containment plans are in place in the unlikely event of spread to the mainland." What the experts at the CSIRO described as an "unlikely event" transpired shortly thereafter: rabbits across many parts of the Australian mainland became infected and died.[15] And non-government-sanctioned spreading of the virus did not stop there. Private individuals in New Zealand, against the express wishes of their government, illegally imported and released RCD, leading to the death of much of the local rabbit population. Animated public debate followed the incident with a certain amount of consensus that there was a moral failure here, although there was disagreement as to how blame was

---

[14] Nick Bostrom, "Existential Risks: Analyzing Human Extinction Scenarios and Related Hazards," *Journal of Evolution and Technology* 9, (2002): 202-14.

[15] Later RCD was purposely released by Australian scientists and had a dramatic effect on the rabbit population.

to be apportioned. Some blamed the individuals who imported the RCD against the express wishes of the government; others blamed the government for not supplying funds for more conventional methods of rabbit population control.

There are two lessons to be drawn from this example. One is that ignorance can lead to biological mishaps. The Australian scientists thought they had their experiment contained, but they failed twice. First was the release from the quarantine area on Wardang Island, and second the escape of the virus to the mainland. The second point is that moral failures can also lead to biological disasters. With respect to biohackers, the point then can be made that through some unforeseen problem, a deadly biological agent, like a virus or bacteria, escapes into the environment. Also, there is the worry that some misanthropic biohacker may hope to destroy all of humanity. (And should it be objected that this would lead to the demise of the biohacker himself, we are all too familiar with deranged killers murdering dozens of innocent victims, only to turn the weapon on themselves).

TRANSHUMANISM: THE MOST DANGEROUS EXPERIMENT SAVE ANY OTHER

I want now to bring several of our lines of discussion together in terms of our options for dealing with civilization ending threats precipitated by twenty-first-century technologies. Broadly construed, our options appear to be three: we eliminate the technologies, we permit them for world engineering purposes only, or we permit them for world- and person-engineering purposes. I'll refer to these, respectively, as the "relinquishment," "steady-as-she goes," and "transhumanist" futures. I want to say a bit more about each, along with some assessment of the likelihood that they will succeed in saving us from a civilization-ending event.

Starting with relinquishment, let us think first about what it means when it says that we ought to forgo any use of twenty-first-century technologies for both world-engineering and person-engineering purposes. Notice here that the question is not whether we ought to permit the development of twenty-first-century technologies. The reason of course is that it is already too late for that. We have developed at least one—genetic engineering—to the point that it potentially could be used for the purpose of ending civilization.

Now it may be thought that these extrapolations about the possible effects of genetic engineering are a little histrionic. Perhaps, but the fact of the matter is that very few have studied the problem of civilization extinction.[16] Among those who have thought about the problem in any detail, there is almost universal agreement that

---

[16] Nick Bostrom, "Existential Risks: Analyzing Human Extinction Scenarios and Related Hazards," *Journal of Evolution and Technology* 9, (2002): 202-14.

the probability here is significant and certainly not where we would like it, namely at zero.[17] And it is not just tweedy academics who take seriously the possibility of bioterrorism and other technological disasters. On December 5, 2008, while I was in the middle of writing this paper, the following headline appeared in my inbox: "U.S. intel panel sees WMD attack in next five years" (*World Tribune*). Former senators Bob Graham and Jim Talen headed the panel. According to the report, the panel "acknowledges that terrorist groups still lack the needed scientific and technical ability to make weapons out of pathogens or nuclear bombs. But it warns that gap can be easily overcome, if terrorists find scientists willing to share or sell their know-how" (*World Tribune*). Also of relevance is that the report suggests "the United States should be less concerned that terrorists will become biologists and far more concerned that biologists will become terrorists." And our concern should only be increasing, since every year it is a little easier to acquire and apply the relevant technical advancements.

So relinquishment requires us to stop not only future developments but also to turn back the hands of time, technologically speaking. If we want to keep ourselves completely immune from the potential negative effects of genetic engineering, we would have to destroy all the tools and knowledge of genetic engineering. It is hard to imagine how this might be done. For example, it would seem to demand dismantling all genetics labs across the globe and burning books that contain information about genetic engineering. Even this would not be enough since knowledge of genetic engineering is in the minds of many. What would we do here? Shoot all those with graduate and undergraduate degrees in genetics and allied disciplines, along with all the basement biohackers we can round up? Think of the analogy with the prohibition experiment. As we said, part of the reason that prohibition was unsuccessful was because the knowledge and rudimentary equipment necessary for brewing was ubiquitous. It is these two features, availability of knowledge and of equipment, that have made biohacking possible. And where would such a policy be implemented? If it is truly a viable and long-term strategy, then relinquishment will have to be adopted globally. Naturally, very few countries with advanced genetic technologies are going to be enthusiastic about genetically disarming unless they have some pretty good assurances that all other countries will also genetically disarm. This leads us to the usual disarmament impasse. In addition to national interests, the relinquishment strategy has to contend with large commercial and military interests in developing and using twenty-first century technologies.

I would rate the chances for relinquishment as a strategy pretty close to zero. In addition to the aforementioned problems, it seems to fly in the face of the first

---

[17]   John Leslie (1996) says there is at least a 30 percent chance of human extinction, while Sir Martin Rees (2003) sees our chances as fifty-fifty of surviving the next century. The most sustained academic discussion can be found in Bostrom and Cirkovic (2008).

law of the ethics of technology: technology evolves at a geometric rate, while social policy develops at an arithmetical rate. In other words, changing societal attitudes takes a much greater time than it does for technology to evolve. Think of the environmental movement. It is almost fifty years since the publication of *The Silent Spring*, a book often linked with the start of the contemporary environmental movement. Only now are we seeing the first portends of a concerted international effort to fight global warming. And unlike polluters, genetic research has the potential to be virtually invisible, at least until disaster strikes. Bill Joy, as noted, calls for relinquishment. But how relinquishment is to be implemented, Joy does not say. It is much like the environmentalist who proposes to stop environmental degradation by stopping pollution. As far as a concrete plan goes, it is missing just one thing: a concrete plan.

The only two options that seem to have any likelihood of being implemented are the steady-as-she-goes and the transhumanism. Recall, the steady-as-she-goes option says that it is permissible to develop twenty-first-century world-engineering technologies but not to use them for person-engineering purposes. The name stems from the fact that, as noted, there are enormous resources devoted at present to the development of genetic and nanotechnologies for world-engineering purposes, and so the proposal is to continue with our current norms.

There are at least two problems with the steady-as-she goes policy. First, there is the worry about how effective a ban on person engineering is likely to be. The likelihood of an effective ban will depend on what policies are adopted, and little thought has gone into this. A notable exception here is Fukuyama, who has made some suggestive recommendations as to how national and international agencies might be built to contain the development of person engineering (2002).[18] If implemented, Fukuyama's recommendations may well reduce the number of attempts to person engineer, but Fukuyama has little to say about the seemingly inevitable underground activities of person engineering. The problem then is that Fukuyama's version of the steady-as-she-goes strategy may reduce the number of person-engineering experiments, but the outcomes of the underground experiments may prove less benign. Unlike what transhumanists propose, a rogue group working clandestinely in opposition to a world ban on person engineering is less likely to be worried about ensuring that their posthuman progeny are as virtuous as possible.

The second, and for our purposes, primary problem with the steady-as-she-goes strategy is that it says nothing about how we are to address the dual use problem: the development of twenty-first-century technologies for peaceful purposes necessarily brings the prospect that the same technology can be used for civilization ending

---

[18]   Francis Fukuyama, *Our Posthuman Future: Consequences of the Biotechnology Revolution* (New York: Farrar, Straus, and Giroux, 2002).

purposes. While I don't agree with Joy about what to do about these threats, I am in full agreement that they exist and that we would be foolhardy to ignore them. Interestingly, this is where Fukuyama is weakest: he has almost nothing to say about the destructive capabilities of twenty-first-century world engineering and about how the institutions he proposes would control their deadly use. A world where we continue to develop twenty-first-century technologies means that the knowledge and limited equipment necessary for individuals to do their own world engineering, and so potentially their own civilization-ending projects (accidentally or purposively), will only increase. So at worst, Fukuyama's proposal is foolhardy; at best, it is radically incomplete.

The transhumanist future is one where both world engineering and person engineering are permitted; specifically, as noted, the transhumanist view is that we should create persons who are smarter and more virtuous than we are. The application to our problem is obvious: our fears about the misuse of twenty-first-century technology reduce down to fears about stupidity or viciousness. Like the Australian research scientists, the worry is that we may be the authors of an accident and, this time, one of apocalyptic proportions: the end of civilization. Likewise, our moral natures may also cause our demise. Or, to put a more positive spin on it, the best candidates amongst us to lead civilization through such perilous times are the brightest and most virtuous: posthumans.

It is worth pointing out that there is no need to deny what Fukuyama claims: there are real dangers in creating posthumans. What Fukuyama fails to address in any systematic way is the fact that there are even greater dangers associated with not creating posthumans. So a prudential and moral reason for creating posthumans is not that this is without risk; rather, it is less of a risk than the alternative here: steady-as-she-goes. If forced to put some hard numbers to these scenarios, I would venture to suggest there is a 90 percent chance of civilization surviving the next two centuries if we follow the transhumanist path, while I would put the chances of civilization surviving a steady-as-she-goes policy at less than 20 percent. But then, I am an optimist.

It might be objected that it is foolhardy or worse to try to put such numbers to futures where so much is uncertain. I have some sympathy with this objection. Thinking about the future is hardly analogous to putting odds on a horse race. On the other hand, a lot more is at stake in thinking about our future, and so we have no choice but to try to estimate as best we can various risks. If it were protested that it is simply impossible to make any meaningful estimate, then this would prove too much. For then there would be no reason to think that the transhumanist future is any more risky than any other future. In other words, the complaint that the transhumanist future is risky has traction only if we have some comparative evaluation in mind. Surgery that has only a one-in-ten chance of survival is not risky, comparatively speaking, if the chances of survival without the surgery are zero. Anyone who criticizes transhumanism for putting civilization at risk, as does Fukuyama, must explicitly or implicitly hold that the chances of survival in a nontranshumanist future are greater. This is what transhumanists deny.

This line of thinking is further reinforced when we consider that there is a limit to the downside of creating posthumans, at least relatively speaking. That is, one of the traditional concerns about increasing knowledge is that it seems to always imply an associated risk for greater destructive capacity. One way this point is made is in terms of "killing capacity" - muskets are a more powerful technology than a bow and arrow, and tanks more powerful than muskets, and atomic bombs even more destructive than tanks. The knowledge that made possible these technical advancements brought a concomitant increase in capacity for evil. Interestingly, we have almost hit the wall in our capacity for evil: once you have civilization destroying weapons, there is not much worse you can do. There is a point in which the one-upmanship for evil comes to an end—when everyone is dead. If you will forgive the somewhat graphic analogy, it hardly matters to Kennedy if his head is blown off with a rifle or a cannon. Likewise, if A has a weapon that can kill every last person, there is little difference between that and B's weapon, which is twice as powerful. So posthumans probably won't have much more capacity for evil than we have, or are likely to have shortly. So at least in terms of how many persons can be killed, posthumans will not outstrip us in this capacity. This is not to say that there are no new worries with the creation of posthumans, but the greatest evil, the destruction of civilization, is something that we now, or will soon, have. In other words, the most significant aspect that we should focus on with contemplating the creation of posthumans is their upside. They are not likely to distinguish themselves in their capacity for evil—since we have already pretty much hit the wall on that—but for their capacity for good.

CONCLUSION

I suspect that those who think the transhumanist future is risky often have something like the following reasoning in mind.

(A)   If we alter human nature, then we will be conducting an experiment whose outcome we cannot be sure of.

(B)   We should not conduct experiments of great magnitude if we do not know the outcome.

(C)   We do not know the outcome of the transhumanist experiment.

(D)   So we ought not to alter human nature.

The problem with the argument is (B). Because genetic engineering is already with us and it has the potential to destroy civilization and create posthumans, we are already entering uncharted waters, so we must experiment. The question is not whether to experiment but only the residual question of which social experiment should we conduct. Should we try relinquishment? This would be an unparalleled social experiment to eradicate knowledge and technology. Should it be the steady-as-she-goes experiment where, for the first time, governments, organizations, and private citizens will have access to knowledge and technology that (accidentally or intentionally) could be turned to civilization-ending purposes? Or, finally, should it be the transhumanist social experiment, where we attempt to make beings brighter and more virtuous to deal with these powerful technologies?

I have tried to make at least a *prima facie* case that transhumanism promises the safest passage through twenty-first-century technologies. Since we must experiment, it would be foolhardy or worse not to put more thought and energy into the problem of our uncertain future. To the extent that we do not put more thought and energy into the problem, one can only lament the sad irony that "steady-as-she-goes" seems an all-too-apt order for a ship of fools.

REFERENCES

Bonner, J. T. *The Evolution of Culture in Animals.* Princeton: Princeton University Press, 1984.

Bostrom, Nick. "Existential Risks: Analyzing Human Extinction Scenarios and Related Hazards." *Journal of Evolution and Technology* 9, (2002): 202-14.

Bostrom, Nick, and Milan Cirkovic (eds.). *Global Catastrophic Risks.* Oxford: Oxford University Press, 2008.

Chan, W. S., A. W. S, C. Marc Luetjens, Tanja Dominko, João Ramalho-Santos, Calvin R. Simerly, Laura Hewitson, and Gerald Schatten. "Foreign DNA Transmission by ICSI: Injection of Spermatozoa Bound with Exogenous DNA Results in Embryonic GFP Expression and Live Rhesus Monkey Births." *Molecular Human Reproduction* 6, no. 1 (2000): 26-33.

Chyba, Christopher F. and Alexander L. Greninger. "Biotechnology and Bioterrorism: An Unprecedented World." *Survival* 24, no. 2 (2004): 143-162.

Fukuyama, Francis. *Our Posthuman Future: Consequences of the Biotechnology Revolution.* New York: Farrar, Straus, and Giroux, 2002.

Fukuyama, Francis. "Transhumanism." *Foreign Policy* no. 144 (2004): 42-43.

Havelock, Eric A. *Preface to Plato.* Cambridge, Mass.: Harvard University Press, 1963.

Holland, Peter W. H., and Tokiharu Takahashi. "The Evolution of Homeobox Genes: Implications for the Study of Brain Development." *Brain Research Bulletin* 66, nos. 4-6 (2005): 484-490.

Johnson, Carolyn Y. "Accessible Science: Hackers Aim to Make Biology Household Practice." *Boston* Globe, September 15, 2008. http://www.boston.com/news/science/articles/2008/09/15/accessible_science/

Joy, Bill. "Why the Future Doesn't Need Us," *WIRED*, April 2000. http://www.wired.com/wired/archive/8.04/joy.html

Leslie, John. *The End of the World: The Science and Ethics of Human Extinction*. New York: Routledge, 1996.

Reese, Sir Martin. *Our Final Hour: A Scientist's Warning: How Terror, Error, and Environmental Disaster Threaten Humankind's Future In This Century—On Earth and Beyond*. New York: Basic Books, 2003.

Walker, Mark. "Prolegomena to Any Future Philosophy." *Journal of Evolution and Technology* 10 (2002).

Walker, Mark. "Genetic Virtue." *Politics and the Life Sciences,* 28(2) (2009), pp. 27-47

Walker, Mark. "Cognitive Enhancement and the Identity Objection." *The Journal of Evolution and Technology* 18 (2008): 108-115.

World Tribune. "U.S. Intel Panel Sees WMD Attack in Next 5 Years." December 5, 2008. http://www.worldtribune.com/worldtribune/WTARC/2008/me_terror0770_12_05.asp.

Wyatt K. B., Campos P. F., Gilbert M.T.P., Kolokotronis S., Hynes W.H., et al. "Historical Mammal Extinction on Christmas Island (Indian Ocean) Correlates with Introduced Infectious Disease," PLoS ONE 3, no. 11 (2008): e3602 doi:10.1371/journal.pone.0003602.

Chapter Seven

From Mind Loading to Mind Cloning: Gene to Meme to Beme A Perspective on the Nature of Humanity

by Martine Rothblatt

INTRODUCTION

A central concern of the pro/anti transhumanist debate is whether to restrict our human bodies to a biological form or to expand our personal existence onto nonbiological platforms. The antitranshumanist position is that we are our DNA-birthed bodies. I suggest that cybernetics may very well offer a means for expanding the human being.

In Jean-Pierre Dupuy's essay "Cybernetics Is An Antihumanism: Advanced Technologies and the Rebellion Against the Human Condition," Dupuy misstates the cybernetics premise. Dupuy suggests that cybernetics in its quest for control is something antihuman. Alternatively, I suggest that cybernetics is simply an extension of life, much like a modern primate digging stick or an insectoid behavioral pattern, all of which quests for control over the environment. Failure to exert control over one's environment is tantamount to extinction, for no environment provides all the requisites for life at all times without manipulation. Even bacteria control their environment by movement through it and by metabolic excretions. To control is not only to be human; it is to survive.

The goal of cybernetic personal existence would be to continue human development rather than to artificially arrest it at the twenty-first-century level after it has developed for countless millennia. For all practical purposes, in the distant future, it is inevitable that the earth will be lost to a cosmic catastrophe of some sort, as that is the fate of all heavenly bodies in the universe. Those, such as Pickering, who oppose cybernetic personal existence condemn humans to astrophysical excision, whereas proponents of cybernetic personal existence provide a potential vehicle for sustaining the human species. Voltaire was correct when he said that the perfect is the enemy of the good, but he did not mean that we shouldn't strive to improve ourselves. To the contrary, Voltaire meant that we ought not stop trying to improve ourselves simply because we cannot be perfect. The same point goes for humanity. We are far from perfect. Cybernetic existence will not make us perfect. But it could make us better, and that is and always has been a worthy cause.

Here I would like to turn to Katherine Hayles's "Wrestling with Transhumanism," wherein she neglects the fact that transhumanists are actually a most socially connected culture because transhumanists want to use technology to overcome the anomie-inducing isolation and desperation of spatiotemporal distance. The very goal of the transhumanist project is realization of the connective consciousness of all humanity, the noosphere (as suggested by Teilhard de Chardin), which is the epitome of social awareness. Our human tribal sense of community is frustrated by physical separation in buildings, economic separation in classes, and social separation in cultures. Is this transhumanist initiative to transcend traditional dysfunctionalities utopian? Ted Peters, in his paper "Transhumanism and the Posthuman Future: Will Technological Progress Get Us There?" seems to think so.

However, Peters mistakes extrapolations for explanations. The transhumanists are no more utopian or naïve than were the sociotechnological pioneers of the nineteenth century who believed in and fought for universal education, railroads, and public health. Our antecedents in the 1800s dreamed of a day when everyone would have a quality education, when transportation would not involve degradation, and when horrifying epidemics did not sweep away our loved ones. It was that lofty—even utopian—goal that invigorated society to introduce compulsory education, the transcontinental railroad, and sanitation. We are still far from the utopian goal, but what sane person could contest the benefits that the utopian vision has created in its wake? It is the same situation with transhumanists. Of course, transhumanists realize that fungible bodies are off in the future, but if that dream can motivate us to relieve the suffering of those stricken by paralysis or other bodily dysfunctions, then it is a dream well worth propagating. Utopia is not so much a place as a direction, a good direction. Transhumanists are taking us in that good direction and cannot be fairly criticized for telling us all that we can do better that we are doing now.

TRANSHUMANISM

The larger issue of transhumanism concerns human transformation rather than what Don Ihde refers to as a superhuman fantasy in his paper "Of Which Human Are We Post?" Ihde ignores the fact that we are continually transforming, from the time we domesticated wolves into dogs and ragweed into crops, to the time we inoculated ourselves with xenoviral fragments to protect against influenza. The difference between transhumanists and many detractors is that transhumanists are out of the closet, whereas the detractors seem to be in a type of denial. The transhumanists simply see the projection of technological trends that are augmenting and enhancing humans, while the detractors *largely* ignore historical trends, deny current trends, and decry many aspects of the future that do not immediately benefit them. Far from hunting for paradise, the transhumanists are simply following an age-old curve of development that goes back thousands of years in human history. Ihde's view of the world seems to be lost in a romantic fantasy of nostalgia for times we would probably not have survived. In an earlier generation, transhumanists would have been called progressives; antitranshumanists would be known as reactionaries, royalists, or racists. The differentiating question is as simple as this: are we to abandon individual humans, as well as human societies, to the random fate of disease and disaster? The transhumanists say no! and will relentlessly aim to enhance humans and their environment until "life is fair" (because we made it so). The antitranshumanists say yes and will lift a finger to save individuals or groups – only so long as there is no cognizable consequence to the kind of human body and human society with which they are familiar.

In a nutshell, for the transhumanist, alleviating suffering and avoiding extinction trumps the comfort of sameness. To the antitranshumanist, maintenance of the status quo trumps ending pain and even human survival. Better evolve than dissolve, says the transhumanist. Nay, better dissolve than evolve, retorts the antitranshumanist.

MIND CLONING

Returning to the concept of cybernetics, Andrew Pickering, in his paper "Brain, Selves and Spirituality in History of Cybernetics," criticizes transhumanism in regard to a goal of cybernetic immortality and perfection by trying to purify and excise humans. With this said, I turn my attention to the concept of copying the mind onto nonbiological platforms. I do this not to provide fodder for unsubstantiated science fiction or utopian thinking, but to invite those who shudder at the idea of the human not remaining an exclusively biological animal to consider a possible future in virtuality within which the mind or minds could exist.

The phrase *mind cloning* conjures weird and perplexing images. Does it mean stamping out an army of people who think the same? Also, how *could* a mind be cloned? We can visualize identical twins as a proxy for body cloning, but no two people have ever had the same mind. And why would anyone *want* to clone minds? Who would want someone else running around with all of our most private thoughts?

In order to explore a world full of mind clones that is now a key R&D project of dozens of government agencies and private companies, I will briefly address the why, how, and when of mind cloning, and propose a sensible framework for its social acceptance.

Let's start with the term *mind cloning*. It means copying the essence of a person's consciousness. We need the wiggle room of "essence" for two reasons. First, there is no such thing as a perfect copy of anything. At least at the subatomic level, things change too quickly to permit any kind of a perfect copy. Even cloned sheep, for example, are not exact copies. One reason for this is that not all of the genetic information of a sheep (or a person) is in their nucleus, the part of a cell used in the cloning process. There are additional strands of genetic information floating in the cytoplasm of each cell, such as mitochondrial DNA, which is not susceptible to cloning using the techniques now employed. Nevertheless, a cloned sheep is certainly a copy of the essence of its mother.

The second reason we need the wiggle room of essence is that consciousness is not an objective quantity like a sheep. Consciousness is subjective, or personal, to its possessor. This means there is only one of each consciousness, by definition of it being a subjective quantity. However, a person who had all of another's mannerisms, personality traits, recollections, feelings, beliefs, attitudes, and values would surely be the essence of the other's consciousness. The mind clone would know they were the same as, but also different from, the original—in much the same way we realize that we are the same as, but different from, the person we were ten years ago.

With today's technology, the copy of one's conscious essence would reside in a computer system. This means that mind cloning results in software that thinks of itself as a human being when running on an appropriate computer. With future technology, it will be possible to download the software mind of a conscious computer into the brain of a fresh body. Such bodies (including brains) could be grown from stem cells the way skin grafts are today, or perhaps be built as nanobiotech hybrids the way artificial joints are today. Until this future arrives, the mind clones would live in virtuality, such as future stages of secondlife.com, and rely upon the Web for their social interaction.

It's not hard for any Web-savvy person to imagine how mind clones will be created. Consider first that there are finite numbers of human mannerisms, personality types, feelings, beliefs, attitudes, and values. The number of different *combinations* of these human attributes is astronomical, far greater than the number of people. And then add in recollections that are unique to each of us—clearly, there is no problem arriving at billions of unique consciousnesses from a few finite sets of human attributes.

Let's zoom in on these attributes. Imagine a Web site that permits you to create an avatar by selecting its human attributes in the way you might order sushi. A click for a certain shy grin; a click on a one-to-ten scale for introversion; clicks for one's beliefs about God, charity; and love, and so on. As you click away, your uploaded image animates with increasing similarity to you, much like a police sketch artist's rendering takes on an increasing likeness. Spend enough time at a well-designed Web site, and a sort of cybertwin or digital reflection of you will arise. This is mind loading. It is a necessary, but not sufficient, step toward mind cloning.

The mind-loaded version of you is a vast set of lookup tables or database preferences. It lacks the wiring of your brain, the multiple subtle interrelationships of your thoughts, the worldly knowledge you have but can't click, the neurohormonal connections that trigger sensations; the curiosity, cautiousness, and conceptualizing that moves you from moment to moment based upon decades of living life. It's the best puppet ever made, but it is still just a cyberpuppet.

Now, there are many smart people out there trying to digitize the brain. They are using brain scanning technology to see which parts of the brain light up and how they light up when we feel awe, bravery, cuddliness, dread, ecstasy, fear, God, hate, isolation, joy, kindness, love, gloom, neglect, outrage, beauty, rowdiness, sadness, trust, understanding, vapidity, wonder, xenophobia, yearning, and zest. For every feeling, some unique set of nerves lights up. There are many ways for neurons to light up with awe, or bravery, or cuddliness—but a finite number of ways. As with personality types and mannerisms, there are a finite number of ways to feel human but an uncountable number of combinations of these ways.

Each feeling amounts to a mental filter that focuses our thoughts moment to moment in a manner consistent with the feeling. Each feeling is a subroutine, an overlaid program on top of a larger program. If I'm sad, things seem sad, and I see the glass as half empty, not half full. The feelings are usually temporary, and in time, our macroprogram reboots to its default settings. But sometimes feelings persist, and the macroprogram cannot recover. Many feelings trigger sensations across our bodies via neurohormonal connections, or, vice versa, sensations trigger feelings. These sensations are select sets of nerves being pinged toward positive or negative polarity. The brain interprets these along a range of ecstasy to agony, and we find ourselves thinking that we feel the brain's interpretation.

Ultimately, feelings are nerves being more or less activated in a plethora of possible combinations. This sort of thing is tailor-made for digitization. Software circuits can be divided into hundreds of feeling elements, scaled from positive to negative, and grouped into emotional bundles. Hence, it is just a matter of time before hackers start selling awe, bravery, and cuddliness modules. The mind loads will feel the emotions with ever more authenticity to human feelings as the software engineers get ever smarter about which neuron pools are associated in which way with which emotions.

In time, mind cloning software will watch a human emote (uploaded digital video, perhaps with some biofeedback such as galvanic skin response) and autotune its feelings modules to match those of the human. As this is done, the mind load will morph into a mind clone. A puppet that feels is a puppet no more. Software that fears for its life, and that quests for more life, is alive.

BEMES

Here I introduce the concept of what I refer to the beme. The word *beme* is an adaptation of the linguist's word *morpheme*, which means the smallest unit of meaning. A beme is the smallest unit of being, or existence. *Being* is usually defined as a state of existing, or as somebody's essential nature or character. Hence, a beme is the smallest unit of someone's essential nature or character.

Bemes are similar to *memes*, units of cultural transmission that behave like genes and were first explicated in 1976 by Richard Dawkins.[1] Memes span a broader field than the linguistic-bound morphemes and are studied more for their transmissibility characteristics than for their inherent meaning. By analogy, a beme is a unit of existence, nature, or character that can behave like a gene. Hence, a beme can produce behaviors like a gene can produce proteins. Also, a beme can be replicated or combined or mutated either within a being (as occurs with genes) or in an offspring (as also occurs with genes).

Bemes might be thought of as specific kinds of memes, although not all small units of existence are also units of cultural transmission. In any event, the growing public familiarity with the concept of memes is helpful in gaining understanding of the new concept of bemes. The following table shows these similarities amongst genes, memes, and bemes:

---

[1] Richard Dawkins, *The Selfish Gene*, (New York: Oxford University Press, 1976). Though Dawkins defined the meme as "a unit of cultural transmission, or a unit of imitation," *memetics*, the study of memes, contains a variety of definitions of meme. They share in common the concept of genetic-like properties to cultural phenomena.

Different definitions of the meme generally agree, very roughly, that a meme consists of some sort of a self-propagating unit of *cultural evolution* having a resemblance to the *gene* (the unit of *genetics*). Dawkins introduced the term after writing that evolution depended not on the particular chemical basis of genetics but only on the existence of a self-replicating unit of transmission—in the case of biological evolution, the gene. For Dawkins, the meme exemplifies another self-replicating unit and, most importantly, one that he thought would prove useful in explaining human behavior and cultural evolution.

Characteristic	Genes	Memes	Bemes
Expression	Proteins Bodies Behaviors	Thoughts Behaviors	Thoughts Behaviors
Replication	Mitosis and (a)sexual reproduction	Talking, media, and education	Digitization and replication of beingness
Mutation	Polymorphisms	Multiple meanings	Ambiguity
Darwinian	Extinct species versus dominant species	Discarded images versus prevalent images	Lost thoughts versus prevalent thoughts

Humans are defined in large part by our thoughts rather than our genes. The concept of a beme, in this regard, could be mightier than the gene.

HUMANITY, TRANSHUMANITY, GENES, AND BEMES

Now, focusing on the question of our humanity, is it our genes or our bemes that are responsible for our uniqueness? Do we reproduce through our genes or our bemes? As is indicated in the above table, these questions cannot clearly be answered one way or the other. Our genes are, of course, responsible for the common features of our bodies, but our human essence lies in our minds not our bodies. Those who have lost their limbs are no less human; those who have lost their minds lose their human rights as well.

Our genes are also responsible for the layout of the brains that give rise to our minds and, consequently for many if not most, of our basic behaviors as well. However, these genetically determined bemes can as well be isolated from the genes, digitally coded, and separately reproduced. And there are many more bemes that arise solely as a result of our experiences in life. These bemes cannot be expressed in genes, but they too can be abstracted, digitally coded, and separately reproduced.

The central thesis of this essay is that, in an Information Age, the beme is mightier than the gene. This means that transmissible units of character or existence are more important than genetic information. For example, most people's love-mate is a person with whom they share no genetic commonality outside of that which is in the general gene pool of their community. However, a lasting interpersonal relationship is only possible if the two partners share a strong appreciation for each other's bemes, their characters, their natures, and their ideational units of existence. To say the "beme is mightier than the gene" is to disagree that "blood is thicker than water." Most people's strongest relationship—that with their spouse or with a best friend—is not a blood relationship.

On the other hand, bemes are not like mere water. A person builds up his or her bemes over time and evolves them as appears most conducive to an enjoyable life. That which we have spent time developing, like a relationship, is more valuable and reliable than that which just appears and claims affinity based solely upon flesh. A better phrase than "blood is thicker than water" is "minds are deeper than matter."

III. H± Point-Counterpoint

Chapter Eight

Of Which Human Are We Post?

by Don Ihde

Human? Posthuman? Transhuman? Did all this bother arise with Foucault? In *The Order of Things*, he claims,

> Man is neither the oldest nor the most constant problem that has been posed for human knowledge . . . taking European culture since the 16th century . . . man is a recent invention within it . . . in the midst of all the episodes of . . . that . . . history [and] now perhaps drawing to a close, has made it possible for the figure of man to appear . . . . As the archaeology of our thought easily shows, man is an invention of recent date. And one perhaps nearing an end.[1]

That is, *if one accepts* a Foucault-like disjunctive-frame *episteme* account of history, *then* man—how *outré,* since feminism, it must now be human—can be invented, and if invented, disinvented or deconstructed. I open in this way because the issues of the human, the posthuman, and the transhuman revolve around distinctive narratives, and these are often highly slippery. I must forewarn you that, as a philosopher, I am *highly skeptical of slippery slope arguments of any kind.* At the same time, I am not unfriendly to the notion of "posts" since I have described, and others have described, my style of analysis as *postphenomenological.*

What is the human? Biologically, modern humans, *homo sapiens sapiens,* are reckoned to be between 100,000 and 200,000 years old. How modern can you get? This is to say that biologically we differ very little from our ancient African ancestors. But is this *nature?* Not entirely. Physical anthropologists argue and

---

[1]   Michel Foucault, *The Order of Things* (New York: Vintage Books, 1973): 386-7.

recognize that many of what once would have been called cultural practices are involved with our own human evolution. Tool use technologies, created and used by our pre-*sapiens* relatives, preceded us by more than a million years. Tool use technologies involving complex eye-hand bodily actions are part of the way in which our brains were formed. More recently, a very provocative thesis has been put forth that the practice of *cooking* may be highly important in the evolution of our physiognomy! Cooking is a sort of "external digestion" technology—as Ernst Kapp, the very first philosopher of technology, already claimed in 1877. Such predigestion provides for two conditions for biological selectivities that help define modern humans: smaller teeth, a key physiological difference between us and most earlier humans, and the loss of the skull crest to which much stronger jaw muscles were attached for chewing. And, as these anthropologists also claim, cooking hearths go back precisely to such early modern sites, but the evolutionary process begins earlier in that charcoal heaps without hearths do go back to pre-*sapiens* sites. I suggest that what is neat about this analysis is that it is much closer to a "natureculture" or "culturenature" notion, as described by Donna Haraway, rather than the too clean division between nature and culture, which presumably defines the "modern settlement" à la Bruno Latour. It also gives a new meaning to "we are what we eat."

Or is the modern human the one who was invented at the beginning of the early modern scientific era of the seventeenth century? This would be the Cartesian-Lockean human—the subject in the camera obscura mechanical body box, but individualized and a subject epistemologically; and also one who has inalienable rights to private pleasures, freedom, and happiness in the sociopolitical arena. Surely, this version of "human" is enigmatically being called into question in a postmodern era—on the one side, the notion of extreme autonomy, without social relations and networkings; but on the other, the possible loss of or weakening of civil liberties—posing an ambiguous threat to hard-won Enlightenment values. Can we have a less self-enclosed, less autonomous, even closer-to-the-animals human, without losing the important political gains made in modernity? The transcending of a now four-century-old interpretation of the human is certainly timely and important.

If we are then at a crucial juncture, a time warp in which we, as self-interpreting animals, must reassess ourselves, then there is a type of parallelism that stretches back to the beginnings of our "modern" era. As it turns out, this summer, one of my commitments was to do a number of entries for a forthcoming Blackwell Companion to the Philosophy of Technology volume, one of which was an introduction to a section on science and technology. In the process, I returned to one of the pioneers of that modernity, Francis Bacon, who in his *Novum Organum* was aware of a turning point in his historical time and who developed the notion of four idols to be avoided in entering the new era. It occurred to me that this device could serve a good purpose for precisely this theme as well. So I shall talk us through four new idols in discussing the human, the posthuman, and transhuman issues here. My idols are the following:

- The *idol of paradise*. This is the idol of much *technofantasy*, which often underlies much of the discussion context we are engaged in.
- The *idol of intelligent design*. This is the idol of a kind of arrogance connected to an overestimation of our own design abilities, also embedded in these discussions.
- The *idol of the cyborg*. Cyborgs, made popular since midcentury, are hybrid creatures of human, machine, and animal combinations, but what do they imply?
- The *idol of prediction*. Projections of futures are always involved in era shifts, but if past projections are taken into account, this turns out to be a very dicey practice.

THE IDOL OF PARADISE

Anyone familiar with much history of the literature on paradise knows that one problem with paradise is that it is likely to be *boring*. From singing angels on a cloud, to the discovery that seventy virgins may turn out to be seventy raisins due to a mistranslation, to Dante's dull paradise in the *Divine Comedy* compared to his imaginative levels of hell—all point to the difficulty of making any utopia exciting and stimulating. I have always argued that to "imagine up" is much harder than to "imagine down." Take for example science fiction presentations, particularly those such as *Star Trek*, *Battlestar Gallactica*, and other series. When the humans and their allies, sometimes quasihumans from other planets, come into the presence of a "superior" set of beings, what do they find? The two most popular variants are these beings have either superior technologies or extraordinary spiritual and mental capacities (i.e., they can see futures, meld with other minds, communicate without technologies, and are usually peaceful mediator types). All of these superior technologies, by the way, can be found in ancient literatures in nontechnology forms: powers of invisibility (now a type of electronic shield, then a cape of invisibility), powers to change forms (now into a transformer or a tech exoskeleton, then a dragon or a spider), and so on. From flying carpets to warp speed, I note there is little new in such fantasies. The difference is that, since modernity, the fantasy embodiments have tended to be *technological* rather than organic, animal-like, or supernatural. Contrast Bruegel's organic animal, supernatural tormentors in his paintings with da Vinci's fantasy technologies, and you get something of the shift.

I have earlier argued that fantasies take shape and form in relation to the relative lifeworlds of the inhabitants.[2] Thus, if one lives in a world in which daily life includes frequent and existentially important interactions with animals—and for that matter, plants—as in hunter-gatherer cultures, then the wish fulfillment fantasies will take the shapes of animal fantasies, dreams, stories, or of plant cycles and growth and decay metaphors. However, if your lifeworld is one saturated with a technological texture, then you get the more "modern" versions suggested above. The technologies will provide the magic answers. Our myths are indexed to our experiences.

Clearly, the implication is that our current debates concerning human/ posthuman/transhuman take this current technomythological shape. Let me begin minimalistically with enhancement desires: Do we want more muscle power? Bigger breasts, fuller lips, or tighter buttocks? Larger penises or better erections? Steroids, breast implants, Botox, liposuction or tucks, penis surgery, or Viagra—this drill is apparent on television and in spam e-mail. (Ironically, my wife gets more penis enlargement spam than I do). This has led to changes in time awaiting the doctor, in which time is shorter for Botox injections than wart removal. This in turn is related to capitalism, in the sense that injections are profitable and easy and wart removal is limited by insurance. All this is part of "modern times" in the post-Charlie Chaplin movie we live in. All these techniques *work*—but not without unintended consequences. Steroids increase the risk of early heart problems; silicone implants can leak and seem to be implicated with autoimmune diseases; long-term Botox use has toxic effects; and in the wrong mix, Viagra can cause critical low blood pressure or blindness. Paradise is not to be found here; calculated risk and compromises are to be found here.

Here then is my thesis: The desires and fantasies are ancient. Historically, they appear in our literatures, our fairy tales, and in our art. The fantasies and desires then want some *kind of magic* to fulfill the desire-fantasy. But the form of the magic differs, according to my thesis, by the textural patterns of historic lifeworlds. From magic potions to magic injections, from an age of alchemy to one of chemistry, the fulfillment technique will differ. But why do I call it magic? Because magic, unlike actual chemistries and technologies, does not have ambiguous or unintended or contingent consequences—trade-offs are lacking; only the paradisiacal results are desired.

How then does this relate to the human-posthuman-transhuman discussion? The answer is simple in one respect: to locate the desire-fantasy, look for the *hype.* Technofantasy hype is the current code for magic. Switch examples now from personal enhancement desires to technologies that will fulfill our social energy desires. Remember the time when the world community, fearful of a nuclear

---

[2]   See my "Technology and Human Self-Interpretation," *Existential Technics* (Albany, NY: SUNY Press, 1983).

holocaust, hyped the "magical" transformation of that power into peaceful uses? One was the technofantasy of limitless, almost free, nuclear supplied power.

This is precisely an example of magical thinking—the hype that projects a noncontingent, nonconsequential, non-trade-off solution. The "infinitely inexpensive" projection did not take into account the need for safety redundancy, for security factors, and for the still problematic need for hundreds of thousands of years of safe waste storage, all of which complicate "paradise," and all of which need to be calculated into the *costs* of this nonneutral technology. Please note here that I am not arguing a dystopian view. It may be possible with very careful planning, with contingency considerations and new technologies to make such an energy source less long-range dangerous than it now is. Rather, I am arguing that magical thinking disregards the ambiguous, nonneutral character of actual technologies. Desire-fantasy, with respect to technologies, harbors an internal contradiction. On the one side, we want the superpowers or enhancements that technologies can confer—long-range vision with telescopes, mountain moving capacity with earth movers, supersonic speed with jet power—but on the other, the technofantasy is to have this enhancement be so totally transparent that it *becomes us*. This is a superman technofantasy: to have and to *be* the power embodied. Such then are the dynamics behind the idol of Paradise.

THE IDOL OF INTELLIGENT DESIGN

Most of you are familiar with this term from the currently raging evolution/creation debates popular in the United States. In that context, *intelligent design* is the notion that various natural phenomena, particularly forms of life, are too complex *not* to be intelligently designed. The implication, of course, is a throwback to the old teleological argument for God, that smart design implies a smart designer. Now, were I to plunge into the evolution-creation argument, I would, in my usually perverse and provocative way, probably *invert* the proposition and argue that evolutionary results are *in fact too complicated to have been designed*! And I would look at the current state of robotics as a very good illustration of this inversion. To date, there are no robots with the gracile motility of even insects in motion, let alone simulacra of upright posture humans playing tennis. Beetles are better at negotiating chaotic terrain than robots, and in terms of flight, bumblebees and humming birds make mockery of the smart bombing Predator of Iraq War fame. Once again, let me warn you that my ironic gestures against this sense of intelligent design are not indicators of a lack of appreciation for technological innovation and modeling-simulation experiments. To the contrary, one of the most delightful and amusing of my observational sidelines over the years has been to witness the way a lone phenomenologist, Hubert Dreyfus, so provocatively influenced the trajectory of both AI (artificial intelligence) and robotics.

Dreyfus's application of Heidegger, picked up by Terry Winograd and Samuel Flores, in programs called "ontological design" changed office systems to much more user-friendly platforms; but in robotics, the Merleau-Pontean notion that bodily motility underlies all intelligent behavior has deflected design notions regarding robot motility. For example, the old dicta regarding a central nervous system centralized in a sort of brain-in-a-vat model for deciding and directing robot motion has gradually begun to be replaced by "smart insect" models of less self-conscious motility, leading to better abilities to locate obstacles and such. Both directions are bodily-being-in-environment models, with greater reliance upon perceptual analogs than upon calculation machine capacities. Perhaps embodied beings are less calculational machines and more sentient animals than modernity usually thinks?

Permit now a shift of example. In this case, human intelligent designers, recognizing the gracile motility of our fellow beings and in line with the previous desire-fantasy dreams, now wish to fulfill the ancient desire for *flight*. As I have suggested, the earliest stages of modernity began to shape such desires into technological forms; and whereas most of the imaginations pre-Renaissance used large birds, dragons, or other flying animals, or sometimes out-of-body dream flights—Leonardo da Vinci began to visualize different flight technologies. Some were quite naively amusing, such as his presumed anticipation of a helicopter, a "flying screw" machine that, of course, could not possibly work! However, he was also an avid observer of birds, and birds have always been icons for the human desire to fly. Leonardo was a keen enough observer to note that bird wings contain curvatures in form, which we now know allows for *lift*, and he incorporated this into his drawings of winged flight machines. None, again, could have worked. But why not? Some have argued that the conceptual design was good, but the lack of lightweight materials and the lack of tensile strength of materials prevented such possibilities. Indeed, when I made remarks of this sort not long ago in a review in *Nature*, I was taken to task by an editor who pointed out that a designer inspired by da Vinci had indeed built a hang glider along da Vinci lines, which did glide. However, when I examined this design, I discovered that a whole series of design modifications totally unknown to da Vinci had been incorporated. In either case, once again the properties and capacities of the technologies needed to be taken into account.

Humans can be stubborn, so the dream of human-powered flight persisted. We look back at the funny home movies of the clumsy attempts at flight technologies at the end of the nineteenth century, and when flight succeeds—with modified bicycle parts and finally a nonhuman engine—a quite different trajectory is born. The finally successful powered flight, the Wright flight in 1903, was actually a combination of many hybrid technologies, light and flexible strong materials, control designs for fixed wings, a small internal combustion engine and propeller (a variation on the ancient screw machine), and an abandonment of the bionic "bird model" of da

Vinci. Rather, the developmental history points to what Andrew Pickering calls the "dance of agency." That is, through much human-material interaction, from which emerged new design and trajectory factors, came today's very non-animal-like flight. So when finally one successful, human-powered aircraft does appear, the Gossamer Albatross—powered by a highly trained bicycle racer turning similar technology which drives a large, slow propeller in a Mylar plastic airframe—which flew across the English Channel in 1979, the stubborn fantasy was fulfilled. Yet it was fulfilled only in ideal, limited conditions and with the appearance of a sort of clumsy, anachronistic success.

Once again the idol of intelligent design gives way to a human-material or human-technology set of interactions, which, through experience and over time, yield to emergent trajectories with often unexpected results. The fantasy model of an intelligent, autonomous designer—working out an intended result upon a purely "plastic" material—gives way to the more realistic notion of human-material interaction, through experienced "resistances and accommodations," in a dance of agency à la Pickering or the invention of an entirely new set of uses for a useless "glue" as in Latour's description of the Post-it.[3]

THE IDOL OF THE CYBORG

Although it was probably Donna Haraway who made the figure of the cyborg into its best known form, as the noninnocent hybrid of human, animal, and machine, moving amidst the technoscience naturecultures of postmodernism, the cyborg was gestated in the *cold-think* of World War II and then the Cold War. From Clynes to Wiener, to von Neumann to Herman Kahn, the technofantasies of moving beyond the humanistic were configured. First, in the Manhattan Project and, thinking the unthinkable, then on to its "peaceful" uses—such as creating huge atom-bomb produced harbors in Alaska—cold-think prided itself on machine thinking replacing human thinking. One of the main technologies of cybernetics, after all, was to create a non-evadable aircraft artillery fire.

But the slippery-slope fantasies are perhaps better seen when science fiction and its filmic expressions are introduced, as in *Terminator*, *RoboCop*, and the variations upon "bionic" men and women. It is here that a history and a phenomenology of *prostheses* can be informative: Prosthetic replacements for limbs and other body parts have an ancient history. Wooden teeth and detachable artificial limbs go back to ancient mummies. In experienced use, these prostheses fall into what I have earlier called *embodiment relations*; that is, we humans can use technologies

---

3   Bruno Latour, *Science in Action* (Cambridge, Mass.: Harvard University Press, 1987): 140.

through which we can experience our environment by "embodying" such devices; and while in use, such devices are "experienced through" in a partial transparency or partial withdrawal. We do not attend to our eyeglasses, or better, our contacts; Merleau-Ponty's lady with the feathered hat, or the blind man with a cane can "feel" through these extensions for bodily motility in an environment. *But* the withdrawal or transparency comes with both a partial incompleteness and, more, with a selectivity such that what is experienced through the prosthesis is both magnified in some aspects and reduced in others. The peg leg or its high-tech Iraqi War hydraulic leg replacement, cannot "feel" the hot, sunbaked surface of the sidewalk the way one's bare foot can. But through the prosthesis, one might be even more sensitive to slipperiness or rough texture. Once again, it is the sensitivity to the materiality of the prosthesis that slippery-slope fantasies forget. Prostheses are compromises; we may have them, but we fall short of experiencing a total transparent embodiment. At a very low and simple level, with a tooth crown, there may be a very high transparency: we are rarely aware of which tooth is crowned. But at a more complex level—say, hearing aids—it becomes obvious that transparency is, at best, partial. In my own case, such painful occasions ranging from dinner parties to a bar, the background noise cannot be dampened even with my high-tech digitals and remote with ambient sound suppressing programs. Nor is music, either live or, worse, on the radio, what I can remember it once being.

Returning to limb prostheses, today the attempt to have the artificial limb mimic likeness to the original or missing limb has sometimes given way to a different variation entirely. In a trajectory away from similarity and away from the contradictory "having and not having," a technological self is the move to have a different kind of prosthesis. Aimee Mullins, who played Cheetah Woman in Matthew Barney's *Cremaster 3,* learned to use from childhood a set of spring like legs. She was born with fibular hemimelia, a birth defect of being born without fibula bones, and underwent stump amputation at age one. The spring legs, subsequently used by a number of athletes with the same defect, are *not like* human limbs, but give a selectivity that magnifies spring-powered speed capacities. Oscar Pistorius, a South African with spring-powered transtibial prosthetic legs, runs almost as fast as normally legged runners but was denied Olympic entry in part because some feared such high-tech devices might give an advantage. This is a trajectory that, while not returning our sentient bodies to us, allows us different capacities than before.

Even more internalized, knee, hip, shoulder, and other *implants* work and work better than damaged parts, *but implants, unlike the fantasized eternality of perfect machines*, also wear out! Metal and plastic "age" and must be replaced every seven or more years, and because more bone must be cut away for the replacement part, this leads to diminishing returns. Here, again, is contingency and trade-offs, and it is better not to have to undergo such procedures unless necessary and hopefully at older ages. The cyborg, when critically examined with a concern for its materiality, does not display its science fiction, technofantasy form. The cyborg, too, can be an idol.

THE IDOL OF PREDICTION

In the same narratives concerning the human, the posthuman, and the transhuman, both dystopian and utopian predictions produce idolatrous technofantasies. Here I could wax eloquent for pages, but I select a few predictions, some of which are made by prominent scientists, others by those extolling utopic virtues in magazines, most selected for deliberate irony by current lights:

- Lord Kelvin (1895): "Heavier-than-air flying machines are impossible."
- Ken Olson (1977) of Digital Equipment: "There is no reason anyone would want a computer in their home."
- Recall the above-cited infinitely cheap atomic energy prediction—this era included other predictions, including the atomic car, which could go 500,000 miles without refueling.
- Or extolling modern magical materials such as the beautification of walls with white lead paint; the amazing material asbestos for floor tiles, roofs, insulation, and decorative interiors.
- How about radioactive suppositories? So every tissue in the body could benefit from healthful radiation.

These are examples from *Follies of Science* (2007).[4] These can more than be matched with lists from Tenner's *Why Things Bite Back* (1996), when he cites Toffler's famous prediction of how the electronic society would be the "paperless society" and how home security systems, by generating false alarms, tied down the equivalent of fifty-eight police officers full time answering 157,000 calls when only 3,000 were genuine, thus likely diverting attention to other crimes. And the list can go on.[5]

David Nye, in *Technology Matters* (2006), points to an in-depth survey of predicted technologies from 1890-1940: 1,500 predictions, and less than one-third occurred. This, by the way, concerned what technologies would be invented, not what uses unintended consequences, or what reversals would occur. Chiding me for pointing this out in *Nature* and claiming these are pretty good odds, my response is that 50 percent odds are normal for a penny toss, and these are less than that!

---

[4]   Eric Dregni and Jonathan Dregni, *The Follies of Science* (Golden, CO: Speck Press, 2007).

[5]   Edward Tenner, *Why Things Bite Back* (New York: Alfred A. Knopf, 1996): 7.

Now, you will note that I have not addressed many of the famous predictions coming from post—and transhumanists, for example, those issued by Hans Moravec, concerning downloading a human mind into a computer, and Ray Kurzweil, concerning the age of intelligent machines. Do these worshippers of the idol of prediction have credibility? Pause for a moment: Just what of a human mind would, should, could be downloaded? The Internet, which plays a strong role in Kurzweil's fantasies, turned out to have some very unpredictable outcomes in relation to its original design and intent. As everyone knows, the decentralization and distributive network technologies of the early Internet—largely restricted to the Cold War university cold-thinkers and the military—were designed to be indefeasible by nuclear attacks. No central authority or power could overcome the distributed networks. Yet once access was expanded—and is still expanding—this lack of central "nervous system" analog control has led to all sorts of unintended consequences. From Andy Feenberg's analysis of the French Minitel with its dating game results, to the current American obsession with hide-and-seek and avatar sting operations for catching pedophiles, indefeasibility has turned out to have lots of unintended consequences. Thus, Kurzweil's almost accidentally correct prediction than the Soviet Empire would fail due to the corrosive power of rising Internet communication—distributed networks did point up the potentially democratic effect, or subversively democratic effect, of this technological complex. But then, turn this back to Moravec's notion of downloading the human mind into a computer—and by extension onto the Internet—and what do we have? Were we all merely cold-thinkers as per von Neumann and Herman Kahn, this might be bad enough; but how about pedophiles and all the rest of the Freudian "unconscious" aspects of the human mind, downloaded and distributed through the Internet? What does it mean to download a mind? If it means downloading all the "bad" parts along with the "good" parts, are we not back at the copying machine, which is, after all, the perfect reading machine that faithfully reproduces precisely the page it is given. Were Moravec himself downloaded, would he be any better than he now is? And if not, are we stuck with a possibly flawed Moravec now and forever?

Note here that my worries are *not* at all those of romantics, objecting because this is "unnatural," nor are they those of the theistically inclined, concerned with human hubris overreaching our natural human limits. They are, rather, worries about unintended consequences, unpredictability, and the introduction of disruptions into an ever-growing and more complex system. They are worries about how "normal accidents" get built into systems as per Charles Perrow. My worries arise precisely from what I have learned about technologies in the now nearly four decades of thinking about technologies. My worries focus upon precisely the *disregard* for the materiality of technologies, the ambiguity of technologies, the multi-stability of technologies and, above all, the intimate role of *humans with technologies*. Thus, I will conclude with another narrative, which I hope will capture the sense of what I have been talking about.

John Henry and Big Blue

The American John Henry legend, expressed in songs and tales, reflects an earlier era in which technologization was feared with respect to replacing humans, but in this case, laboring humans. John Henry was depicted as a big black man, known for his exceptional skills at driving spikes for setting up rails for the advancing railroad; in another version, he was depicted as a tunnel digger. In both cases, an invention—of a steam-powered spike driver in the first, or a steam-powered digger in the second—threatened to outdo and replace John Henry. So a contest is set up between John Henry and the steam machine, and with superhuman effort, John Henry scores a very tight victory over the steam machine. However, his efforts ended with a heart attack, and he collapsed at the finish line, dead.

Of course, we know the outcome. The machine actually wins, since once driving spikes or digging tunnels became automated, steam machines replaced human muscle power. And as the moral of the story goes for labor unions and a social left, the armies of coolies who did that work on our nineteenth century railroads were left unemployed. But fast-forward to today: who today bemoans the replacement of hard, "chain gang-like" labor with efficient machines?

I switch to my observed version from two events at my retreat in the Green Mountains of Vermont. Now almost a decade ago, a devastating ice storm coated the forests of my region and mountainside, damaging many trees and downing others. I had a managed forest plan and, on the advice of my forester, accepted a selective cut. The end result was that seven double truckloads of logs were cut and sold, and the stumps cut down to the ground and brush burned or removed. How did this happen? One tough old Vermonter, armed with a large chain and a four-wheel machine, complete with road-making blade, chainsaw in hand, by himself—*no, by himself plus his technologies*—in a matter of weeks, completed the task. Then, again this summer, this time wanting selective trees that had grown up in my lower meadow and apple orchard, now threatening my highly taxed view (there is a view tax in Vermont!), I had my meadow-mowing Vermonter do the job. This time, with a large excavator with clasping arm, dozer blade, and another of the large four-wheel machines, again by himself—no, by himself with the large machines—he does the job in a few days. I imagined a century ago when both these jobs would have called for a gang of Vermonters, horses and sledges, and hand-powered two-man saws, undertaking what would have been a month's work. So what is my point? The technologies *did not* replace the humans; rather, different technologies *plus* the humans changed the nature of the task.

Today, here in the context of the human, posthuman, transhuman narratives, the variant is, once again, the humans *versus* the machines; this time, not with respect to muscle power, but with respect to *calculating power.* AI, VR, and the range of more "mind-related" technologies are again mythologizing the human versus machine myths long embedded in our culture. Now frankly, were my computer able to simply ingest all my tax-related data for my annual income tax report and spit out a legal and yet maximal result for me, I would cheer and accept giving up the task entirely. That is, of course, not the way it happens. Instead, it happens—if I borrow from Latour's human-and-nonhuman-collectives notion—more like this: I collect and organize my now enormous and complicated annual data and turn it over to my tax advisor. He, now with four others in his office, formats it for the programs that are responsible for analysis, and last year, he said he tried some seven variants to produce the most effective result. This is a simulation and modeling process now so common for complex phenomena problems for which such calculation machines are at their best. However, again, it is clearly not human versus machine—it is humans in conjunction with machines that produce the result.

And this is where I finally turn to my last legend, the 1997 presumed *defeat* of champion chess player Kasperov by the IBM computer with the Big Blue program. The PR—and the Minskys and Moravecs and all the other technofantasizers—hyped this occasion as the ultimate, inevitable result of yet another mythical "machine beats human" contest, a mental and century-later version of "John Henry." However, that is not what happened, and the history of the event not only is different from its mythical version, but also precisely needs to be reframed in human *plus* machine interpretation. From the first, of course, it is human plus machine in the creation of the software. The software did not create itself; it was honed and refined by many skilled programmers, as per the previous tales in amongst the idols, and gradually perfected through resistances and accommodations and the dance of agency peculiar to computer programming. But there is more: during the match, after each game, but behind the scenes, somewhat like the gang of water dabbers and cleaners at a boxing match, Big Blue was aided by its programmers, who tweaked and re-tweaked its programs before the next round. This was not machine versus Kasperov; this was the collective machine plus programmers—a collective versus Kasperov! Is it then any wonder that Kasperov is as much exasperated by the behavior of the "machine" as he is by the lightning-quick moves it can make with hyperspeed calculations?

I suggest here that only if humans are stupid enough to end up worshiping the very idols they create could the fantasized replacement of humans by machines take place. The changing technologies with which we interact, form collectives, and experience the dances of agencies, do forecast vastly changed conditions of work and play (and even love), but it is not them versus us. In Long Island, my living room has a number of pieces of "art" from the Sepik River region of New Guinea. I bought these pieces in Australia from a shop in Sydney that specialized in this sculpture art. Now, in their own cultural context, such pieces were not at all what we would think of as art but were simultaneously more a sort of "practical religious" set of objects. They served fertility, ritual, healing, and many other social functions; they were what older anthropologists might have called "sacred" objects—or *idols*. However, if they are sacred, how could I acquire them? The answer is one that I find appropriate for my conclusion here. These sacred objects, idols, are in their original context, thought to gradually lose power, to deteriorate, even to break down—*amazingly just like technologies*—so when they reach a certain stage of uselessness, they are discarded. And so I have collected some of these discarded idols and reformulated their use into "art objects" in my home. Here lies the moral of my tale concerning the human, the posthuman, and the transhuman.

REFERENCES

Dregni, Eric, and Jonathan Dregni. *The Follies of Science.* (Golden, CO: Speck Press, 2007).

Foucault, Michel. *The Order of Things: An Archaeology of Human Sciences.* New York: Vintage Books, 1973.

Ihde, Don. *Existential Technics.* Albany, NY: SUNY Press, 1983.

Latour, Bruno. *Science in Action.* Cambridge, Mass.: Harvard University Press, 1987.

Nye, David. *Technology Matters.* Cambridge, Mass.: MIT Press, 2006.

Tenner, Edward. *Why Things Bite Back.* New York: Alfred A. Knopf, 1996.

Chapter Nine

True Transhumanism: A Reply to Don Ihde

by Max More

In his *Global Spiral* essay, "Of Which Humans Are We Post?" Don Ihde wonders whether "all this bother" about the concepts of human, transhuman, and posthuman arose with Foucault. The answer is no, they did not. Much earlier thinkers raised these questions in one form or another. Foucault's discussion in *the Order of Things* appeared only in 1973. Even if we limit ourselves to modern discussions of these concepts, Foucault is almost irrelevant. This is certainly true of the kinds of thinkers with whom Ihde concerns himself. The only people he actually names are Hans Moravec, Marvin Minsky, and Ray Kurzweil, but Ihde is clearly commenting on the general thrust of modern transhumanist thought. Our modern biologically and genetically defined subspecies, *Homo sapiens sapiens*, has been around for 100,000 to 200,000 years. There's some plausibility in Ihde's suggestion that the modern concept of human formed only in the last three or four centuries: the Cartesian-Lockean human. The emphasis on the rational capacities of human beings, however, lies further back with Plato and Aristotle (in their two quite differing ways). Aristotle didn't have the Lockean notion of individual rights, but they weren't a big stretch from the great Greek's view of the individual good as personal flourishing through the development of potential—development that would need a protected space. The Cartesian-Lockean human was crucially followed by the Darwinian and Freudian human, which took human beings out from the center of creation and some distance away from the transparently rational human of the old philosophers. Even so, I heartily agree that reassessing our interpretation of the "human" is timely and important.

The biologists' conception of what it is to be a member of the human species so far remains useful: Our species is a group of "interbreeding natural populations that are reproductively isolated from other such groups."[1] Although useful, that species-based definition and the related genetically delimited identification of "human" is becoming increasingly inadequate as our further evolution depends more on the scientific and technological products of our minds. The transhumans or posthumans we may become as individuals (if we live long enough) or as a species may quite possibly share our current DNA, but implants, regenerative medicine, medical nanotechnology, neuron-computer interfaces, and other technologies and cultural practices are likely to gradually render our chromosomes almost vestigial components of our individual and species identity.

While I agree with Ihde on the need for (further) discussion of the concepts and significance of human, transhuman, and posthuman, I find many of his comments to be directed at transhumanists who barely exist (if at all). I resonate with the project of understanding potentially obfuscating "idols" such as Bacon described. But Ihde's discussion of his own four idols seems to be more of a straw man than an accurate critique of contemporary transhumanist views. I find this to be true especially of his idol of paradise and idol of prediction. The other two idols—of intelligent design and the cyborg contain relatively little critical commentary, and so I find less in them to object to.

TRUE TRANSHUMANISM

A few years ago, I received a telephone call from researchers from the Oxford English Dictionary who were looking into the possibility of adding *transhumanism* to that authoritative bible of word usage. That addition has just now happened—a little behind the widespread adoption of the term around the world. Although Dante and Huxley used the term earlier, I first (and independently) coined the modern sense of the term around two decades ago in my essay "Transhumanism: Toward a Futurist Philosophy." My currently preferred definition, shared by other transhumanists is as follows:

> *Transhumanism is both a reason-based philosophy and a cultural movement that affirms the possibility and desirability of fundamentally improving the human condition by means of science and technology. Transhumanists seek the continuation and acceleration of the evolution of intelligent life beyond its currently human form and human limitations by means of science and technology, guided by life-promoting principles and values.*

---

[1]   Ernst Mayr, *Population, Species, and Evolution* (Cambridge, Mass.: Harvard University Press, 1963), 12.

Since I will argue that most of Ihde's critical comments and idols succeed in damaging only views that few or no transhumanists actually hold, it makes sense for me to establish my knowledge of those views. Apart from first defining and explaining the philosophical framework of transhumanism, I wrote the principles of extropy and cofounded Extropy Institute to explore it and to spur the development of a movement (for want of a better term) based on transhumanism. That movement has grown from numerous sources in addition to my own work and has become a global philosophy attracting a remarkable amount of commentary, both pro and con. In some minds (certainly in that of Francis Fukuyama), it has become "the most dangerous idea in the world."

Ihde's own four idols of thought refer more to straw positions than to real views held by most contemporary transhumanists. That doesn't mean that he went astray in choosing Francis Bacon and his four idols from his 1620 work *Novum Organum*[2] as an inspiration. Around the same time that I defined "transhumanism," I also suggested that transhumanists consider dropping the Western traditional but terribly outdated Christian calendar for a new one in which year zero would be the year in which *Novum Organum* was published (so that we would now be entering 389 PNO, or post-Novum Organum, rather than 2009). Despite Aristotle's remarkable work on the foundations of logic and his unprecedented study "On the Parts of Animals," Bacon's work first set out the essence of the scientific method. That conceptual framework is, of course, utterly central to the goals of transhumanism—as well as the key to seeing where Ihde's idols (especially that of paradise) fail accurately to get to grips with real, existing transhumanist thought.

Bacon's own four idols still have much to recommend them. His idols of the tribe and of the cave could plausibly be seen as the core of important ideas from today's cognitive and social psychology. These idols could comfortably encompass the work on biases and heuristics by Kahneman and Tversky and other psychologists and behavioral finance and economics researchers. The idols of the cave are deceptive thoughts that arise within the mind of the individual. These deceptive thoughts come in many differing forms. In the case of Don Ihde's comments on transhumanist thinking, we might define a subspecies of Bacon's idol and call it the idol of non-situated criticism (a close cousin of the idol of the straw man).

Many of Ihde's comments sound quite sensible and reasonable, but to whom do they apply? The only transhumanists Ihde mentions (without actually referencing any specific works of theirs) are Hans Moravec, Marvin Minsky, and Ray Kurzweil. In "The Idol of Prediction," Ihde says, "In the same narratives concerning the human, the posthuman and the transhuman . . ." but never tells us just *which* narratives he's talking about. The lack of referents will leave most readers with a distorted view of true transhumanism. There are silly transhumanists of course, just as silly thinkers

---

[2]   Francis Bacon, *Novum Organum* (1620).

can be found in any other school of thought. I take my job here to be distinguishing the various forms of transhumanism held by most transhumanists from the easy but caricatured target created by Ihde (and many other critics).

Critics' misconceptions are legion, but here I will focus on those found in Ihde's paper. I declare that

- Transhumanism is about continual improvement, not perfection or paradise.
- Transhumanism is about improving nature's mindless "design," not guaranteeing perfect technological solutions.
- Transhumanism is about morphological freedom, not mechanizing the body.
- Transhumanism is about trying to shape fundamentally better futures, not predicting specific futures.
- Transhumanism is about critical rationalism, not omniscient reason.

From Utopia to Extropia

According to Ihde, "technofantasy hype is the current code for magic." As an example, he picks on the poor, foolish fellow (Lewis L. Strauss) who fantasized that nuclear fission would provide a limitless supply of energy "too cheap to meter." Technofantasy is magical thinking because magic produces outcomes that are completely free of trade-offs and unclear and unintended consequences. Magical technologies simply "make it so." In these technofantasies, "only the paradisical [*sic*] results are desired." It might have been better if Ihde had talked of "divine thinking" rather than "magical thinking" since, in a great many fables and other stories, the use of magic *does* bring unintended consequences (perhaps most famously in the various genie-in-a-bottle tales). Still, the point is clear. But does it apply to actual transhumanist thinkers? After all, Ihde's well-worn example is not from a transhumanist, but from an excessively enthusiastic promoter of nuclear fission as an energy source.

It is easy to throw around a term like *technofantasy*. But what exactly is it? What appears to be fantasy, what appears to be a magical technology depends on the time frame you adopt. Clearly many of today's technologies would appear magical to people from a few centuries ago. That point was stated memorably in Arthur C. Clarke's third law: "Any sufficiently advanced technology is indistinguishable from magic."[3] Take someone from, let's say, the fifteenth century and expose them to air

---

[3]   Arthur C. Clarke, "Hazards of Prophecy: The Failure of Imagination," in *Profiles of the Future* (1973).

travel, television, or Google, and they would probably ask what powerful demon or mage created them.

Of course there *is* such a thing as technofantasy: it is imaginary technology that ignores the laws of physics as we currently understand them. Any remarkable technology, so long as it is not physically impossible, cannot reasonably be described as magical thinking. Projecting technological developments within the limits of science is projection or "exploratory engineering," not fantasy—a distinction crucial to separating the genres of "hard science fiction" from "soft" SF and outright fantasy. Seamless and "magical" operation remains a worthy goal for real technologies, however difficult it may be to achieve (as in "transparent computing"). Hence the ring of truth from Gehm's corollary to Clarke's third law: "Any technology distinguishable from magic is insufficiently advanced."

Although seamless and reliable technologies deserve a place as a *goal* for transhumanists, the ideas of perfection and paradise do not. We find those concepts in religious thinking but not in transhumanism. There are one or two possible exceptions: Some Singularitarians may be more prone to a kind of magical thinking in the sense that they see the arrival of greater-than-human intelligence almost instantly transforming the world beyond recognition. But even they are acutely aware of the dangers of super-intelligent AI. In contrast to Ihde's straw man characterization, most transhumanists—and certainly those who resonate with the transhumanist philosophy of extropy—do not see utopia or perfection as even a *goal*, let alone an expected future posthuman world. Rather, transhumanism, like Enlightenment humanism, is a meliorist view. Transhumanists reject all forms of apologism—the view that it is wrong for humans to attempt to alter the conditions of life for the better.

The Idol of Paradise and the idea of a Platonically perfect, static utopia is so antithetical to true transhumanism that I coined the term *extropia* to label a conceptual alternative. Transhumanists seek neither utopia nor dystopia. They seek perpetual progress—a never-ending movement toward the ever-distant goal of extropia. One of the principles of extropy (the first systematic formulation of transhumanist philosophy that I wrote two decades ago) is perpetual progress. This states that transhumanists "seek continual improvement in ourselves, our cultures, and our environments. We seek to improve ourselves physically, intellectually, and psychologically. We value the perpetual pursuit of knowledge and understanding." This principle captures the way transhumanists challenge traditional assertions that we should leave human nature fundamentally unchanged in order to conform to "God's will" or to what is considered "natural."

Transhumanists go beyond most of our traditional humanist predecessors in proposing fundamental alterations in human nature in pursuit of these improvements. We question traditional, biological, genetic, and intellectual constraints on our progress and possibility. The unique conceptual abilities of our species give us the opportunity to advance nature's evolution to new peaks. Rather than accepting the undesirable aspects of the human condition, transhumanists of all stripes challenge natural and traditional limitations on our possibilities. We champion the use of science and technology to eradicate constraints on life span, intelligence, personal vitality, and freedom.

Or as I put it in a "Letter to Mother Nature": "We have decided that it is time to amend the human constitution. We do not do this lightly, carelessly, or disrespectfully, but cautiously, intelligently, and in pursuit of excellence. We intend to make you proud of us. Over the coming decades we will pursue a series of changes to our own constitution . . ."

Ihde's positioning of transhumanist thinking as paradisiacal is particularly odd and frustrating given the rather heavy emphasis on risks in modern transhumanist writing. Personally, I think that emphasis has gone too far. Reading Ihde and many other transhumanist-unfriendly critics, you get the impression that transhumanists are careening into a fantastically imagined future, worshipping before the idols of technology and progress while giving the finger to caution, risk, trade-offs, and side effects. These critics cannot have actually read much transhumanist writing—certainly not anything written in the last decade. If they had, they would have immediately run into innumerable papers on and discussions of advanced artificial intelligence, of runaway nanotechnology, of "existential risk." They would have come across risk-focused worries by organizations such as the Foresight Institute and the Council on Responsible Nanotechnology. They would have come across my own proactionary principle, with its explicit and thorough consideration of risks, side effects and remote, unforeseen outcomes, and the need to use the best available methods for making decisions and forecasts about technological outcomes.

INTELLIGENT DESIGN AND INTELLIGENT TECHNOLOGY

In what seems to me like something of a tangent to his discussion of magical thinking, Ihde says that "Desire-fantasy, with respect to technologies, harbor an internal contradiction." He sees a contradiction in wanting to *have* a technological enhancement and in having that enhancement become (a part of) us. On one hand, if we define the terms just right, it has to be a contradiction to *simultaneously* have an enhancement and to be enhanced.

But there is no contradiction in the idea that a technology can develop so that it enhances us and eventually becomes part of us. I explored this idea in detail in my doctoral dissertation, *The Diachronic Self: Identity, Continuity, Transformation*.[4]

---

[4]   Max More, *The Diachronic Self: Identity, Continuity, Transformation* (PhD diss, University of Southern California, 1995).

If we absorb a technology, integrating it into ourselves, we *can* both have and be the technology in the relevant senses. This is much like taking a vaccine now—it's an externally devised technology that alters our immune system, but it alters and becomes part of us. Or consider how an externally developed technology like gene therapy or artificial neurons can become integrated into who we are.

Ihde refers to the idol of intelligent design as "a kind of arrogance connected to an overestimation of our own design abilities, also embedded in these discussions." Again, he provides no referents for "these discussions." He contrasts this idol with a "human-material or human-technology set of interactions which through experience and over time yield to emergent trajectories with often unexpected results." This idol is indeed a problem. But Ihde's discussion implies that it's a problem among transhumanist thinkers. Given the absence of actual examples, it's hard to evaluate this implicit claim. His loaded term "arrogance" doesn't help. When does confidence become arrogance? Were the Wright brothers arrogant in their belief that they could achieve flight?

What really distinguishes transhumanist views of technology is expressed by what I called "intelligent technology" in the philosophy of extropy. I declared that "technology is a natural extension and expression of human intellect and will, of creativity, curiosity, and imagination." I expressed the transhumanist project of encouraging the development of ever more flexible, smart, responsive technology. I spoke for practically all transhumanists in suggesting that "we will co-evolve with the products of our minds, integrating with them, finally integrating our intelligent technology into ourselves in a posthuman synthesis, amplifying our abilities and extending our freedom." As bold and unapologetic a statement as this is (befitting a transhumanist *declaration*), it says nothing about expecting perfectly reliable technologies that have no unintended consequences or outcomes that may trouble us.

Along with an overall (practical or active) optimism regarding technology, there's a strong strain among transhumanists (and especially in the principles of extropy) of critical rationalism and spontaneous order. It's true that older technophiles—especially those who might reasonably be labeled "technocrats"—have sought to impose on society a technologically mediated vision of a better future. Transhumanists have far more often challenged this approach—what Hayek called "constructivist rationalism," preferring a self-critical rationalism (or pancritical rationalism[5]). Critical rationalism distinguishes us from Bacon, who, like Descartes, believed that the path to genuine knowledge lay in first making a comprehensive survey of what is reliably known rather than merely believed.

Adding to the limits to confidence imposed by critical rationalism as opposed to constructivist rationalism, many transhumanists show a great appreciation for spontaneous order and its attendant unintended consequences, as outlined in my

---

[5]   Max More, "Pancritical Rationalism: An Extropic Metacontext for Memetic Progress" (Paper presented at the Extro 1 conference, 1994b).

"Order Without Orderers."[6] Outcomes of people using technologies will never be quite as we might expect. Technology in use can differ drastically from technology as designed. When particle physicists started using Tim Berners Lee's hypertextual Web at the start of the 1990s, they had no idea what would quickly develop out of it. But these unexpected outcomes and spontaneous developments don't mean that we should stop trying to design better technologies and to improve our abilities at foreseeing ways in which they could go wrong.

THE BODY IN TRANSHUMANISM

Ihde is right that the cyborg can be an idol. In his discussion of this idol, however, he never explicitly suggests that transhumanists idolize the cyborg. That's just as well since transhumanists generally look down on the cyborg concept as primitive and unhelpful. It is the critics who try to force the square peg of transhumanist views of the body into the round hole of the "cyborg." This most often takes the form of accusing us of seeking to mechanize the human body, or of fearing, hating, or despising our fleshiness, the fallacies of which I discussed in "Beyond the Machine: Technology and Posthuman Freedom."[7] A classic example of this straw man construction can be found in Erik Davis's *Techgnosis*. Thankfully, Ihde does not repeat this error.

True transhumanism doesn't find the biological human body disgusting or frightening. It does find it to be a marvelous yet flawed piece of engineering, as expressed in Primo Posthuman.[8] It could hardly be otherwise, given that it was designed by a blind watchmaker, as Richard Dawkins put it. True transhumanism *does* seek to enable each of us to alter and improve (by our own standards) the human body. It champions what I called *morphological freedom* in my 1993 paper, "Technological Self-Transformation."

THE ROLE OF FORECASTING

"Idolatrous technofantasies" arise again, according to Ihde "in the same narratives concerning the human, the posthuman and the transhuman." *Which*

6   Max More, "Order Without Orderers," *Extropy* #7 (1991).

7   Max More, "Beyond the Machine: Technology and Posthuman Freedom," in proceedings of Ars Electronica, *FleshFactor: Informationmaschine Mensch*, Ars Electronica Center (Wien, New York, Springer, 1997).

8   Natasha Vita-More, "Primo Posthuman Future Body Prototype," 1997; "The New [human] Genre—Primo Posthuman" (Paper presented at Ciber@RT Conference, Bilbao, Spain, April, 2004).

narratives are these? Again, we are left without a referent. The point of his discussion of prediction is to repeat his point about unintended consequences and difficulties in knowing how technologies will turn out. In this section, Ihde does finally mention two people who might be called transhumanists—Hans Moravec and Ray Kurzweil—although Kurzweil definitely resists the label. Ihde calls them "worshippers of the idol of prediction" and asks if they have any credibility. Instead of addressing that, he makes some comments on unintended consequences that might arise from downloading the human mind into a computer.

Both Moravec's and Kurzweil's forecasts of specific technological trends have turned out rather well so far. Of course, it is easy to find lists of predictions from earlier forecasters that now, with hindsight, sound silly, and Ihde treats us to a few of them. Even there, and even with the assumption that accurate predicting is what matters in the whole transhuman/posthuman discussion, he fails to make a strong case for the futility or foolishness of predicting. He mentions an in-depth survey of predicted technologies from 1890 to 1940, noting that less than one-third of the 1,500 predictions worked out well. He adds: "Chiding me for pointing this out in *Nature* and claiming these are pretty good odds, my response is that 50% odds are normal for a penny toss, and these are less than that!?"

The critics who chided Ihde for this are perfectly justified. He just digs himself deeper into the hole of error by bringing up the coin toss analogy. A coin has two sides, yielding two possibilities, so that the chance of a random prediction coming true is 50 percent. But technologies can develop in innumerable ways, not only because of future discoveries about that technology, but also because of interactions with other technologies. Technologies largely develop based on how they are used. This error is especially odd considering how frequently Ihde flogs the dead horse of trade-offs and unintended consequences.

More importantly for these discussions of the transhuman and posthuman, it seems to me that Ihde doesn't understand futurology or forecasting. The purpose of thinking about the future is not to make impossibly accurate pinpoint *predictions*. It's to *forecast* possible futures so that we can prepare as well as possible for the upsides and downsides—so we can try to anticipate and improve on some of the trade-offs and side effects and develop resilient responses, policies, and organizations. Rather than throwing up our hands in the face of an uncertain future, transhumanists and other futurists seek to understand our options better.

Ultimate skepticism concerning forecasting is not tenable, otherwise no one would ever venture to cross the road or save any money. Should we look at the uncertainty inherent in the future as an impenetrable black box? No. We need to distinguish different levels of uncertainty and then use the best available tools while developing better ones to make sense of possible outcomes. At the lowest level of uncertainty, there is only one possible outcome. In those situations, businesses use tools such as net present value.

Raise the level of uncertainty a bit and you're in a situation where there are several distinct possible futures, one of which will occur. In these situations, you can make good use of tools such as scenario planning, game theory, and decision-tree real-options valuation. At a higher level of uncertainty, we face a range of futures and must use additional tools such as system dynamics models. When uncertainty is at its highest and the range of possible outcomes is unbounded, we can only look to analogies and reference cases and try to devise resilient strategies and designs.[9]

Transhumanists are far from being dummies when it comes to looking ahead. But it's true that many transhumanists are far from perfect in their approach to forecasting and foresight. My biggest complaint with many of my colleagues is that their vision is overly technocentric. Rather than "the idol of prediction," a better critical construct would have been "the idol of technocentrism." Not surprisingly, many transhumanists have a heavily technical background, especially in the computer and information sciences and the physical sciences. With my own background in economics, politics, philosophy, and psychology, I see a paucity of the social sciences among even sophisticated seers such as Ray Kurzweil, which I debated with him in 2002.[10]

None of Ihde's idols apply to true transhumanism. But they do add up to a simple message: People's actions have unintended consequences, people are clueless about possible futures, and it is arrogant and hubristic to pursue fundamental improvements to the human condition. This ultimately pessimistic and existentially conservative message does indeed conflict directly with true transhumanism. Transhumanists do in fact understand unintended consequences and limits to our understanding, but they continue to strive for fundamental advances. I am wary of all "isms," but these kinds of critiques of transhumanism spur me to renew my identification with that label even as I engage more deeply in cleaning up such misconceptions.

References

Bacon, Francis. *Novum Organum*. 1620.

Clarke, Arthur C., "Hazards of Prophecy: The Failure of Imagination" in *Profiles of the Future* Rev. ed. New York: Henry Holt & Co., 1984.

Courtney, Hugh. *20/20 Foresight: Crafting Strategy in an Uncertain World*. Cambridge, Mass.: Harvard Business School Press, 2001.

Davis, Erik. *Techgnosis: Myth, Magic & Mysticism in the Age of Information*. New York: Harmony Books, 1998.

Ihde, Don. "Of Which Human Are We Post?" *The Global Spiral* 9, no. 3, (2008). http://www.metanexus.net/magazine/tabid/68/id/10552/Default.aspx.

---

[9] Hugh Courtney, *20/20 Foresight: Crafting Strategy in an Uncertain World* (Cambridge, Mass.: Harvard Business School Press, 2001).

[10] Ray Kurzweil and Max More, "Max More and Ray Kurzweil on the Singularity," KurzweilAI.net (2002), http://www.kurzweilai.net/articles/art0408.html?m=1.

Kurzweil, Ray. *The Singularity is Near: When Humans Transcend Biology*. New York: Penguin, 2006.

Kurzweil, Ray and Max More. "Max More and Ray Kurzweil on the Singularity." KurzweilAI.net, 2002, http://www.kurzweilai.net/articles/art0408. html?m=1.

Mayr, Ernst. *Population, Species, and Evolution*. Cambridge, Mass.: Harvard University Press, 1963, 1970.

More, Max. "Principles of Extropy," *Extropy*, 1990, 1992, 1993, 1998.

———. "Transhumanism: Toward a Futurist Philosophy." *Extropy* #6, 1990, 1994, 1996.

———. "Order Without Orderers," *Extropy* #7, 1991.

———. "Technological Self-Transformation: Expanding Personal Extropy." *Extropy* #10, vol. 4, no. 2 (1993): 15-24.

———. "On Becoming Posthuman." *Free Inquiry*, 1994a.

———. "Pancritical Rationalism: An Extropic Metacontext for Memetic Progress," Paper presented at the Extro 1 conference, 1994b.

———. *The Diachronic Self: Identity, Continuity, Transformation*. (PhD diss, University of Southern California, 1995), http://www.maxmore.com/disscont. htm.

———. "Beyond the Machine: Technology and Posthuman Freedom." Paper in proceedings of Ars Electronica, *FleshFactor: Informationmaschine Mensch*, Ars Electronica Center, Springer, Wien, New York, 1997.

———. "Virtue and Virtuality" (Von erweiterten Sinnen zu Erfahrungsmaschinen) in *Der Sinn der Sinne*. Kunst und Austellungshalle der Bundesrepublik Deutschland, Gottingen, 1998.

———. "Letter to Mother Nature" (part of "The Ultrahuman Revolution: Amendments to the Human Constitution.") Paper presented at Biotech Futures Conference, U.C. Berkeley, 1999.

———. The Proactionary Principle, 2004. http://www.maxmore.com/proactionary. htm.

———. "Superlongevity without Overpopulation." In *The Scientific Conquest of Death*. Immortality Institute, 2004b.

———. "How to Choose a Forecasting Method," ManyWorlds, 2005, http:// contribute.manyworlds.net/301/content/Models/CO1118051055599.pdf.

Vita-More, Natasha, 1997. "Primo Posthuman future Body Prototype," 1997, http://www.natasha.cc/primo.htm and http://www.kurzweilai.net/meme/frame. html?main=/articles/art0405.html.

Vita-More, Natasha. "The New [human] Genre—Primo Posthuman." Delivered at Ciber@RT Conference, Bilbao, Spain, April, 2004.

Chapter Ten

Transhumanism and the Posthuman Future: Will Technological Progress Get Us There?

by Ted Peters

The prospect of a posthuman future replete with ecological harmony, cybernetic immortality, and the imbuing of the entire universe with evolving intelligence tantalizes our imagination with a utopian vision. All we need do is turn a couple of technological corners and, suddenly, the abundant life will be ours. We will be liberated from the vicissitudes of biological restraints such as suffering and death, and we will be freed by enhanced intelligence to enjoy the fulfilling life of a cosmic mind. The transhumanist, or H+, vision is as inspiring as it is extravagant.

How do we get there from here? How do we make the leap from our biological inheritance to a future of machined mind? How do we accelerate evolutionary development to carry the present generation into an unprecedented new era of posthuman flourishing? How can our technological future gain a decisive victory over our biological past?

What we find in transhumanist prognostications is reliance on the doctrine of progress. Transhumanists assume that progress, understood as betterment over time, is inherent in nature and inherent in culture. Evolution constitutes progress in biology. Technological advance constitutes progress in culture. Betterment is inevitable as the inexorable wheels of progress keep turning. The direction of progress is set, and the task of transhumanist technology is to increase the speed forward.

In this essay, I would like to begin with a brief exposition of the central claims and promises being lifted up by members of the transhumanist school of thought, explicating especially their assumptions regarding the nature of progress. I will place the futurist orientation of today's transhumanists in the broad context of futurist thinking, which has developed over the last half century. I will distinguish between two types of futurist thinking: *futurum*, relying upon growth or progress, versus *adventus*, which anticipates the advent of the new. I will show how transhumanism fits squarely into the first of these, not the second. Finally, I will turn to distinctively theological resources to critique the concept of progress with which the transhumanists work. I will explicate briefly the positions taken by neo-orthodox theologians such as Reinhold Niebuhr and Langdon Gilkey, who helped make us aware that progress is ambiguous—that is, all technological advances can be pressed into the service of either good or evil. Progress in technology does not in itself foster progress in culture or morality.

My thesis is this: transhumanist assumptions regarding progress are naïve because they fail to operate with an anthropology that is realistic regarding the human proclivity to turn good into evil. It is my own view that researchers in the relevant fields of genetics and nanotechnology should proceed toward developing new and enhancing technologies, to be sure, but they should maintain constant watchfulness for ways in which these technologies can become perverted and bent toward destructive purposes.

In the process I would like to correct one mistake made by transhumanist theorists. They presume that religion will attempt to place roadblocks in their way on the grounds that the religious mind is old fashioned, out of date, Luddite, and dedicated to resisting change. When this image is applied to Christian theology or even Jewish theology, it is mistaken. The Hebrew Scriptures include the prophets who look forward to the future, because God promises new things. "I am about to do a new thing," says God in Isaiah 43:19. The most significant of the new things God promises is the coming kingdom of God, the transformation of this creation into a new creation. The Bible closes in Revelation 21:5 with God saying, "See, I am making all things new." Rather than fixate things in the past, biblical theologians are inspired to anticipate the new, to look forward to transformation, to celebrate innovation. If a theologian would become critical of a transhumanist, it would not be in defense of what has been. Rather, it would be because of a naïveté in thinking that we could accomplish with technology a transformation that can be achieved only by the eschatological act of a gracious and loving God.

What Is a Transhumanist?

Astounding changes belong to our medium-range future. A transformation of apocalyptic proportion is imminent. According to the Transhumanist Declaration of the World Transhumanist Association, "humanity will be radically changed by technology in the future. We foresee the feasibility of redesigning the human condition, including such parameters as the inevitability of aging, limitations on human and artificial intellects, unchosen psychology, suffering, and our confinement to the planet earth."[1]

The human race of the present generation has the opportunity to speed up its own evolution through technological self-transformation. "Transhumanism is the view that humans should (or should be permitted to) use technology to remake human nature" is the definition offered by Heidi Campbell and Mark Walker.[2] It is a science and a philosophy that seeks to employ genetic technology, information technology, and nanotechnology to greatly enhance the healthy life span of persons, increase intelligence, and make us humans happier and more virtuous. The key is to re-contextualize humanity in terms of technology. This leads to a vision of a posthuman future characterized by a merging of humanity with technology as the next stage of our human evolution. Humanity plus (H+) is calling us forward. *Posthuman* refers to who we might become if transhuman efforts achieve their goals.

The transhumanist movement seeks to fill the widening cultural void in Western civilization due to the disintegration of the former religious glue that held us together in a common spirit. In addition to the failure of tradition to hold us together, so also postmodernism is failing because this nihilistic philosophy refuses to recognize the gifts of the modern scientific age, namely, reason and progress. What we need at this moment is an inspiring philosophy that reveres scientific reason and that will pull us toward a positive future. To meet this need, transhumanism offers a "totalized philosophical system"[3] with a three-level worldview: a metaphysical level, a psychological level, and an ethical level.

At the metaphysical, or cosmological, level, the transhumanist sees a world in a "process of evolutionary complexification toward evermore complex structures, forms, and operations." At the psychological level, transhumanists believe we human beings are "imbued with the innate Will to Evolve—an instinctive drive to expand abilities in pursuit of ever-increasing survivability and well-being." These two lead to the ethical level, where "we should seek to *foster* our innate Will to Evolve, by continually striving to expand our

---

[1]   http://www.transhumanism.org/index.php/WTA/declaration/ (accessed January 22, 2008). Transhumanism is an expansion on *extropianism*. Extropy, in contrast to entropy, refers to a system's capacity for growth based upon its functional order, intelligence, vitality, energy, and experience. Extropianism or extropism is a set of values oriented toward improving the human condition through technology that might some day bring immortality.

[2]   Heidi Campbell and Mark Walker, "Religion and Transhumanism: Introducing a Conversation," *Journal of Evolution and Technology* 14, no.2 (2005): 1. See: Nick Bostrom, home page 2005, http://www.nickbostrom.com/tra/values.html.

[3]   Simon Young, *Designer Evolution: A Transhumanist Manifesto* (Amherst, NY: Prometheus Books, 2006), 87.

abilities throughout life. By acting in harmony with the essential nature of the evolutionary process—complexification—we may discover a new sense of purpose, direction, and meaning to life, and come to feel ourselves *at home in the world* once more."[4] What Simon Young plans is to replace "Darwinian Evolution with Designer Evolution—from slavery to the selfish genes to conscious self-rule by the human mind."[5]

The future will differ from the past. Whereas in the past we have been prisoners of our biology, in the future we will become liberated. Our liberation will come from increased intelligence, intelligence that itself will find a way to remove itself from our deteriorating bodies and establish a much more secure substrate for endurance. Our mental lives in the future may take place within a computer or on the Internet. What we have previously known as *Homo sapiens* will be replaced by *Homo cyberneticus*. "As humanism freed us from the chains of superstition, let transhumanism free us from our biological chains."[6]

Once freed from the limits of our inherited bodies, the expansion of human intelligence would be limited only by the size of our universe. What the transhumanist foresees is a cosmic imbuing of matter with consciousness. "Liberated from biological slavery, an immortalized species, *Homo cyberneticus*, will set out for the stars. Conscious life will gradually spread throughout the galaxy . . . until finally, in the unimaginably distant future, the whole universe has come alive, awakened to its own nature—a cosmic mind become conscious of itself as a living entity—omniscient, omnipotent, omnipresent."[7] The entire universe will be converted into an "extended thinking entity," writes Hans Moravec.[8]

The mood of transhumanism is aggressively Promethean. Here is the promise: we humans will arrest from the gods and from nature the principles and resources we need to take our destiny into our own hands. With a wave of the philosophical hand, we will expel the old fatalisms, the naysayers, the Luddites. "Bio-fatalism will increasingly be replaced by techno-can-do-ism—the belief in the power of the new technology to free us from the limitations of our bodies and minds . . . . In the twenty-first century, the belief in the Fall of Man will be replaced by the belief in his inevitable transcendence—through Superbiology."[9] The torch of Prometheus will lead us into the new world of transhumanism. "Let us cast aside cowardice and seize the torch of Prometheus with both hands."[10]

---

[4]   Ibid., 19 italics in original; see: 202.

[5]   Ibid., 207.

[6]   Ibid., 32, italics in original.

[7]   Ibid., 44.

[8]   Hans Moravec, *Mind Children: The Future of Robot and Human Intelligence* (Cambridge, Mass.: Harvard University Press, 1988), 116.

[9]   Young, *Designer Evolution*, 20.

[10]   Ibid., 40.

This Promethean confidence in the advance of technology is accompanied by a utopian vision, a vision of future human fulfillment or even posthuman fulfillment in a kingdom where rational intelligence has transcended its previous biological imprisonment. Not only as individuals but also as a social community and even as a cosmic community we will experience ecstatic human flourishing, the abundant life that previous religious visionaries could only dream of.

THE SINGULARITY IS ALMOST HERE

How will we get there from here? Crossing the threshold of the Singularity—the creation of smarter-than-human intelligence—will mark the transition.[11]

Ray Kurzweil prophesies a dramatic future event—not in the distant future but rather just around the corner, 2045 to be exact. This will be a threshold event, an event known in his field as the "Singularity."[12] Leading up to the Singularity we will see how the pace of technological change will be so rapid and its impact so deep that human life will be irreversibly transformed. The nose on this transformation face will be enhanced human intelligence. What follows this nose is the observation that human intelligence will leap from human bodies to machines, making high-tech machines more human than we are. This can happen because intelligence is not dependent upon our biological substrate; rather, as information in patterns, intelligence can be extricated from our bodies. Our intelligence can live on in an enhanced form even when extricated from our bodies and placed in a computer. "Uploading a human brain means scanning all of its salient details and then reinstantiating those details into a suitably powerful computational substrate. This process would capture a person's entire personality, memory, skills, and history."[13]

On the one hand, this would require disembodied intelligence. On the other hand, we would have new bodies, namely, machines. "Future machines will be human even if they are not biological," writes Kurzweil. "This will be the next step in evolution."[14] Rather than a biological substrate, humans of a future generation will rely upon a machine substrate. When we have escaped our biological limitations, we will be able to program a much longer life, a disembodied yet intelligent life. "The Singularity will allow us to transcend these limitations of our biological bodies

---

[11] Singularitarians are friends of the Singularity, believers who are working to make it happen. The Singularity Institute for Artificial Intelligence (SIAI), for example, was founded in 2000 to develop safe artificial intelligence (AI) and to raise awareness of both the dangers and potential benefits it believes AI presents. http://www.singinst.org/.

[12] Ray Kurzweil, *The Singularity Is Near: When Humans Transcend Biology* (New York: Penguin, 2005), 136.

[13] Ibid., 198-199.

[14] Ibid., 30.

and brains. We will gain power over our fates. Our mortality will be in our own hands. We will be able to live as long as we want . . . . By the end of this century, the nonbiological portion of our intelligence will be trillions of trillions of times more powerful than unaided human intelligence."[15]

Living in cyberspace could seem attractive. One would not be alone. One's cybermind would be in community with all other cyberminds, a variant on Teilhard's noosphere. One might even celebrate a new higher level of community. This is what Margaret Wertheim celebrates. Despite the dangers lurking in our computers, she thanks cyberspace for establishing a network of relationships. Further, the global community of electronic relationships is eliciting a sense of responsibility toward one another. "If cyberspace teaches us anything," writes Wertheim, "it is that the worlds we conceive . . . are communal projects requiring ongoing communal responsibility."[16] Once Kurzweil has successfully uploaded our minds into cyberspace, we will enjoy a communal network of shared intelligence.

Even though we can thank our evolutionary past for bringing us to the point of intelligence, we the human race must move still further forward. Our generation has the opportunity to enhance our intelligence, to advance still further in evolutionary development. Computers along with GNR—genetics, nanotechnology, and robotics—are all tools whereby we can build a dramatically new future for abundant living and cosmic community.

What we note here is how Kurzweil conflates biological evolution and technological progress. He sees the latter as an extension of the former. The key characteristic of both evolutionary and technological progress is inevitability, according to Kurzweil. Both natural evolution and human technology benefit from a guiding purpose, a built-in purpose. And this built-in *Logos*, or entelechy, virtually guarantees the future he is forecasting. What is this built-in purpose? Increased intelligence. "The purpose of the universe reflects the same purpose as our lives: to move toward greater intelligence and knowledge . . . we will within this century be ready to infuse our solar system with our intelligence through self-replicating non-biological intelligence. It will then spread out to the rest of the universe."[17]

How do we get there from here? Through applying our existing intelligence to leaping the hurdles that currently need technological transcending. "Insight from the brain reverse-engineering effort, overall research in developing AI [Artificial Intelligence] algorithms, and ongoing exponential gains in computing platforms make strong AI (AI at human levels and beyond) inevitable. Once AI achieves human levels, it will necessarily soar past it because it will combine the strengths of human

---

15   Ibid., 9.

16   Margaret Wertheim, *The Pearly Gates of Cyberspace: A History of Space from Dante to the Internet* (New York: W. W. Norton, 1999), 304.

17   Kurzweil, *Singularity*, 372.

intelligence with the speed, memory capacity, and knowledge sharing that nonbiological intelligence already exhibits."[18] Note Kurzweil's confident vocabulary: "inevitable" and "necessary." Simon Young makes this explicit, "The furtherance of human evolution through advanced biotechnology is not only possible, but *inevitable*."[19]

SALVATION FROM THE ENVIRONMENTAL CRISIS

This technological utopia will bring not only maximized intelligence, but it will also bring ecological harmony. Working for clean alternative technologies that not only preserve but also restore the biosphere sits high on the agenda of what some transhumanists embrace as *technogaianism*, an ethic for technology that supports the Gaia philosophy.

Kurzweil believes that nanotechnology will rescue us from our environmental crisis. By building devices at the molecular scale out of nanoparticles, we can reduce the size and surface area of such devices, lowering their impact on the surrounding environment. In addition, new biological properties will be introduced so that nanotechnology "will eventually provide us with a vastly expanded toolkit for improved catalysis, chemical and atomic bonding, sensing, and mechanical manipulation, not to mention intelligent control through enhanced microelectronics. Ultimately we will redesign all of our industrial processes to achieve their intended results with minimal consequences, such as unwanted by-products and their introduction into the environment."[20]

In short, manufacturing in the future will do less damage to our surroundings. In addition, we will develop better methods of cleaning up pollution. And we will even overcome hunger and poverty. "Emerging technologies will provide the means of providing and storing clean and renewable energy, removing toxins and pathogens from our bodies and the environment, and providing the knowledge and wealth to overcome hunger and poverty."[21] Nanotechnology in the service of progress can lead today's world into a tomorrow of social justice and ecological harmony.

THE COMING TECHNOLOGICAL VICTORY OVER AGING AND DEATH

Transhumanism can be described as a philosophy of life with a central tenet: "the belief in overcoming human limitations through reason, science, and

---

18 Ibid., 407.
19 Young, *Designer Evolution,* 22, italics in original.
20 Ibid., (2005) 251.
21 Ibid., 371-372.

technology."[22] One limitation on the transhumanist list to be overcome is aging. Death too. Aubrey de Grey says he is "not in favor of aging." When one is not in favor of something, then it is time to apply technology to overcome it. This is what de Grey plans. If we could eliminate aging, then "we will be in possession of indefinite youth. We will die only from the sort of causes that young people die of today—accidents, suicide, homicide, and so on—but not of the age-related diseases that account for the vast majority of deaths in the industrialized world today."[23] Now, we might ask: might this be realistic?

Until recently, demographers assumed that once gains made by reducing mortality in early and midlife had reached completion, then growth in longevity would level off and we would see a fixed maximum for human age. However, to our surprise, this is not happening. In much of the developed world, life expectancy continues to increase, and people reach old age in healthier condition than their grandparents did. Might realism be on the side of the transhumanists?

Why do we grow old? Can we do something about it? "Clear consensus now exists that aging is caused by the gradual, lifelong accumulation of a wide variety of molecular and cellular damage. At the heart of the genetic determination of lifespan is the extent to which the organism's genome invests in survival." With the many tasks genetic expression needs to perform, why waste time and energy on repairing what is broken in order to lengthen the life span of the host organism. After all, the body is expendable, at least according to the disposable soma theory. Now if the genome does not care about life span, might we with the help of our medical scientists care? Might we intervene to patch up molecular and cellular damage? Yes. "If aging is a matter of things falling apart, can research realistically hope to achieve anything useful? The answer is emphatically yes—there is plenty of evidence that it is possible to intervene in the underlying causative mechanisms."[24]

Ray Kurzweil offers an ebullient version of this otherwise cautious forecast: "We are beginning to understand aging, not as a single inexorable progression but as a group of related processes. Strategies are emerging for fully reversing each of these aging progressions, using different combinations of biotechnology techniques."[25] With emphasis, Kurzweil trumpets, "We have the means right now to live long enough to live forever."[26]

Can we slow down, if not actually stop, the aging process? Kurzweil answers affirmatively. He claims he has already achieved something notable in his own

---

[22]   Ibid., 15.

[23]   Aubrey de Grey, "Foreword: Forever Young," Ibid., 9.

[24]   Thomas B. L. Kirkwood, "A systematic look at an old problem," *Nature* 451: 7179: 644-647 (February 7, 2008) 645.

[25]   Kurzweil, *Singularity,* 212-213.

[26]   Ibid., 371.

case. At age fifty-six, his biological age is only forty. How has he accomplished this? "I have been very aggressive about reprogramming my biochemistry," he writes. "I take 250 supplements (pills) a day and receive a half-dozen intravenous therapies each week (basically nutritional supplements delivered directly into my bloodstream, thereby bypassing my GI tract). As a result, the metabolic reactions in my body are completely different than they would otherwise be."[27]

Taking vitamin supplements enhances the health of the body, and this indirectly supports the operations of our intelligent brains. Might we do more? Might we find a way for our intelligence to escape the limits of our aging bodies entirely? Yes, say the transhumanists. Our minds can move into a computer and then into cyberspace. "Currently, when our human hardware crashes, the software of our lives—our personal 'mind file'—dies with it. However, this will not continue to be the case when we have the means to store and restore the thousands of trillions of bytes of information represented in the pattern that we call our brains . . . . They [the bodiless intelligences] will live out on the Web, projecting bodies whenever they need or want them, including virtual bodies in diverse realms of virtual reality, holographically projected bodies, foglet-projected bodies, and physical bodies comprising nanobot swarms and other forms of nanotechnology."[28]

Such a personal eschatology consisting of immortalized intellectual life is reminiscent of Socrates, who found comfort when anticipating the death of his body. Once liberated from his temporal body, Socrates's disembodied mind could go on to contemplate eternal ideas.[29] Once the transhumanist has liberated our intelligence from our biological bodies and placed our minds into computers or into cyberspace, we will be able to think cosmically and escape the threat of extinction through death.

How do we get there from here? Technological progress will carry us from our biologically inherited bodies into a future of cybernetic immortality. Socrates presumed that his intellectual soul was inherently immortal. Transhumanists presume that progress is inherent to evolution and that our future liberation from biological constraints is inevitable. Like a rocket taking off from a launching pad, our computer generation has been thrust by evolution upward into the stratosphere of technological progress, and very soon we will find our immortalized minds winging throughout the cosmos.

TRANSHUMANIST ETHICS

What kind of ethical deliberation or moral code might transhumanism lead to? It leads in two opposite directions. One direction is toward laissez-faire capitalism.

---

[27]   Ibid., 211.

[28]   Kurzweil, *Singularity,* 325.

[29]   Plato, *Crito* and *Phaedo.*

After all, only the sectors of the modern economy flushed with money can afford to invest in GNR: genetics, nanotechnology, and robotics. Capital investment and technological advance provide cyclical support for one another. Investors invest in GNR, and the sales earnings from GNR increase the amount of capital available for reinvestment. "It's the economic imperative of a competitive marketplace that is the primary force driving technology forward and fueling the law of accelerating returns . . . . Economic imperative is the equivalent of survival in biological evolution."[30] What we find here is an ethical principle—the "will to evolve," mentioned earlier—drawn from evolutionary biology and applied to economics, "survival of the fittest."

The other direction taken by transhumanist ethical thinking is toward increased cooperation, even altruism or benevolence. Support for altruism takes the form of a common sense admonition to cooperate with one other for the betterment of all. Benevolence is more highly valued than selfishness, according to transhumanist ethics. When this direction is taken, the Darwinian struggle for existence with its competitive aggression is replaced.

Simon Young, for example, asserts that we should advance from *genethics* to *nurethics.* By the former term, he is referencing Richard Dawkins's theory that the "selfish gene" directs the course of evolution and that human ethics are a social expression of the selfish gene's pressure to replicate.[31] Dawkins's selfish gene theory is his interpretation of nineteenth-century social Darwinism, where the "struggle for existence" in nature provided justification for a social ethic celebrating the "survival of the fittest." Should we today construct an ethic based upon our selfish genes? Should today's society be governed by the competition between all those struggling to survive? Young answers in the negative. Now that we have brains and reason and science, however, we are no longer puppets dancing on the strings of our DNA; we are no longer merely struggling for biological existence. Our brains can transcend our biological inheritance. We can devise a rational ethic. This rational ethic Young describes as benevolence, a "common sense" ethic that includes altruistic care for one another. "Morality is the replacement of Genethics with Nurethics—from control by the selfish genes, to self-rule by the human mind . . . . In the language of Nurethics, the self-governing mind may learn to inhibit *stupidly selfish* instincts in its own best interests of ever increasing survivability and well-being."[32] The problem with selfish human behavior is that it is stupid. In contrast, benevolence is smart. As our intelligence increases, we will replace stupid selfish morality with more reasonable benevolent behavior such as cooperation.

---

[30]   Kurzweil, *Singularity*, 96.

[31]   See: Richard Dawkins, *The Selfish Gene* (Oxford and New York: Oxford University Press, 1976).

[32]   Young, *Designer Evolution,* 35, italics in original.

What Young perceives as a contradiction between the naturalistic ethics tied to evolution and his more benevolent values was a contradiction already seen during the era of social Darwinism. American pragmatist Charles Sanders Peirce pointed this out in the late nineteenth century. "The *Origin of Species* of Darwin merely extends politico-economical views of progress to the entire realm of animal and vegetable life . . . . As Darwin puts it on his title-page, it is the struggle for existence; and he should have added for his motto: Every individual for himself, and the Devil take the hindmost! Jesus, in his Sermon on the Mount, expressed a different opinion."[33] If today's transhumanists affirm values akin to those of Jesus, they will have to do so in opposition to the values inherent in previous forms of evolutionary ethics.

Theologian Jûrgen Moltmann has offered a similar analysis. If in our era of biomedical progress human existence is no longer oriented toward mere survival, then we are ready to reorient our lives around a new purpose, namely, fulfillment. Darwinian values that may have supported survival of the fittest will need replacing by values that promote cooperation and social harmony. "The change in human interests evoked by biomedical progress can be described as a transition from the struggle for existence to striving for fulfillment," writes Moltmann. "The principle of self-preservation against others can be transformed into the principle of self-fulfillment in the other. Systems of aggression can be overcome by systems of co-operation."[34] The implication for transhumanist ethics is this: despite the conflation of biological evolution and technological progress, Darwinian values such as self-preservation in the competition for existence cannot be thought to be progressive in light of the picture of the future that transhumanists are painting. Yet their reliance upon the "will to evolve" in the form of laissez-faire capitalism reiterates the nineteenth-century reliance on social Darwinism, the very value system that apparently needs replacing. In sum, transhumanist ethics is torn by a tension between the capitalist values adhering to survival of the fittest and the altruistic values of a benevolent community.

THE ETHIC OF RELINQUISHMENT

With this in mind, we turn to another question: should a transhumanist ethic place us totally at the beck and call of every proposal for technological progress?

---

[33] Charles Sanders Peirce, *Collected Papers of Charles Sanders Peirce*, edited by Charles Hartshorne and Paul Weiss (8 Volumes: Cambridge, Mass.: Harvard University Press, 1931-58) 6:293 or *The Essential Peirce: Selected Philosophical Writings,* edited by Nathan Houser, Christian Kloesel, and Peirce Edtion Project (2 Volumes: Bloomington: Indiana University Press, 1992)1998) 1:358-360.

[34] Jûrgen Moltmann, *The Future of Creation,* translated by Margaret Kohl (Minneapolis: Fortress Press, 1979) 147.

Does this mean unbridled social subservience to any and every advance? No. We must be selective, say the transhumanists. We might find we need to relinquish some opportunities while embracing others. Discerning which to relinquish and which to support is one of the ethical tasks consciously taken on by transhumanists.

Kurzweil addresses ethical issues with his concept of relinquishment. Should we relinquish the opportunity for technological advance? If so, at what level? Kurzweil objects to naturalists who advocate "broad relinquishment"—that is, the broad rejection of technology in order to preserve what nature has bequeathed us. Yet Kurzweil is drawn toward "refined relinquishment"—that is, relinquishing select technologies that threaten our safety or the safety of the environment. Saying no to developing physical entities that can self-replicate in a natural environment makes sense to Kurzweil, even though the principle of self-replication will be necessary in certain cases such as self-replicating intelligence.[35] We want to avoid inundation by "gray goo," by unrestrained nanobot replication. What we need is "blue goo"—that is, "police" nanobots that will combat the criminal nanobots.[36]

We cannot avoid at this point introducing the phenomenon of the computer virus. In the case of the computer virus, we find an example of a nonbiological self-replicating entity that has appeared on the scene along with the spread of Internet communication. This software pathogen threatens to destroy our computer network medium, but the bright inventors of computer software can design an "immune system" to prevent serious damage. What is Kurzweil's interpretation? "Although software pathogens remain a concern, the danger exists mostly at a nuisance level," he comments. Then he adds, "When we have software running in our brains and bodies and controlling the world's nanobot immune system, the stakes will be immeasurably greater."[37]

Anticipating my theological analysis yet to come, I recommend that we pause for a moment to consider the significance of the computer virus for understanding the human condition. The invention of the computer virus is an invention with one sole purpose, namely, to destroy. Despite the benefits or even blessings of computer connections around the world, something at work in the human mind leads to the development of brute and unmitigated destruction. No increase in human intelligence or advance in technology will alter this ever-lurking human proclivity.

Is the transhumanist understanding of human nature realistic enough? Does the transhumanist vision include a realistic anticipation of our human proclivity for twisting good things into the service of evil? What we see in transhumanism is a vague awareness of this ever-lurking threat. But is it being taken with

---

[35]   Kurzweil, *Singularity*, 410-414.

[36]   Ibid., 416.

[37]   Ibid., 414.

sufficient seriousness? Does confidence in progress as inherently inevitable blind transhumanists from seeing the potholes in the road they are traveling?

Transhumanists seek protection from evil in the free market. Here is the path their ethical logic follows. Society should organize itself to foster the advances they are proposing. Technology needs money, private money, so society should be ready and willing to provide funding. This is where capitalism becomes incorporated into the transhumanist ethic. Laissez-faire capitalism will protect us from evil and will keep progress progressing. "Inherently there will be no absolute protection against strong AI. Although the argument is subtle, I believe that maintaining an open free-market system for incremental scientific and technological progress, in which each step is subject to market acceptance, will provide the most constructive environment for technology to embody widespread human values."[38] The free market will provide enough good to overcome the evil nuisances.

Again we ask: how will we get there from here? The highway of technological progress will take us there, and free market capitalism will clear the road of evil obstructions. So the transhumanists assume. In another essay, I parse the various ethical issues arising from within the advancing field of nanotechnology, one of the service roads that connect to the transhumanist highway.[39] Here, at a more abstract level, I simply wish to point out that the ethical values the transhumanists think they are trucking are likely to hit a detour, because investors from the free market will most likely divert the technology they fund into the service of their own economic ends.

DOES RELIGION BLOCK PROGRESS?

Such detour signs are apparently invisible. What transhumanists think they see in front of them are roadblocks put there by religion. Religion is allegedly Luddite. Through the eyes of today's transhumanists, religion looks like a roadblock, an obstruction. What the transhumanists think they see in religion is an atavistic commitment to the past, to the status quo, to resistance against anything new. This image is misleading; although we must admit that some religious reactions to scientific and technological advance can take Luddite form. Be that as it may, later in this paper I will show that Christian theology strongly affirms change. It even looks forward to radical transformation. The reluctance to embrace progress on the part of theologians does not come from a posture of resistance. Rather, it comes

---

[38] Ibid., 420.

[39] "Are we Playing God with Nano Enhancement?" *Nanoethics: The Ethical and Social Implications of Nanotechnology,* ed. by Fritrz Allhoff, Patrick Lin, James Moor, and John Weckert. New York: Wiley, 2007, chapter 4.3.

from an entirely different source, namely, a critique of the naïveté on the part of those who put their faith in progress, especially technological progress. What is so naïve about transhumanism, I will try to show, is its dismissal of the ambiguity that unavoidably accompanies all technological progress. What a Christian theologian can in good conscience do is encourage the advance of life-enhancing technology while keeping a wary eye open for the potential destructive proclivities of sinful human beings.

Simon Young provides an example of one who would like to clear religious blockage to make way for transhumanism. He assumes that a religious faith in God is necessarily atavistic and recalcitrant. After all, if God created the world the way it is, then it follows that it is immoral to change it. After all, if God allowed a child to be born with a genetic defect, it follows that it is immoral for medical therapists to repair it. This is Young's logic, applicable to the Christian faith, if not other religions. "The greatest threat to humanity's continuing evolution is theistic opposition to Superbiology in the name of a belief system based on blind faith in the absence of evidence."[40]

However, the historical evidence does not fit Young's assumptions. The God of the Bible does "new things," says Isaiah. God even promises a new creation, a renewing of nature. And if one only looks in the local telephone book or an online directory, more than likely a Good Samaritan hospital can be found just around the corner. Medical care for those who suffer began with Jesus the healer and continues right down to present day Christian consciousness. No Christian opposition to biology, either regular unleaded or the super type, exists, especially when biology is pressed into medical service. So Young's complaint regarding at least Christian recalcitrance is based upon blind assumptions rather than open-eyed observation.

What about the transhumanist attempt to attain everlasting life? Out of an apparent fear that religious tradition might attempt to slow down technological innovation, transhumanists accuse religious representatives of holding a vested interest in provenance over matters of death and immortality. One of the impediments to the advance toward cybernetic immortality is religion, they say. Religion stands in the way. Religion threatens to block progress. This is because religion has traditionally sought to provide a palliative for people faced with death. Religion brings acceptance of death, and comfort with that acceptance. Ready to engage in combat with traditional religion, in Promethean style, Kurzweil wants to defy death and use nanotechnology as a weapon to defeat death. "The primary role of traditional religion is deathist rationalization—that is, rationalizing the tragedy of death as a good thing."[41] In order to benefit from what the Singularity can bring, we need to overcome our deathist rationalization. We need to sweep traditional religion out of our road.

---

[40]   Young, *Designer Evolution,* 324.

[41]   Ibid., 372.

Given what was mentioned just above, it would appear to me that any improvement in human health or even longevity would be greeted by Christian moralists as a blessing from science, a gift to be thankful for. No theological recalcitrance would block progress toward human betterment through medical technology. On the other hand, a Christian theologian is likely to contend that the extension of the present form of human life for the indefinite future offered in the transhumanist scenario simply does not correspond to the biblical vision of resurrection from the dead. Our redemption through resurrection into the new creation does not correspond to cybernetic immortality. But that is another matter, and not one I want to make central in this essay. Rather, I would like to understand more clearly the ramifications of transhumanist assumptions regarding progress in light of the Bible's promise of a coming future transformation.

FUTUROLOGY AND ESCHATOLOGY

The appearance of transhumanist thinking and future forecasting has been made possible by recent advances in technology nested within a three-century tradition of belief in progress. What belief in progress has done for Western civilization is hold in front of us a positive vision of the future. Transhumanism holds up a positive vision of the future, a variant of visions that have become quite familiar over the last half century.

Here let us expand the context for understanding the place of transhumanist thinking within the wider horizon of Western culture and also within Christian theology. Two key elements in the transhumanist vision I would like to analyze are these: belief that the future will be different from the past plus the confidence that we can rely upon progress to bring this new future to pass. I would like to analyze these two commitments within a review of just what the concept of the future entails.

Two distinctive yet complementary ways for viewing the future stand before us. The first way is to foresee the future as growth, as an actualization of potentials residing in the present or the past. The second way is to anticipate something new, to prophesy a coming new reality. The first can be identified with the Latin term *futurum*. This term suggests growth, development, maturation, or fruition. An oak tree is the actualized futurum of a potential that already exists in the acorn. The Latin term *adventus*, in contrast, is the appearance of something new, a first, so to speak. It is a future that can be expected or hoped for, but it cannot be planned for. Whereas futurum provides an image of the future that can result from present trends, adventus provides a vision of a future that only God can make happen.[42]

---

[42]   "*Futurum* means what will be; *adventus* means what is coming." Jürgen Moltmann, *The Coming of God: Christian Eschatology* (Minneapolis: Fortress Press, 1996) 25.

The now nearly effete era of futurology relied upon futurum. We might date the birth of futurology with the founding of the World Future Society in 1967, although pioneering thought in the 1950s led up to it. Alvin Toffler spoke of the futurists as "a growing school of social critics, scientists, philosophers, planners, and others who concern themselves with the alternatives facing man as the human race collides with an onrushing future."[43] That school of futurists who flourished before many of today's transhumanists were born is all but dead now, but their legacy remains instructive for us today.

The Earth Day futurists of the late 1960s and 1970s set forth projections based upon then present trends. They forecasted alternative scenarios of damage to our planet and terrifying diebacks of starving people if trends continued toward increased population growth, increased natural resource depletion, increased agricultural and industrial production, increased pollution, along with increased threats to the ozone layer. They even warned us of global warming. These futurists structured their thinking according to what I call the understanding-decision-control (udc) formula: we need to *understand* present trends along with the alternative scenarios they could lead to; we need to make a *decision* regarding which alternative future we should actualize; and then we the human race can take *control* over our destiny rather than be pilloried by the onrush of an otherwise uncontrollable future.[44] Futurology provided the science that was thought would provide human control over our planetary future.

Whereas the path to the future pictured by the futurists was a movement from here to there, the path envisioned by Christian theologians reversed the direction. The vision of God's future would require the advent of something new, the arrival of a reality that we ourselves could not control. Roman Catholic theologian Karl Rahner spoke of God's future as a "mystery," as a coming reality beyond our rational control. Human consciousness transcends present reality with an openness toward the future, to be sure, Rahner said; but we must rely on the fact that "this future wills to give itself through its own self-communication . . . which is still in the process of historical realization."[45] Lutheran theologian Carl Braaten sharply defined the difference between futurology and eschatology: "A crucial difference

---

[43]   Alvin Toffler, editor, *The Futurists* (New York: Random House, 1972) 3.

[44]   I offered this analysis in two books, *Futures—Human and Divine* (Louisville: Westminster John Knox Press, 1977) and *Fear, Faith, and the Future* (Minneapolis: Augsburg Press, 1980). Here I challenged futurists with the *eschatological problem:* how do we get there from here? If the future is to be significantly different from the past, how on the basis of past resources can the change be accomplished? How can a leopard change its spots?

[45]   Karl Rahner, *Foundations of Christian Faith* (New York: Searbury Crossroad Press, 1978), 458.

between secular futurology and Christian eschatology is this: the future in secular futurology is *reached* by a process of the world's *becoming*. The future in Christian eschatology *arrives* by the *coming* of God's kingdom. The one is a *becoming* and the other a *coming*."[46]

In light of these understandings of the future, it is clear that the concept with which transhumanists work is the future as *futurum,* the future as a futurologist would grasp it.[47] New and startling things await us in the future, but the way from here to there is growth, technological advance. Human and posthuman flourishing will be the result of step-by-step advances. This understanding of the posthuman future depends on a related concept, namely, progress.[48] To the doctrine of progress we now turn.

PROGRESS IN TECHNOLOGY

As we have seen, transhumanism relies on the doctrine of progress. Adherence to progress lies at the level of assumption. One might ask: is such an assumption warranted? There is no doubt that progress in technology is a reality. Technological progress is the poster child of the Enlightenment civilization Yet we have reason to ask whether progress is limited to technology or whether all of reality is being

---

[46] Carl E. Braaten, *The Future of God* (New York: Harper, 1969), 29.

[47] It is my judgment that Robert M. Geraci is mistaken when he insists that the AI movement is apocalyptic (*adventus*) in "Apocalyptic AI: Religion and the Promise of Artificial Intelligence," *Journal of the American Academy of Religion* 76, no. 1 (2008): 138-166. Geraci rightly recognizes that the transhumanists replace divine action with evolutionary progress (p. 159); but then he fails to acknowledge that this implies a non-apocalyptic form of transformation. In addition, Geraci offers a reductionistic interpretation of Jewish and Christian apocalyptic, presuming it is caused by a "breakdown of a proper social order" and a sense of alienation (pp.140-141; 146-147). He even describes Hans Moravec and Ray Kurzweil as alienated. It is difficult to see how millionaire industrial leaders or authors who publish with Harvard University Press belong to the class of alienated victims of social breakdown.

[48] The doctrine of progress and the science of futurology may look different from eschatology, but they are all children of the same religious family. "Alone among the major world religions, and in special contrast to those of the East, Christianity postulated that the world was going somewhere, that the future was not simply an unchanging or cyclically repeating replica of the past. The idea of progress—central to the development of science and the modern world—had its roots in Christian eschatology." Victor C. Ferkiss, *Technological Man: The Myth and the Reality* (New York: New American Library, Mentor Books, 1969), 43.

carried toward the future by the flow of progress. Specifically, is it reasonable to think of human nature as progressive?

The backbone of the doctrine of progress is that "*something* is better than it had been and promises to get better still in the future."[49] This Western idea burst forth during the Renaissance and originally included a vision of a better future for culture. Eventually, cultural advance was eclipsed by industrial and then scientific or technological progress. Since the Enlightenment, "contemporary science and technology in effect co-opted the idea of progress, claiming improvement as self-evident."[50] We find ourselves today thinking objectively about the progressive advance of technology and, to some extent, science; but we cannot be confident that we see progress culturally or morally. "Because the notion of purpose or end in relation to nature was abandoned in modern science, there is no basis in science or in technology for judging the value of the ends to be served by technologies and therefore no basis for judging that changes to natural entities are improvements. This isolation of ends from means creates an ethical gulf between technical knowledge and its applications."[51]

What is key here is that our post-Enlightenment civilization has witnessed a split between technological progress and moral values. This split can be invisible, however, when the idea of progress seems to assume its own inherent definition of "better" and places this value in conflict with the values of the surrounding culture. When this happens, culture feels overrun by progress, and then technology is viewed as dehumanizing.

Despite the threat of dehumanization, it is clear that technological progress is driving our civilization. So we ask: in what direction? Does technology determine the direction for us? Or do we draw upon values from other sources and press technology into the service of actualizing those values? Does the dazzle of technological innovation temporarily blind us to the need for retrieving our fundamental value stance? Writing in the 1960s and 1970s, Georgetown University futurist Victor Ferkiss cautioned against allowing technology to follow its own course without being directed by human commitment to values such as justice, equality, and human well-being. "To control technology, to control the direction of human evolution, we must have some idea of where we are going and how far, else we will be mere passengers rather than drivers of the chariot of evolution."[52]

Over the last four decades, futurists such as Ferkiss have wrestled with the role of technology in bearing our civilization toward its future. Not merely the machines

---

[49]   Steven Goldman, "Progress," in *Encyclopedia of Science, Technology, and Ethics,* edited by Carl Mitcham (4 Volumes: New York: Macmillan, Gale, 2005) 3:1519.

[50]   Ibid., 1520.

[51]   Ibid.

[52]   Ferkiss, 203.

we invent are relevant. Perhaps more relevant is the technological mindset, the cultural incorporation of the machine into our self-understanding as human beings. The nearly primordial concept of *techne*, or *technique*, refers to the complex of standardized means for attaining a predetermined result. The technical mind converts otherwise spontaneous and unreflective behavior into behavior that is deliberate and rationalized. What distinguishes our modern world is the sheer delight we take in *technique*, finding fascination at more complex computers, faster jets, and bigger bombs. New nouns such as *technological man* or *technological civilization* have come to describe the ever-expanding and apparently irreversible rule of technique in all domains of life. Technique has expanded not only our practical lives, but it has also entered into our inner lives. Technique has become constitutive of the identity of modern human being. "Technology is what has made man man," wrote Ferkiss.[53]

But we might ask: could progress take us to the point where a fully "technological man" or perhaps a fully "technologized humanity" could emerge? To believe such a thing is either possible, let alone desirable, is to embrace a myth. "Technological man is more myth than reality," warned Ferkiss.[54] Why? Because of the split between technique and value. Technique is still pressed into the service of values that transcend it, whether we observe this or not. And what critical observers have seen during the industrial age in the modern West is the subordination of both science and technology to the service of economic greed and political domination. Today's technology is still supported and guided by yesterday's bourgeois values. Nothing suggests this arrangement will change. "What if the new man combines the animal irrationality of primitive man with the calculated greed and power-lust of industrial man, while possessing the virtually Godlike powers granted him by technology? This would be the ultimate horror."[55]

Now just how is this relevant to our analysis of the transhumanist project? Note two things: first, note the false assumption that technological progress has a built-in direction or purpose—false because it fails to recognize the split between progress and value; second, note the close alliance between transhumanist progress and free market capitalism. The values allegedly inherent within evolution and progress will not be able to sustain themselves in the face of the pressure to serve the demands of the funders. Money talks. What money says goes. No way exists to liberate technological progress from the vested interests of the economic and political powers that make such progress possible. Despite their feeble whisperings of liberal values such as altruism, cooperation, and ecology, the progress transhumanists anticipate will be unavoidably pressed into the service of consolidating and expanding the wealth of its investors.

---

[53]   Ibid., 36.

[54]   Ibid.,202.

[55]   Ibid.,34.

Does Technology Dehumanize Us?

Chief Scientist of Sun Microsystems Bill Joy opened the twenty-first century with a prophetic essay "Why the Future Doesn't Need Us." Can we imagine a future in which we, members of the human race as we know it, will be no longer? Will downloading our intelligence into a machine threaten the continuance of or humanity? "But if we are downloaded into our technology," Joy asks, "what are the chances that we will thereafter be ourselves or even human?"[56] The transformation of the natural world around us along with the transformation of ourselves into something new that surpasses us raises the question: will the kind of technological progress advocated by transhumanists actually dehumanize us? Would such dehumanization be due to this specific technological proposal, or is it due to the very nature of technique itself?

Watching the incorporation of technique into human self-understanding has alarmed both theologians and secular humanists for half a century now. Some fear that technology applied to the inner life dehumanizes us, that it cuts us off from our otherwise spontaneous joy at being natural creatures. "Technique is opposed to nature," writes French social critic and Reformed theologian Jacques Ellul. "It destroys, eliminates, or subordinates the natural world, and does not allow this world to restore itself or even to enter into a symbiotic relation with it."[57] Now Ellul's pitting human nature in opposition to technique is a bit extreme, because most anthropologies would affirm that the pursuit of technological innovation is one of the obvious attributes of human nature. We are *Homo faber,* the species that makes things. So the threat of dehumanization comes not from technological advance per se; rather, the threat comes from our temptation to so identify with our technological production that we forget our relationship to the natural world. In order to protect us from such forgetfulness, Ferkiss proposes a new norm: "man is part of nature and therefore cannot be its conqueror and indeed he owes it some respect."[58]

Just how it is that technology threatens our humanity is subtle. On the one hand, transhumanists propose a technology that will enhance our humanity, at least the intelligent aspect of humanity. On the other hand, once technology takes over and replicates itself, it will leave our present stage of humanity in the evolutionary dust. An emerging posthumanity will replace us. We might ask: if we replace ourselves

---

[56] Bill Joy, "Why the Future Doesn't Need Us," *Wired,* April 2000. http://www.wired.com/wired/archive/8.04/joy.html.

[57] Jacques Ellul, *The Technological Society,* translated by Robert K. Merton (New York: Vintage Books, 1964), 179.

[58] Ferkiss, *Technological Man,* 209.

with posthumanity, will we have given expression to our essential human potential for self-transcendence through technology? Just how should we think about this?

If yesterday's futurists could speak to us about today's challenge, they would most likely warn us of tendencies to surrender what is human to the mindset of technique. "While it is untrue that technology determines the future independently of human volition, there is no question that that human individuals and human society are increasingly under pressure to conform to the demands of technological efficiency, and there is a real possibility that the essence of humanity will be lost in the process, that human history will come to an end and be converted into a mere prelude to the history of a posthuman society in which machines rather than men rule."[59] Ferkiss admonishes us to avoid this pitfall. "Man must maintain the distinction between himself and the machines of his creation . . . not only must man stand above the machine, he must be in control of his own evolution."[60] Almost presciently anticipating today's proposal to create a posthuman intelligence, Ferkiss declares that we should preserve our humanness; we should maintain today's humanity over against the temptation to replace it with something more advanced. "Man's greatest need is not to transcend his species as such but to develop it fully . . . . Man is not a superape; he is no longer an ape at all. Before we abandon man for a machine-man or a genetic mutant, we should learn what he can do in his present form once liberated from hunger, fear, and ignorance."[61] Perhaps Ferkiss the humanist would represent the religious roadblock the transhumanists would like to clear out of the way.

Now this observation that we human beings belong to nature and are embedded in nature is important, to be sure, yet this is not the point I would like to stress here. What is more important to the present analysis is the naïve sense of control or false sense of dominance that technological victories over nature might elicit. University of Chicago theologian David Tracy alerts us to the dangers of sacrificing our better judgment to naïve trust in technological progress. "Now *techne* becomes the product of the will to domination, power and control . . . a power on its own, leveling all culture; annihilating all at-home-ness in the cosmos, uprooting all other questions in favor of those questions under its control; producing a planetary thought-world where instrumental reason, and it alone, will pass as thought . . . . The object cannot think. The subject will not. We began as technical agents of our willful destiny. We seem to end as technicized spectators at our own execution."[62]

---

[59]   Victor Ferkiss, *The Future of Technological Civilization* (New York: George Braziller, 1974), 5.

[60]   Ferkiss, *Technological Man,* 210.

[61]   Ferkiss, *Technological Man,* 216.

[62]   David Tracy, *The Analogical Imagination: Christian Theology and the Culture of Pluralism* (New York: Crossroad, 1981), 352.

THE THEOLOGICAL CRITIQUE OF PROGRESS

The assignment given me by the conference leadership is to examine the concept of progress underlying the transhumanist vision and to look at it from the distinctive perspective of a Lutheran theologian. For resources, I will turn to a theological sub-tradition that is not exclusively Lutheran but relies upon Luther's Reformation insights into human nature. This is the neo-orthodox school of theological thinking that reigned during the middle of the twentieth century. One key figure was Reinhold Niebuhr, long time professor of social thought at Union Seminary in New York, along with one of his disciples, Langdon Gilkey, the late professor of theology at the University of Chicago. In the tradition of Augustine and Luther, they proffered a version of "Christian realism" regarding the sinful condition in which we human beings find ourselves, and they cautioned against overestimating what we can achieve within history apart from the gracious action of God.

In his writings during the 1930s and 1940s, Niebuhr shows awareness that our modern post-Enlightenment culture, which plays host to both natural science and European imperialism, is a branch growing on a larger historical tree. The tree's trunk stands with roots in classical Greece and Rome, as well as in the soil of Israel's history and the Christian Bible. The modern idea of progress, he avers, is both an outgrowth and a pruned version of biblical eschatology. The prophets and the apocalypticists of Scripture saw human history as dynamic, as changing, as moving from promise to fulfillment. But human advance is also subject to divine judgment. What this means is that all events within history are ambiguous—that is, the advance of each human potential can lead to either a good actualization or an evil actualization. Unambiguous goodness is not guaranteed by progress. Only eschatologically—only at the advent of God's kingdom, which will come by an act of divine grace—will unambiguous fulfillment be possible. In the meantime, we live in the paradox of being able to envision fulfillment while experiencing the inescapable dialectic of success and failure.

"The idea of progress is the underlying presupposition of what may be broadly defined as 'liberal' culture. If that assumption is challenged the whole structure of meaning in the liberal world is imperiled . . . . The creed is nevertheless highly dubious . . . . It is false in so far as all historical processes are ambiguous."[63] The ambiguity of which Niebuhr speaks is the ever-present potential created by human freedom, namely, the potential to choose evil and chaos, as well as what is good and fulfilling. The problem is that today's believers in progress are blind to this ambiguity. They trust that inherent to the progress of history is a built-in Logos, or

---

[63] Reinhold Niebuhr, *The Nature and Destiny of Man,* 2 Volumes (New York: Charles Scribner's Sons, 1941-1942) 2:240.

guiding principle that transforms otherwise meaningless growth into a process of betterment. This belief is a truncation of the biblical eschatology, which preceded it. It is an outgrowth of the effect of Scripture on Western culture, to be sure, but the concept of progress prunes off this growth the previous recognition of the ineluctable continuation of creative evil. "The 'idea of progress,' the most characteristic and firmly held article in the *credo* of modern man, is the inevitable philosophy of history emerging from the Renaissance. This result was achieved by combining the classical confidence in man with the Biblical confidence in the meaningfulness of history. It must be observed, however, that history is given a simpler meaning than that envisaged in the prophetic-Biblical view . . . . [Progress] did not recognize that history is filled with endless possibilities *of good and evil* . . . . It did not recognize that every new human potency may be an instrument of chaos as well as of order; and that history, therefore, has no solution of its own problem."[64]

We moderns have inherited the optimism of the Renaissance while tacitly rejecting the realism regarding human nature given us by the Reformation. A sinner in need of divine grace was the starting point of Reformation anthropology, a starting point quickly forgotten during our eras of science building and nation building. "Original sin really means that human nature has completely fallen," writes Reformer Martin Luther. "The intellect has become darkened, so that we no longer know God and His will . . . our conscience is no longer quiet but, when it thinks of God's judgment, despairs and adopts illicit defenses and remedies. These sins have taken such deep root in our being that in this life they cannot be entirely eradicated."[65] We are soiled by sin, so to speak. No amount of progress will wash it away. "Sin remains, then, perpetually in this life, until the hour of the last judgment comes and then at last we shall be made perfectly righteous."[66] No amount of human intelligence, wit, will power, creativity, reform, or revolution can enable us to dig ourselves out of this hole. We are unable to transform ourselves. Only God can deliver us.

Now, says Niebuhr, without this acknowledgement of who we are as human beings, we will find ourselves with something less than a purchase on the reality of our situation. "This tragic aspect of history, towards which the Renaissance was partly oblivious, was precisely that aspect of history which the Reformation most fully comprehended. This comprehension is contained in the Reformation polemic against all doctrines of sanctification, whether Catholic, secular or sectarian-Christian, in which it detects a too-simple confidence in historical

---

[64] Ibid., 2:154-155, italics in original.

[65] Martin Luther, *Luther's Works*, American Edition, Vols. 1-30, edited by Jaroslav Pelikan (St. Louis: Concordia Publishing Company, 1955-1967); Vols. 31-55, edited by Helmut T. Lehmann (Minneapolis: Fortress Press, 1955-1986) 1:114.

[66] Ibid., 34:167.

possibilities. Its doctrine of 'justification by faith' contains implications for an adequate interpretation of history which have never been fully appropriated or exploited."[67] No historical ideology or scientific technology can possibly provide us with unambiguous sanctification—that is, unambiguous improvement, let alone perfection. Failure to realize this leaves us in unreality.

Realism requires an accurate portrayal of the human situation. It requires an honest recognition of human sinfulness. At any time and in any place, otherwise happy and fulfilled human beings may initiate evil and destruction. This ever-present risk of sinful activity is a universal contingent—that is, though unnecessary, it is always and everywhere possible. "Sin is natural for man in the sense that it is universal but not in the sense that it is necessary."[68] At the birth of the computer age, we should have been able to predict the coming of the computer virus, or something like it. Now, at the birth of transhumanist technology, similar predictions would be in order. A transhumanist spirituality would need to incorporate this kind of realism regarding human nature, a human nature not capable of changing through augmentation of intelligence.

When it comes to spiritual health, the realism of Luther's Reformation becomes Niebuhr's prescription. Niebuhr structures the insights of the Reformation paradoxically so that they shine with a double dimensional illumination upon our experience. Here is Niebuhr's list of "the 'yes' and 'no' of its dialectical affirmations: that the Christian is *justus et peccator*, 'both sinner and righteous'; that history fulfills and negates the Kingdom of God; that grace is continuous with, and in contradiction to, nature; that Christ is what we ought to be and also what we cannot be; that the power of God is in us and that the power of God is against us in judgment and mercy; that all these affirmations which are but varied forms of the one central paradox of the relation of the Gospel to history must be applied to the experiences of life, from top to bottom. There is no area of life where 'grace' does not impinge."[69] Because of who we human beings are, subject to sin, our fulfillment will require gracious divine action on our behalf. The good news of the Christian gospel is that God promises us such grace.

---

[67]   Niebuhr, *Nature and Destiny*, 2:155.

[68]   Ibid., 1:242. Robert John Russell introduces the term, "universal contingent," in reference to Niebuhr's position. Like human history, nature is also ambiguous—that is, a mixture of beauty and suffering. "The Groaning of Creation: Does God Suffer with All Life?" in *The Evolution of Evil,* edited by Gaymon Bennett, Martinez Hewlett, Ted Peters, and Robert John Russell (Göttingen: Vandenhoeck & Ruprecht, 2008), 120-142.

[69]   Niebuhr, *Nature and Destiny.*, 2:204. Quite like Niebuhr, Moltmann comments: "Everything that can be used can also be misused. Consequently biomedical progress is ambivalent as long as man is an unreliable being." *Future of Creation,* 135.

Progress Under Judgment

The core worry of the Christian theologian here is the naïveté with which believers in progress remove the ambiguities of human history, with which they maintain confidence in the good that progress can bring while denying the potential growth of evil. What the theologian ought to steadfastly maintain is that our vision of human abundance and human flowering must hold on to its transcendence; we must hold on to the judgment that the eschatological kingdom of God renders against the accomplishments of human history. "There is a great temptation today to confuse sociological evolution with spiritual progress," writes Jacques Ellul. "The Bible expressly tells us that the history of mankind ends in judgment."[70]

That Christian reliance upon a transcendent judgment against human history is a necessary antidote to the naïveté of faith in progress seems confirmed by events during the first half of the twentieth century. Technological and even cultural advance in the European West were insufficient to prevent political tyranny, mass genocide, and global war. Langdon Gilkey recites the litany of events that confirmed the need for seeing a dialectic between immanent progress and God's transcendent kingdom. "In the First World War—despite the refinement of European culture and the moral idealism of that culture's self-understanding—Europe experienced the apparent self-destruction of this most modern and developed of societies in a prolonged and senseless bath of blood. In the Depression and its aftermath, the West as a whole experienced the self-contradiction of its economic forms, and the consequent rise of fascist and communist totalitarianisms that dissolved the hard-won political freedoms of modernity. And in the Second World War, with its slavery, genocide and technology of ultimate destruction, the world experienced an eruption of technological and sophisticated evil: personal, political and social, unknown to history before. History seemed to manifest demonic regress not progress in the social, political and moral realms."[71]

Gilkey's theological judgment reiterates that of Reinhold Niebuhr and was shared by the influential school of neo-orthodox theologians subsequent to World War II. "It seemed the obvious lesson of current events that morals do not advance in history. Hence, a progress of technology may in fact augur a regress in social harmony and social justice, and thus all that is cumulative, instead of 'saving' mankind, can threaten to become the demonic instrument of mankind's destruction. This permanent ambiguity of historical process, this continuation of sin even in an

---

70   Jacques Ellul, *False Presence of the Kingdom,* translated by C. Edward Hopkin (New York: The Seabury Press, 1972), 20.

71   Langdon Gilkey, *Reaping the Whirlwind: A Christian Interpretation of History* (New York: Seabury Press, 1976), 223.

advancing culture, meant that if there be a kingdom, it could not be realized through a sociohistorical development leading to a perfect society in history."[72]

When considering our evolutionary history and technological future, what direction should a realistic anthropology follow? Paul Jersild, in a recent article on science and faith, points a cautious way. "In some respects, a more civilized society does emerge with the evolution of cultures, but there is ample evidence that evolving societies invent still more horrific ways to exalt themselves and destroy their neighbors. Evolution, whether biological or cultural, does not mean inexorable progress on the road toward perfection."[73] In sum, we should move forward, but we should not presume progress in every respect is inevitable or guaranteed.

CONCLUSION

It is my conclusion that members of the transhumanist school of thought are naïve about human nature, and they are overestimating what they can accomplish through technological innovation. They are naïve because they take insufficient account of the propensity we human beings have for using neutral things or even good things for selfish purposes, resulting in chaos and suffering. The assumption transhumanists seem to make that both biological evolution and technological progress have their own built-in entelechy, or purpose from which we can derive our social ethic, overlooks the threat to their values posed by the funders. By depending on private capital and even building laissez-faire capitalism into their value system, they risk subjugating all their technological achievements to the values of the bourgeois class. The result will be technological advances that benefit the investors, to the detriment of the wider society and the ecosphere they would like to rehabilitate.

The forecast of a future replete with cybernetic immortality and cosmic consciousness seems extravagant and fantastic. Whether it is possible for our intelligence and self-consciousness to be reduced to information patterns and then uploaded on to a nonbiological substrate is not a question I can address here. But I would like to point out that there is no warrant for believing that all our human problems will be solved by transhumanist technology. There is no warrant for thinking that the currently selfish human race will be able to transform itself into an altruistic or benevolent one. There is no warrant for thinking that we human beings, with our history of economic injustice and ecologically unhealthy habits, are willing

---

[72] Ibid., 222-223.

[73] Paul Jersild, "Rethinking the Human Being in Light of Evolutionary Biology," *Dialog* 47, no.1 (2008): 42.

or able, on our own, to eliminate poverty and protect the ecosphere. No amount of increased intelligence will redeem us from what the theologians call *sin*.

I call this the *eschatological problem*. I ask: how do we get there from here? If we in the human race have been responsible for selfishness, economic injustice, and environmental degradation, how can we then become capable of benevolence, economic justice, and ecological health? How can a leopard change its spots? What transhumanists are hoping for is *adventus*, but they have only *futurum* to work with.

God has promised some of what appears in the transhumanist vision. But the transformation of the human heart so that it exudes benevolence and justice requires divine grace. The advent of the new creation will require much more than what our evolutionary history by itself can deliver. It will require God's transforming power. Increased human intelligence cannot on its own accomplish what it will take divine grace to make happen.

One more observation. I would like to point out that this near-apocalyptic vision projected by the transhumanists includes some elements that appear irreconcilable with the biblical promise of a new creation. The biblical promise begins with Jesus' Easter resurrection as a model. This includes suffering and death, complete death. It also includes a divine act of raising the dead to new life. What happened to Jesus is what will happen to us. New Revised Standard Version (NRSV) 1 Corinthians 15:20: "But in fact Christ has been raised from the dead, the first fruits of those who have died." The New Testament does not look forward to living forever in our present state; rather, it presumes we will pass through death to the new life God promises. Eternal life is not the same thing as extended life.

The picture of cybernetic immortality painted by the transhumanists does not look like the Bible's promise of resurrection. Even if genetic enhancement and nanotechnology are able to increase human longevity or even lead to cybernetic immortality, the uploaded self-consciousness will still need to pass through the purgatorial cleansing of death and resurrection. Apart from the fulfillment of this promise, the future of human history will remain like its past, ambiguous.

Finally, a Christian theologian can only encourage continued scientific research into genetics and nanotechnology when the goals are improved human health and well-being. Attempts to enhance human intelligence through technological augmentation might also be greeted with approval, although probably not with overwhelming enthusiasm. Because the theologian looks forward to the advent of divine transformation, he or she can celebrate anticipatory transformations brought by advances in science and technology. Biblical theology need not be recalcitrant or Luddite. Biblical theology can be ready to celebrate technological breakthroughs while remaining realistic about what to expect from human nature.

REFERENCES

Bostrom, Nick. Home Page 2005. http://www.nickbostrom.com/tra/values.html.

Braaten, Carl E. *The Future of God.* New York: Harper, 1969.

Campbell, Heidi and Mark Walker. "Religion and Transhumanism: Introducing a Conversation." *Journal of Evolution and Technology* 14, no.2 (2005): 1.

Dawkins, Richard. *The Selfish Gene.* Oxford and New York: Oxford University Press, 1976.

Ellul, Jacques. *False Presence of the Kingdom.* Translated by C. Edward Hopkin. New York: The Seabury Press, 1972.

Ellul, Jacques. *The Technological Society.* Translated by Robert K. Merton. New York: Vintage Books, 1964.

Ferkiss, Victor C. *The Future of Technological Civilization.* New York: George Braziller, 1974.

Ferkiss, Victor C. *Technological Man: The Myth and the Reality.* New York: New American Library, Mentor Books, 1969.

Geraci, Robert M. "Apocalyptic AI: Religion and the Promise of Artificial Intelligence." *Journal of the American Academy of Religion* 76, no. 1 (2008): 138-166.

Gilkey, Langdon. *Reaping the Whirlwind: A Christian Interpretation of History.* New York: Seabury Press, 1976.

Goldman, Steven. "Progress." In *Encyclopedia of Science, Technology, and Ethics,* edited by Mitcham, Carl. 4 Volumes: New York: Macmillan, Gale, 2005.

Houser, Nathan, Christian Kloesel, and Peirce Edition Project, eds. *The Essential Peirce: Selected Philosophical Writings.* 2 Volumes: Bloomington: Indiana University Press, 1992,1998.

Jersild, Paul. "Rethinking the Human Being in Light of Evolutionary Biology." *Dialog* 47, no.1 (2008): 42.

Joy, Bill. "Why the Future Doesn't Need Us." *WIRED*, April 2000. http://www.wired.com/wired/archive/8.04/joy.html.

Kirkwood, Thomas B. L. "A Systematic Look at an Old Problem." *Nature* 451 (2008): 644-647.

Kurzweil, Ray. *The Singularity is Near: When Humans Transcend Biology.* New York: Penguin, 2005.

Luther, Martin. *Luther's Works*, American Edition. Vols. 1-30, edited by Jaroslav Pelikan (St. Louis: Concordia Publishing Company, 1955-1967); Vols. 31-55, edited by Helmut T. Lehmann (Minneapolis: Fortress Press, 1955-1986).

Moltmann, Jûrgen. *The Coming of God: Christian Eschatology.* Minneapolis: Fortress Press, 1996.

Moltmann, Jûrgen. *The Future of Creation*, translated by Margaret Kohl. Minneapolis: Fortress Press, 1979.

Moravec, Hans. *Mind Children: The Future of Robot and Human Intelligence.* Cambridge, Mass.: Harvard University Press, 1988.

Niebuhr, Reinhold. *The Nature and Destiny of Man.* 2 Volumes: New York: Charles Scribner's Sons, 1941-1942.

Peirce, Charles Sanders. *Collected Papers of Charles Sanders Peirce.* Edited by Charles Hartshorne and Paul Weiss. 8 Volumes: Cambridge, Mass.: Harvard University Press, 1931-58.

Peters, Ted. "Are We Playing God with Nano Enhancement?" *Nanoethics: The Ethical and Social Implications of Nanotechnology,* edited by Fritz Allhoff, Patrick Lin, James Moor, and John Weckert. New York: Wiley, 2007, chapter 4.3.

_____. *Futures—Human and Divine.* Louisville: Westminster John Knox Press, 1977.

_____. *Fear, Faith, and the Future.* Minneapolis: Augsburg Press, 1980.

Rahner, Karl. *Foundations of Christian Faith.* New York: Searbury Crossroad Press, 1978.

Russell, Robert John. "The Groaning of Creation: Does God Suffer with All Life?" In *The Evolution of Evil,* edited by Gaymon Bennett, Martinez Hewlett, Ted Peters, and Robert John Russell. Göttingen: Vandenhoeck & Ruprecht, 2008: 120-142.

Transhumanist World Association (WTA). "Transhumanist Declaration." http://www.transhumanism.org.

Toffler, Alvin, ed. *The Futurists.* New York: Random House, 1972.

Wertheim, Margaret. *The Pearly Gates of Cyberspace: A History of Space from Dante to the Internet.* New York: W. W. Norton, 1999.

Young, Simon. *Designer Evolution: A Transhumanist Manifesto.* Amherst, NY: Prometheus Books, 2006.

Chapter Eleven

Trite Truths about Technology: A Reply to Ted Peters

by Russell Blackford

INTRODUCTION

I have been asked to comment, in particular, on the contribution of Ted Peters entitled "Transhumanism and the Posthuman Future: Will Technological Progress Get Us There?"[1] Though Peters's article is the main focus of what follows, I must also refer to some other pieces in the same edition of *The Global Spiral* in order to explain my position on the merits of transhumanist thinking. I will argue that Peters and others have reminded us of some trite truths about technology and that the reminder may serve as a reality check for transhumanists (just in case some of them need it). At the same time, it would be foolishly condescending to assume that most transhumanists are unaware of the trite truths that I will isolate. More likely, these are so well known that they usually go without saying.

TRANSHUMANISM: THE ESSENTIAL IDEA

In its essence, transhumanism involves a rather simple idea: within certain limits that require investigation, it is desirable to use emerging technologies to enhance human physical and cognitive capacities and to make other beneficial

---

[1] Ted Peters, "Transhumanism and the Posthuman Future: Will Technological Progress Get Us There?" *The Global Spiral* 9, no. 3 (2008). http://www.metanexus.net/magazine/tabid/68/id/10546/Default.aspx.

alterations to human traits. Stated so broadly, transhumanism's essential idea is, I believe, defensible. Note, however, that it allows enormous scope for discussion and debate among people who accept it as a general proposition. Questions abound. What, exactly, *are* the limits that I've described as requiring investigation? How quickly or slowly will the transition take place and where might it end? Should we be attempting to accelerate it, slow it down, or direct its course in some way? All of these issues and many others can be—and are being—discussed with sophistication, and often with passion, within the contemporary transhumanist movement. Many positions are taken, and the ferment of opinions and arguments is surely a sign of the movement's intellectual health.[2]

On the other hand, such ferment and internal debate can create confusion. Some participants in the transhumanist movement may want little more than the greenlighting and fast-tracking of certain controversial technologies—therapeutic cloning technology, for example. At the other extreme, some imagine grand schemes for reengineering the cosmos, perhaps turning entire stars, planets, or galaxies into a complex, intricately functioning substrate that experiences blissful consciousness. Here speculative thought runs wild, though that is not always a bad thing. There are, of course, many intermediate (or simply different) transhumanist positions.

Some individuals may feel considerable ambivalence about the label, seeing the force of conflicting considerations. That is, indeed, my own situation. Still, the essential idea of transhumanism is no longer especially recherché: it is increasingly familiar and plausible.

It is intellectually legitimate to challenge transhumanism's essential idea, but I have never seen a promising argument along such lines, much less a convincing one. Perhaps such an argument is "out there" waiting to be discovered, but that remains to be seen. A different approach—also intellectually legitimate, but more nuanced—would attempt to identify some of the specific transhumanist positions on offer and then consider their respective merits. Unfortunately, I see no indication that the contributors to the June 2008 edition of *The Global Spiral* have made a serious effort to adopt either approach.

By contrast, it is not intellectually useful to challenge a specific viewpoint within transhumanism or to synthesize some composite viewpoint out of the (perhaps conflicting) writings of a few prominent or not-so-prominent transhumanist thinkers, then attack this—and *then* claim to have refuted or discredited transhumanism itself. This could leave the essential idea of transhumanism untouched. All too often, Peters and other critics seem to take this approach, perhaps because they

---

2   A good starting point for anyone interested in the ferment of ideas among transhumanists and other thinkers with similar interests would be to consult the pages of the *Journal of Evolution and Technology*, available online at http://jetpress.org/.

understand transhumanism as a comprehensive system of dogma rather than as a diverse cultural and philosophical movement.

Peters devotes much of his discussion to the views of one of transhumanism's high-profile fellow-travelers, Ray Kurzweil, and those of Simon Young, who has published a recent book on the subject.[3] However, Young's book has no general acceptance within the transhumanist movement and really represents no more than its author's personal views. The same applies to the ideas of Kurzweil. Peters's synthesis of propositions from the published works of Kurzweil and Young may reflect the views of some, perhaps even many, transhumanists, but it is nonetheless Peters's own synthesis. It certainly does not represent the position of the transhumanist movement as a whole. No elaborated position can, because transhumanism is not that sort of thing.

Two Side Skirmishes

A full commentary on Peters's article would involve many side skirmishes, some of them important. I don't wish to become lost in these, but two merit some (necessarily limited) discussion.

The roadblocks of religion. The first is an issue that seems dear to Peters's heart. He argues against what he claims is a "mistake" made by transhumanists.[4] The so-called mistake is an expectation that religion, and particularly Christianity, will put roadblocks in the way of transhumanist aspirations. In the space available to me, I cannot address this at length. However, I believe that Peters underestimates the degree to which religion is likely to create such roadblocks. I will briefly sketch why.

Before I do so, however, I must point out that Peters and I both have biases. He writes as a Lutheran theologian, whereas I am an outspoken atheist. All the same, while I have certain antireligious leanings, I am not so ignorant as to imagine that Abrahamic theology is a featureless monolith. Even within Christianity, there are many theological schools, disputes, and emphases, and it would be churlish to presume that nothing good can ever come out of any of them. It would certainly be mistaken to lump the ideas of, say, Pierre Teilhard de Chardin or Reinhold Niebuhr or Martin Luther King with those of, say, Fred Phelps or Jerry Falwell or Joseph Ratzinger. Christian theology is (like transhumanism) a rich and complex field; it may sometimes be weakened by its internal divisions and debates, but (again like transhumanism) it is sometimes strengthened by its ferment of ideas.

---

3   Simon Young, *Designer Evolution: A Transhumanist Manifesto* (Amherst, NY: Prometheus Books, 2006).

4   Peters, "Transhumanism and the Posthuman Future": 1.

With all that duly noted, Peters seems disingenuous when he argues that Judeo-Christian theology welcomes change and will not oppose transhumanist aspirations. He does not support this claim with any empirical study—or even with an impressionistic overview—of the views of actual theologians. Rather, he refers to passages from the Old and New Testaments that might be said to presume the value of novelty. In Isaiah 43:19, God is represented as saying, "I am about to do a new thing." In Revelation 21:5, God says, "See, I am making all things new."[5]

These verses are obviously open to interpretation, like all passages in the Abrahamic holy books, but let's concede that they exalt the idea of transformation, of making things new, at least when the transformation is for the better. But no one denies that the Abrahamic monotheisms allow a positive place for change. Of course they do. Even the most vulgar forms of Christian fundamentalism value individual transformation when the recipient of salvation is "born again," and they look forward to comprehensive eschatological transformation at the end of days, when the current order of things will be overturned and ultimately annihilated by divine intervention. Christianity has traditionally displayed a linear rather than cyclical view of time and history, with time's arrow pointing to the ultimate triumph of good over evil.

But none of this entails that all, or even most, Christian leaders and theologians would countenance the technological boosting of human capacities that transhumanists advocate. Changes of *those* kinds might well be regarded by many leaders and theologians as hubristic, or otherwise morally impermissible, and as fair (perhaps even urgent) targets for political suppression.

Later in his article, Peters points out that Christian hospitals are not opposed to advanced technology; on the contrary, they use it extensively for patient care.[6] No doubt they do, but what follows from this? It by no means follows that Christian leaders and theologians have tended, in the past, to favor new technologies that assist medicine or alter bodily functioning. The widespread historical opposition to anesthesia and the contraceptive pill are good examples to consider. The Catholic Church still views the use of contraceptive technologies, such as condoms or the Pill, as a sin against the God-given natural order: an impermissible suppression of the human genitals' proper functions.[7] Against that background, it is not necessarily a "mistake" to fear that some or many Christian leaders and theologians will have grave reservations about technologies that could enhance human capacities beyond merely healthy functioning.

---

[5]   Ibid.

[6]   Ibid., 5.

[7]   *Humanae Vitae*. Encyclical letter of Pope Paul VI. July 25, 1968. See http://www.vatican. va/holy_father/paul_vi/encyclicals/documents/hf_p-vi_enc_25071968_humanae-vitae_en.html.

Whatever the range of Christian views, Peters might reply: the *correct* theological position is one that holds enhancement of human capacities to be at least permissible. Perhaps so, but Peters is trying to reassure transhumanists that Christian theology will not, in fact, create roadblocks for them. That, of course, does not depend upon which theological views, if any, may—all things considered—actually be correct, but upon which views are well positioned to exert political influence. Viewed in this way, transhumanist fears of religious roadblocks are perfectly rational.

Evolution and ethics. Another side skirmish involves the relationship between transhumanism and evolutionary ethics. Here Peters argues that transhumanism encounters an intellectual problem because (so he believes) it bases its moral claims on values implicit in Darwinian evolution while simultaneously affirming the altruistic values of benevolent community. Peters sees a tension in this, and he adds that transhumanists find themselves in opposition to the values of earlier forms of evolutionary ethics, such as nineteenth-century social Darwinism.[8]

This issue is worth some brief discussion for two reasons. First, Peters may be correct that some transhumanists are committed to an implausible interpretation of Darwinian evolution as inherently directional or progressive. Accepting this, at least for the sake of argument, is there anything essential to transhumanism that is inconsistent with a more plausible account of evolution and its relationship to morality? Second, I have an additional reason for sketching such an account: it may be helpful for assessing Peters's own theological conception of human nature.

Contrary to Peters's line of argument, Darwinian evolution does not contain implicit values.[9] The process of evolution simply *is*. Current (well-corroborated) scientific theory postulates that some organisms are likely to survive and reproduce more efficiently than others in any given environment, and that those which do so tend to pass down their genetic material to the next generation. So long as there are also mechanisms that produce genetic variations, the repetition of this process over time is sufficient to generate the diversity of life on Earth. Sufficiently long stretches of time may allow highly complex organisms to emerge, but there is no reason to believe that the average complexity of organisms is—or somehow *must*

---

[8] Peters, "Transhumanism and the Posthuman Future," 3-4.

[9] The views in this paragraph and the four that immediately follow it are mine, but I claim no particular originality for them. They are based on my reading of numerous works in the fields of evolutionary psychology and evolutionary ethics. I owe thanks to many authors who have helped shaped my general picture of the relationship between evolution and ethics. One who deserves special mention—though as a preference utilitarian he would probably disapprove of the idea of living within deontic constraints—is Peter Singer. See especially Singer's *A Darwinian Left: Politics, Evolution and Cooperation* (London: Weidenfeld & Nicolson, 1999).

be—increasing, or that the process has any inbuilt direction, or that organisms which appear later are necessarily superior (by whatever standards we might adopt) to organisms that appear earlier. At most, there is some tendency in a reasonably stable environment for later organisms to be more efficiently engineered than earlier organisms that are morphologically similar and exhibit similar behaviors. Nothing earthshaking follows from this last point.

Against that background, it should be acknowledged on all sides that our own species has evolved over countless years, during which time *Homo sapiens* eventually emerged in Africa as a social primate. Doubtless we evolved certain broad psychological proclivities—just like other primates. These may well include a strong tendency to act in our self-interest as individuals (and in the interests of our children, other family members, and those whom we see as allies). But we also appear to have evolved a considerable degree of sympathetic responsiveness to others, even to the sufferings of nonhuman animals.

There is quite a complex relationship between our evolved psychology (whatever its exact content) and the demands of morality. Certain behavioral tendencies may well have been adaptive for our ancestors, in the sense that they tended to lead to reproductive success in the environments in which *Homo sapiens* gradually evolved. However, while we may have an inherited tendency to act in certain ways, it does not follow (certainly not directly) that we *should* act in those ways. Perhaps it is sometimes possible to derive an *ought* from an *is*, but as Hume famously commented, we are at least owed an explanation as to *how* this could ever be done.[10] To the extent that past forms of evolutionary ethics have attempted to leap without adequate explanation from *is* to *ought*, there is no shame in disagreeing with them.

Even if certain behavioral propensities enhanced the reproductive fitness of our distant ancestors, this does not entail that they advance our current, reflectively endorsed values. We do not act immorally when we reject our immediate (and perhaps, in a sense, "natural") impulses, under the guidance of other values that we endorse. Nor are human societies mistaken when they develop moral norms that constrain their members from acting in ruthless pursuit of their individual self-interest. On the other hand, any workable system of moral norms must be one that is practical for the needs of beings like us, who are, by and large, neither angelically selfless nor utterly uncaring about others' perceived sufferings. Thus,

---

[10]   In fact, talk of "constraints" oversimplifies. Developed moral systems do more than forbid certain actions and require others. They may, for example, identify some actions as morally praiseworthy (but not obligatory) and others as morally distasteful (but not forbidden). They may identify certain dispositions of character as virtuous and others as vicious. And so on. None of this detracts from my main point that such systems leave considerable scope for self-interested action.

our evolved psychology may impose some limits on what real-world moral systems can realistically demand of human beings.

Accordingly, a realistic moral system will allow considerable scope for individuals to pursue their own interests and happiness, but within deontic constraints.[11] It will not condemn all pursuit of self-interest as "sinful," nor will it allow the pursuit of self-interest—perhaps in competition for scarce resources or for potential mates—with no restraints at all. Literally ruthless competition would lead to widespread insecurity, suffering, and disorder. Given all this, we typically have good reasons, as individuals, to uphold the respective moral systems that we are born into, though not necessarily in every detail. Upon reflection, we may find that we have reasons to resist or flout some of the moral norms that we encounter, or, indeed, to seek deletions, extensions, and changes.[12]

If some transhumanists paint a picture of Darwinian evolution, and of its relationship to morality, that is significantly inconsistent with the above, then they are, I believe, open to legitimate criticism.[13] However, the important conclusion to draw at this point is that my sketchy picture of evolution and ethics is not inconsistent with the essential transhumanist idea. So long as we give reflective endorsement to the value of increasing human capacities, and so long as there is a realistic prospect of pursuing this by technological means, the essential idea is defensible.

SIX TRITE TRUTHS ABOUT TECHNOLOGY

While transhumanists take a defensible position when they support the development of emerging technologies to enhance human capacities, they should not assume that it will be easy sailing. In particular, transhumanists should acknowledge the following four points, which appear to be the gist of Don Ihde's contribution to the June 2008 issue of *The Global Spiral*.[14] Whether or not Ihde would agree with my formulation of them, these points appear highly plausible:

---

11   David Hume, *A Treatise of Human Nature* (first published 1739 and 1740; rpt. London: Penguin, 1984), 521. Hume did not argue that *oughts* cannot be explained; his point is that adequate explanations make reference to such psychological phenomena as human desires and sympathies.

12   Compare J. L. Mackie, *Ethics: Inventing Right and Wrong* (London: Penguin, 1977), 120-24, 146-48.

13   However, it is not apparent to me that Simon Young, the example discussed by Peters, has made any such error.

14   Don Ihde, "Of Which Human Are We Post?" *The Global Spiral* 9, no. 3 (2008). http://www.metanexus.net/magazine/tabid/68/id/10552/Default.aspx.

1. In the real world, technological advances involve compromises and trade-offs.
2. Technological advances take place in unexpected ways and find unexpected uses.
3. Implanted technologies have disadvantages as well as advantages: e.g., prostheses and implants are often experienced as imperfect and obtrusive, and they wear out.
4. Predictions about future technologies and how they will be incorporated into social practice are unreliable.

We can go further and add a fifth truth about technology, taking into account a realistic understanding of human nature:

5. Future technologies will sometimes be used for spiteful or malevolent purposes and will typically be used for self-interested ones.

Finally, the following is not directly a truth about technology, but about the representation of technology in science fiction. A similar point is made by Katherine Hayles in her contribution to *The Global Spiral*,[15] though again she may not agree with my formulation:

6. Science fiction is one—though certainly not the only—resource available to people, including transhumanists, who want to think about possibilities for our future.

I don't propose to defend these six points individually. I cannot imagine that anyone would disagree with them, once they are stated plainly and concisely (but perhaps I'm in for a surprise!). However, all six require elaboration, qualification, and the disclaimer that they are not laws of nature, just useful pragmatic generalizations based on historical experience. The other thing that must be said is that these are *trite* truths. If they are not explicitly stated in transhumanist theories and manifestos, it is most likely to be because they are considered so obvious that they go without saying, rather than that the authors are unaware of them or disagree with them.

The trite truths about technology suggest that it will be difficult to invent useful technologies to enhance human capacities, and even our attempts to imagine appropriate inventions will be sketchy and fallible. However, it by no means follows that we should abandon or forbid all attempts to develop such technologies, any

---

[15] Katherine Hayles, "Wrestling with Transhumanism," *The Global Spiral* 9, no. 3 (2008). http://www.metanexus.net/Magazine/tabid/68/id/10543/Default.aspx.

more than our inability to emulate the grace and freedom of birds was a reason to abandon or forbid efforts at powered, heavier-than-air flight.

MUST TRANSHUMANISTS BE NAÏVE?

Although I see no reason to think that transhumanists are unaware of the trite truths about technology, any who actually *are* surely need a reality check. Peters appears to think that transhumanists are sufficiently naïve to be unaware of the fifth of the trite truths. Indeed, throughout his article, he repeats the words *naïve* and *naïveté* like a mantra (to the point, I confess, where I found it irritating). The alleged naïveté of transhumanists consists in an unwarranted optimism that they are supposed to have about human nature and about the prospect that things will always get better.

Peters offers an interesting, but ultimately unconvincing, argument that transhumanists are committed to an overoptimistic account of progress that would compel them to reject the fifth trite truth about technology. He begins by distinguishing between the notion of a future that emerges from the present (*futurum*) and the notion of a future that can be brought into being only by the intervention of God (*adventus*). He insists that transhumanists are committed to *futurum* rather than *adventus*. But, so he claims, a commitment to *futurum* depends upon a prior commitment to a doctrine of progress. Therefore, transhumanism depends upon a doctrine of progress. But such a doctrine is naïve. Therefore, transhumanists are naïve when they rely on it.

Let's assume that transhumanists are committed to the idea that the future will emerge from the present via natural causal mechanisms without divine intervention. Most transhumanist thinkers probably believe this, and to *that* extent it might be said, correctly, that transhumanism is committed to *futurum* rather than *adventus*. However, such a commitment does not depend on the acceptance of any naïve or implausible doctrine of progress.

These days, it is commonplace to imagine that future societies will differ radically from our own in social and economic organization, but as Robert Scholes has explained, this was probably unthinkable before the seventeenth and eighteenth centuries. Scholes adds that the transformation of societies by irreversible technological change became apparent only in the nineteenth century.[16] Thus, the idea of a future greatly different from the present as a result of continuing advances in knowledge and technology is a rather new one, historically. Note, however, that

---

[16]   Robert Scholes, *Structural Fabulation: An Essay on Fiction of the Future* (South Bend and London: Notre Dame University Press, 1975), 15-16.

it does not depend on any further idea that all change must be for the better, e.g., morally or culturally. It is based on the observed facts of social transformation over the last three or four centuries and the continuing impact of new knowledge and new technologies on the way we live.

By contrast, *adventus*, or something much like it, is a very old idea. Many mythological systems imagine that there will be tumultuous changes in the future brought about by the actions of supernatural beings. The mere antiquity of the idea does not discredit it, of course, but such actions and changes as it posits have never been observed.

Transhumanists do assume that the future derives causally from the present, but that should not be especially controversial. One could make such an assumption while simultaneously worrying that the actual future might turn out unpleasant or even dystopian. Perhaps transhumanists are committed to the idea that it's possible to devise (as-yet-unspecified) technologies that will enable the enhancement of human capacities, but they need not hold that the emergence of such technologies is simply inevitable or that it will bring no dangers. Nor must transhumanists make any absurd claims that fly in the face of what we know about the development and use of technology. They need not deny that new technologies will sometimes be used spitefully or malevolently, or that they will typically be used for self-interested purposes.

At the same time, there is no need to adopt the overly pessimistic assumption that emerging technologies will typically be used for purposes that lie outside of reasonable deontic constraints. As I've explained above, realistic systems of morality do not condemn all self-interested actions as morally impermissible or "sinful"; they require only that self-interest be pursued subject to certain conditions or within certain boundaries. Peters offers no good reason to believe that the technologies of the future will typically be used in ways that transgress defensible boundaries.

Doubtless we should be alert for possible dangers from new technologies or possible misuses of them. Doubtless the appropriate boundaries need to be discussed. In short, Peters is on strong ground when he asks us to be watchful for ways in which new technologies could be used for destructive purposes. No one ought to take issue with that. Not surprisingly, however, transhumanists are well aware of the point and often devote much of their energy to identifying risks and considering ways to reduce them.[17] Things could go very badly. At the same time, let's not approach the future with unrealistic pessimism.

---

[17] The classic article on this topic by a leading transhumanist philosopher is Nick Bostrom, "Existential Risks: Analyzing Human Extinction Scenarios and Related Hazards," *Journal of Evolution and Technology* 9, no. 1 (2002). http://www.jetpress.org/volume9/risks.html.

SIN

Peters makes much of the need for realism, and we should indeed be realistic about future prospects rather than blithely imagining that, come what may, all will be well. New technologies cannot be predicted with any certainty, and Peters is correct that they are likely to be misused, at least by some. Nonetheless, one can be unrealistically pessimistic just as one can be unrealistically optimistic. As a Christian theologian, Peters is very impressed by what he sees as humanity's essential sinfulness. As he puts it, "something at work in the human mind leads to the development of brute and unmitigated destruction." His example, in the relevant passage, is the phenomenon of computer viruses, strings of code that are, as he expresses it, created "with one sole purpose, namely, to destroy."[18]

But all this fails to convince. No doubt there are young people (and perhaps some older ones) who take gleeful pleasure in the creation of computer viruses and the havoc they can cause. However, Peters neglects to observe that most computer users do *not* create viruses or look on their effects with glee. Most of us regard the creators of computer viruses as antisocial pests. Maybe we'll always have people like them among us, but human beings are not universally inclined to malice and spite. Of course, some human beings are malevolent in far more horrible and destructive ways than computer hackers . . . but again this is a small minority. If destructiveness, malevolence, spiteful glee in others' discomfort, and so on are asserted by Peters to be hallmarks of human nature—in the sense that humans are always, or typically, like that—he is just wrong. He is operating with a philosophical anthropology that is unrealistically blind to the strong human propensities for sympathy, cooperation, and compromise.

He is on stronger ground when he writes of the inevitability that new technologies will be used by individuals and corporations for self-interested purposes.[19] But that is an entirely different point. Acting in one's own self-interest should not, in itself, be regarded as morally wrong or a "sin." People who are largely motivated by self-interest can still flourish side by side in reasonable and mutually productive cooperation. The important questions are whether fair deontic constraints on the pursuit of self-interest can be set by human societies and, if so, whether most people will abide by them most of the time. Here, I see no need at all for pessimistic answers. (If we were *that* "sinful," human society would be impossible.)

Peters's main point seems to be that we should follow in the tradition of Christian thought that stresses "he sinful condition in which human beings find themselves" and cautions "against overestimating what we can achieve within

---

18   Peters, "Transhumanism and the Posthuman Future," 4.

19   Ibid., 5-6.

history apart from the gracious action of God."[20] As is evident by now, I don't find the religious concepts of sinfulness and divine grace helpful, but of course there is a weaker secular equivalent of this thought. For all the reasons contained in the six trite truths that I listed above, we should not be too optimistic about what is achievable or when. We can agree with Peters when he states near the end of his article: "In sum, we should move forward, but we should not presume progress in every respect is inevitable or guaranteed."[21]

But this claim can stand without any theological scaffolding to support it, and there is no reason for thoughtful transhumanists to disagree with it. Such a position could just as easily be advanced *within* the transhumanist movement as outside it.

CONCLUSION

I am puzzled as to why Peters has adopted such a disdainful attitude toward transhumanist thought, given that he shares considerable common ground with transhumanists. It would have been more realistic to identify specific transhumanist thinkers, or specific ideas promoted by certain transhumanists, with which he disagrees—rather than attempting a sweeping, but clearly fallacious, argument that is supposed to demonstrate transhumanism's fundamental naïveté. It is not as if he has a good argument against transhumanism's essential idea, nor does he oppose the development of new technologies. He correctly stresses the need for alertness and caution, but there is no reason for transhumanists to reject this. Why, then, has he not taken a more tentative and conciliatory approach toward people with whom he shares much common ground?

The same question could be asked of other contributors to the June 2008 issue of *The Global Spiral*. Often they give an impression of seeking to discredit transhumanism rather than to establish any useful dialogue with transhumanist thinkers. This might be understandable if transhumanism were a dominant social paradigm, wielding great and detrimental political influence. In those circumstances, there might be a burning need to challenge transhumanist ideas. That, however, is very far from the situation we are in.

Transhumanist thinkers might be tempted to respond to the views of Peters and others with similar disdain. Perhaps I have yielded too much to that temptation. Allow me, then, to conclude by emphasizing yet again that there is common ground between transhumanists and at least some of the contributors to the June 2008

---

[20]   Ibid., 7.

[21]   Ibid., 8.

transhumanism issue of *The Global Spiral*. I hope that future dialogue may produce greater understanding, mutual respect, and possibly some shared insight.

REFERENCES

Bostrom, Nick. "Existential Risks: Analyzing Human Extinction Scenarios and Related Hazards." *Journal of Evolution and Technology* 9, no. 1 (2002). http://www.jetpress.org/volume9/risks.html.

Hayles, Katherine. "Wrestling with Transhumanism." *The Global Spiral* 9, no. 3 (2008). http://www.metanexus.net/Magazine/tabid/68/id/10543/Default.aspx.

Humanae Vitae. Encyclical letter of Pope Paul VI. 25 July 1968. See http://www.vatican.va/holy_father/paul_vi/encyclicals/documents/hf_p-vi_enc_25071968_humanae-vitae_en.html.

Hume, David. *A Treatise of Human Nature*. First published 1739 and 1740; rpt. London: Penguin, 1984.

Ihde, Don. "Of Which Human Are We Post?" *The Global Spiral* 9, no. 3 (2008). http://www.metanexus.net/magazine/tabid/68/id/10552/Default.aspx.

Mackie, J. L. *Ethics: Inventing Right and Wrong*. London: Penguin, 1977.

Peters, Ted. "Transhumanism and the Posthuman Future: Will Technological Progress Get Us There?" *The Global Spiral* 9, no. 3 (2008). http://www.metanexus.net/magazine/tabid/68/id/10546/Default.aspx.

Singer, Peter. *A Darwinian Left: Politics, Evolution and Cooperation*. London: Weidenfeld & Nicolson, 1999.

Scholes, Robert. *Structural Fabulation: An Essay on Fiction of the Future*. South Bend and London: Notre Dame University Press, 1975.

Young, Simon. *Designer Evolution: A Transhumanist Manifesto*. Amherst, NY: Prometheus Books, 2006.

Chapter Twelve

Brains, Selves, and Spirituality in the History of Cybernetics

by Andrew Pickering

This essay is a revised version of a paper presented at the Max Planck Institute for History of Science, Berlin, November 3, 2007.

I was pleased to be invited to this meeting—I knew almost nothing about transhumanism when I got the invitation, and thinking about it seemed like an interesting challenge. I had intended to write a paper just for the meeting; somehow the time evaporated (my return to England), so I sent along a recent paper deriving from my research into the history of cybernetics that touches on some relevant issues, I think, and in these remarks I'll try to join up a few dots.

First remark: if transhumanism didn't exist, it would be necessary to invent it. The aspiration to transcend the human form does a wonderful job in inviting the numinous question: what does it mean to be human? Or as Don Ihde put it, "of which human are we trans?" So that is the question that I want to dwell on—what does it mean to be human? And the best way I've found to proceed is to contrast the answer that I'm inclined to give based on my analyses of scientific practice and my more recent work on the history of cybernetics, with the answer offered by the transhumanists. Immediately we run into a problem—I think the transhumanists might not have a single agreed position. So for the purpose of exposition I will narrow my definition of transhumanism down to the goal of "cybernetic immortality" as a sort of defining outer limit of transhumanist thought.

So what is cybernetic immortality? I take it be the idea that we can achieve a sort of immortality by downloading (or uploading) our consciousness into a computer (and then it can move around from machine to machine forever). What can we say about this idea? First, it exemplifies the transhuman aspiration very nicely—it envisages shuffling off the material form of the human body entirely.

Second, it answers the question "what does it mean to be human?" very clearly. A certain timeless *essence* of humanity (consciousness, the mind) is to achieve immortality, with all the useless paraphernalia of humanity (the body, even the unconscious and subconscious reaches of the mind) to be sloughed off.

How might we react to this version of what it means to be human? We could start by noting that there is something very odd about it. Its vision of the human essence is actually a historical construction, invented by the Enlightenment. Of course, you might like the Enlightenment, and you might want to make its privileging of the mind and reason a permanent feature of humanity, as in cybernetic immortality. However, it's worth noting that what is envisaged here is a *freezing* and a *narrowing* of the human form—the imposition of a historically specific definition rather than the liberation of an eternal essence. Actually, it's this impulse toward freezing that worries me most about transhumanism.

As I move toward my own work, a few more thoughts spring to mind. In my book *The Mangle of Practice: Time, Agency, and Science* (Chicago: University of Chicago Press, 1995) I was led to emphasize two aspects of being in the world: what I called a *posthumanist* entanglement of the human and the nonhuman, and temporal *emergence*, the continual bubbling up of irreducible novelty in the world. My sense of "posthumanism" is thus more or less the inverse of how the same word is used in connection with transhumanism. The latter refers to a splitting off of consciousness from materiality, whereas I want to argue for a decentered analysis that foregrounds the constitutive coupling of consciousness, reason, the self, etc. with the material world. Where does this divergence leave us? I'm inclined to stick to my story, but that doesn't mean I have to regard cybernetic immortality as a totally mistaken idea. Presumably, even downloaded consciousnesses would have something to interact with—the material world via some sort of motor organs, or just each other—so, oddly, a decentered posthumanist analysis, in my sense, would still go through. These disembodied consciousnesses would still be constitutively plugged into the world as we are, but *differently*—not through the medium of the fleshly body.

This, of course, raises the question of whether the medium of being matters. And this, in turn, is the sort of question that phenomenologists like to meditate on, so maybe I should leave it for Don Ihde to answer. However, for myself, I have to say that, as mentioned in my paper, I'm taken by a very literal understanding of Michel Foucault's notion of *technologies of the self*. Different technologies, different material setups indeed elicit different inner states. And I'm willing to bet that cybernetic immortality would entail some sort of technologies of the self, and that the selves they elicit would be very different from the selves we have today. And the moral of this is that, even if transhumanists aim at the simple liberation of some timeless human essence, they would end up with something they did not expect—which again problematizes their version of what it means to be human. And, of course, we could have reached the same conclusion by thinking about emergence—we have to expect new selves to be continually bubbling up in our dealings with the material world, even dealings that aim to hold the self constant.

I should think more now about this phrase, *cybernetic immortality*, and I want to make a distinction concerning the referent of *cybernetic*. The sense invoked by the transhumanists appeals to the information theory branch of cybernetics, and more broadly to anything to do with AI and computers. This hangs together perfectly with the Enlightenment image of reason as the human essence. However, in *The Mangle*,[1] I argued that we cannot get to grips even with Enlightenment science itself by focusing on reason alone. Instead, we need to begin with *performance*—the idea that we humans are linked into the world via dances of agency, coupling our performances with those of the world. This emphasis on performance is a very different answer to the question of what it means to be human than the Enlightenment's answer, and, as it happens, there is a very different branch of cybernetics that stages and acts out this vision for us, the branch that flourished in Britain after the war and that I talk about in my paper. And one interesting aspect of this difference is that it invites very different fantasies of immortality from Enlightenment cybernetics.

This revolves around the biological computers that I mentioned in my paper below—meaning, naturally occurring adaptive systems enrolled into human projects as performative brains.[2] Stafford Beer and Gordon Pask imagined these as substitutes for human factory managers and went so far as to devise ways to train them to function as such. The basic idea was that the human manager would monitor the performance of the adaptive system and somehow reinforce moves that he or she approved of, until the system achieved a level of performance that the human could live with—at which point the human could withdraw and leave the factory, to be managed by a pond or some electrochemical threads or whatever.

The simple point I want to make here is that, after training, one can regard the computer as a sort of *model* of the human manager, inheriting his or her performative competence—and I cannot see why one should not think of this as a species of genuinely cybernetic immortality: the key competence of the human would here be indeed downloaded, not into a digital machine but into some lively and adaptive nonhuman material. However, something very different from consciousness gets downloaded here, into a medium very different from a digital computer. Hence, we can see that very different modes of immortality are imaginable depending on what one thinks it means to be human. To put it another way, we can see more concretely

---

[1] Andrew Pickering, *The Mangle of Practice: Time, Agency, and Science*, (Chicago: University of Chicago Press, 1995).

[2] See Andrew Pickering, "Beyond Design: Cybernetics, Biological Computers and Hylozoism," *Synthese* 168 (2009): 469-91 and *The Cybernetic Brain: Sketches of Another Future*, (Chicago: University of Chicago Press, 2010).

through this example how current discussions of cybernetic immortality amount to a freezing and narrowing of the space of future possibilities. I would hate to see the Enlightenment story of humanity made irrevocably true by biotech and AI.

I could say some more about my cyberneticians. If I wanted to persuade you to take them seriously, I would go on about their work in robotics, complex systems theory, management, and so on—nice down to earth topics that Enlightenment thinkers can recognize—but one thing that interests me a lot about them is precisely that they had some unconventional ideas about the *self*, as discussed at some length in my paper. These follow immediately from the notion of the brain and the self as performative. The Enlightenment self is given and conscious—it's the kind of self that does IQ tests and that AI models—which is why academics can mistake it for an essence. The performative self, in contrast, is opaque to consciousness, the sort of thing one can *find out about* experimentally. And in my paper, I show how, in the history of cybernetics, this sort of curiosity about the performative self has been entangled with all sorts of technologies of the self (including flickering strobe lights and hallucinogens, as well as meditation) and with associated altered states, explorations of consciousness, strange performances, magic, the *siddhis*, the decentered dissolution of the self, tantric yoga, and union with the divine. The self, as revealed here, turns out to be inexhaustibly emergent, just like the world—the antithesis of the given human essence of the Enlightenment and cybernetic immortality. And again, for me, this shows the extent of the freezing and narrowing of the human that transhumanism entails—the severity of *its editing of what the human might be*. Of course, all of the practices and states that I talk about in my paper are already marginalized in contemporary society—it feels vaguely embarrassing to talk about them in public. But at least the margins exist, and one can go there if one likes. The transhumanists would like to engineer them out of existence entirely and forever. Yes, I'm starting not to like transhumanism.

As an aside here, I could state the obvious: that cybernetic investigations of the self lead straight into the space of the spiritual, though the immediate resonances and affiliations are with Eastern spirituality rather than Christianity. There is, of course, an important and distinctly Christian line of the critique of transhumanism that emphasizes a deep significance of death and resurrection that transhumanism skates over. However, it is worth emphasizing a certain isomorphism here of critique and criticized: both positions assume that they already know substantively what it means to be human. Both would like to freeze the human in place; neither acknowledges a significant space for emergence. From this spiritual angle, then, the mangle, cybernetics and Eastern spirituality all serve to thematize the narrowness of current debates both for and against transhumanism. "Who knows what a body can do?" Do we want to foreclose this question?

Let me come at this topic from one last angle. Transhumanism has a *telos*: it thinks it can see the future and how to mobilize science and technology to get there.

Clearly, the mangle and cybernetics contest this idea. But I find it interesting to confront it historically too. In a paper available on the web ("Facing the Challenges of Transhumanism: Philosophical, Religious, and Ethical Considerations"), Hava Tirosh-Samuelson credits the word *transhumanism* to Julian Huxley in 1957, but traces the origins of the idea back to the 1920s and 1930s in the writings of J. B. S. Haldane, J. D. Bernal, and Julian's brother, Aldous Huxley. I would be interested to know more about Haldane's and Bernal's thinking in this area, but I know something about Aldous and Julian Huxley from my work on cybernetics and the 1960s. Their writings are, for example, central to the present-day human potential movement, which focuses on precisely the sort of altered states and strange performances that I just mentioned as edited out of the transhumanist vision. The canonical recent text here would be Michael Murphy's enormous 1992 book, *The Future of the Body: Explorations into the Further Evolution of Human Nature.*

So there is a continuing, if marginal, tradition here of imagining an emergent rather than essentialized answer to the question of what it means to be human. It interests me that, also back in the 1920s and 1930s, one can find important works of fiction that point in the same direction. A couple of weeks ago, I happened to read a canonical fantasy novel from the period, David Lindsay's *Voyage to Arcturus*, and in it Lindsay elaborates the idea of an unstable material and physical environment in which humanity continually develops entirely new limbs and sense organs. I also think of Olaf Stapledon's 1931 novel *Last and First Men*. This sketches out an imaginary *longue durée* history of the future of the human race stretching over millions of years, in which humanity eventually seizes control of its own evolution, as the transhumanists would say. However, instead of freezing our form in the name of transhumanist perfection, we experiment with it. In the chapter that I remember best, the human race acquires wings and takes to the air, and Stapledon elaborates the posthumanist (in my sense) point brilliantly by conjuring up the changes in subjectivities and social relations that go along with the new aerial existence—flight as a technology of the self, producing a new kind of people.

Why do I mention this now? For three reasons: First, because *Last and First Men* is a very nice example of the sort of vision of the future that might go with the mangle and cybernetics—a vision of open-ended experimentation, emergence, and transformation, with no fixed end. Second, because an interesting project in the history of ideas comes into sight here. I would like to know how it came to be that, in the twenties and thirties, people were able to imagine radical transformations of the human form, when no evident technological possibilities were at hand. And third, from the opposite angle, I am struck by the impoverishment of our imagination that has since come to pass. Now we have biotechnology, now we really could dream of equipping ourselves with wings or new senses, but we don't. Instead of experimentation with the endless possibilities of humanity, we dream transhumanist dreams of purification and the excision of what already exists, of downloading consciousness. Something profoundly sad has happened to our imagination. That, in the end, is what transhumanism brings home to me.[3]

II

My research in the history of cybernetics in Britain has taken me to strange and unexpected places.[4] Grey Walter's 1953 popular book, *The Living Brain*, is, on the one hand, a down-to-earth, materialist, and evolutionary story of how the brain functions. I know how to deal with that. However, it is also full of references to dreams, visions, ESP, nirvana, and the magical powers of the Eastern yogi, such as suspending the breath and the heartbeat—*siddhis* as they are called. I never knew what to make of this, except to note how strange it is and that respectable scientists don't write about such things now. But then I realized that I should pay attention to it. Walter was by no means alone on the wild side. All of the other cyberneticians were there with him. In his private notebooks, Ross Ashby, the other great first-generation cybernetician in Britain, announced that intellectual honesty required him to be a spiritualist, that he despised the Christian image of God, and that instead he had become a "time worshipper." Gordon Pask wrote supernatural detective stories. Stafford Beer was deeply absorbed by mystical number systems and geometries, happily sketched out his version of the great chain of being, taught Tantric yoga, and attributed magical powers like levitation to his fictional alter ego, the Wizard Prang. Echoing Aldous Huxley on mescaline, Gregory Bateson and R. D. Laing triangulated between Zen enlightenment, madness, and ecstasy.

Strange and wonderful, surprising stuff. What is going on here? I want to try to sort this out and tie it back to a distinctive conception of the human brain.[5]

Meditating on the history of cybernetics has helped me see just how deeply modern thought is enmeshed in an endlessly repetitive discourse on *how special*

---

[3] There is, of course, no shortage of genres that circle around the *fear* of variations on the human form. Canonical works would have to include Mary Shelley's *Frankenstein* and H. G. Wells's *The Island of Dr Moreau*, but it seems to me that this genre really flourished after WWII and during the Cold War: endless American B-movies about mutants, John Wyndham's *Midwich Cuckoos*, Greg Bear and *Darwin's Radio* (though, as usual, Bear is more interesting, portraying the promise as well as the fear of the next stage of human evolution).

[4] Documented and analyzed at great length in Andrew Pickering, *The Cybernetic Brain: Sketches of Another Future*, (Chicago: University of Chicago Press, 2010).

[5] A much fuller treatment of the topics to follow (and much else) complete with citations to sources is to be found in my forthcoming book: *Sketches of Another Future: The Cybernetic Brain, 1940-2000* (Chicago: University of Chicago Press, forthcoming).

we are, how *different* human beings are from animals and brute matter. It is, of course, traditional to blame Descartes for this *human exceptionalism*, as we might call it.[6] However, while we may no longer believe we have immortal and immaterial souls, the human sciences seem always to have been predicated on some immaterial equivalent that sets us apart: language, reason, emotions, culture, the social, the dreaded knowledge or information society in which are now said to live. This sort of master narrative is so pervasive and taken for granted that it is hard to see, let alone to shake off and imagine our way out of. This is why we might learn from cybernetics. It stages a nondualist vision of brains, selves, and the world that might help us put the dualist human and physical sciences in their place and, more importantly, to see ourselves differently and to act differently. Let me talk about how this goes.

We should start with the brain. The modern brain, as staged since the 1950s by AI for example, is cognitive, representational, deliberative—the locus of a certain version of human specialness. The key point to grasp is that the cybernetic brain *was not like that*. It was just another organ of the body, an organ that happens to be especially engaged with bodily *performance* in the world. In this sense, the human brain is no different from the animal brain except in mundane specifics: Ashby, for example, noted that we have more neurons and more neuronal interconnections than other species, making possible more nuanced forms of adaptation to the environment. And, of course, the defining activity of first-generation cybernetics was building little electromechanical models of the performative brain—Walter's tortoises and Ashby's homeostats—thus completing the effacement of difference between humans on the one side and animals, machines, and brute matter on the other. This is what I like about cybernetics: it was and is nowhere in the Cartesian space of human exceptionalism. It reminds us that we are performative stuff in a performative world—and then elaborates fascinatingly on that. Now I want to try to make sense of some of these elaborations as they bear on non-Cartesian understandings of minds, selves, and spirit.

Altered States and Strange Performances

The Cartesian brain is available for introspection. We know our own special cognitive powers and feelings, and it is the job of AI, say, to reproduce those powers in a computer program. However, the performative brain is not like that.

---

[6] The canonical transhumanist dream of downloading consciousness to a computer is, of course, a species of human exceptionalism writ very large. My idea here is to explore a different mode of being in the world and where it might lead us, especially across spiritual terrain.

195

Walter's tortoises navigated their environments without representing them at all. In general, cybernetics understood performance as largely happening below the level of consciousness and, as thus, unavailable to inspection. Ashby's model for the performative brain was bodily processes of homeostasis—keeping the blood temperature constant—something that all mammals do, but not by thinking about it. This unavailability of the performative brain at once made it an object of *curiosity*—who knows what a performative brain can do? This simple curiosity in turn explains much, though by no means all, of the cyberneticians' travels in forbidden lands. If mainstream Western culture defines itself by a rejection of strange performances, well, then other cultures can be seen as a repository of possibilities, hence Walter's interest in nirvana and the yogic *siddhis*. He was happy to recognize that Eastern yogis have strange powers; he just wanted to give a naturalistic explanation of them in terms of the performative brain. The *siddhis* were thus, according to Walter, instances of disciplined conscious control of otherwise autonomic bodily functions; nirvana was the absence of thought in the achievement of perfect homeostasis—the disappearance of the last relic of the Cartesian mind. Beer thought differently. He practiced yoga; the *siddhis* were real to him, the incidental powers that arise on a spiritual journey. We can come back to spiritual matters in a minute.

With the exception of Beer, *siddhis* and the like were matters of distant report to the cyberneticians, not personal experience; and another hallmark of early cybernetics was the pursuit of parallel phenomena that were accessible to Western means of investigation, hence the interest in ESP phenomena. Hence, several of my cyberneticians belonged to the British Society for Psychical Research, as I recently found out. However, the key discovery in this respect was undoubtedly Walter's of *flicker*. In the course of EEG research in 1945, Walter and his colleagues discovered that gazing with eyes closed at a strobe light flickering near the alpha frequency of the brain induced visions: moving, colored patterns, often geometrical ones but also visions of events like waking dreams. This flicker experience was important to the cyberneticians and psychical researchers precisely as a vindication of an understanding of the brain as performative and endlessly explorable rather than cognitive and immediately available. So a couple of comments are appropriate here.

First, flicker vividly problematized any notion of the brain as an organ of representation. One indeed sees strange and beautiful patterns in a flicker setup, but the patterns are equally obviously *not there* in the world. The strobe just flashes on and off, but the patterns move and spiral through space. Second, flicker thematizes a nondualist coupling of the brain to the world. The brain does not choose to see moving patterns; the external environment elicits this behavior from the brain. To see what is going on here, I can't help thinking of Michel Foucault's idea of *technologies of the self*. In Foucault's own work, these are technologies that produce a distinctly human, self-controlled self—the kind of self that sets us apart from animals and things. Flicker, then, is a different kind of nonmodern, non-Cartesian technology of self—a technology for *losing control* and going to unintended places, for *experiment* in a performative sense. Much of the literature in this area can be read as devoted to strange performances and the technologies of the self that elicit them. Aldous Huxley's second book on his mescaline experience, *Heaven and Hell* (1956), is one long catalogue of technologies for eliciting nonmodern selves open to mystical experiences, including holding one's breath, chanting, and flagellation, as well as psychedelic drugs and, yes, flicker.

What interests me most here, I think, is how drastically these technologies and their associated altered states undercut our notions of the modern self. They remind us that there are other ways to be, other selves that we can inhabit. They show vividly and by contrast just how straitened the modern self is and just how constrained the human sciences that celebrate the modern self are.

The Decentered Self

We can think about another aspect of the cybernetic brain. I said that it was performative, and now I need to add that in the main line of cybernetic descent, the brain's role in performance was that of *adaptation*. The brain, above all the organs, is what helps us cope with the unknown and get along in a world that can always surprise us in its performance. Adaptation is an interesting concept in the present connection because it is intrinsically relational. One adapts to specific others as they appear, not to the world in general once and for all. This in turn implies a sort of *decentering* of the self that, again, cybernetic technologies of the self help stage for us. When Allen Ginsberg, the Beat poet, took LSD for the first time, it was in conjunction with a feedback-controlled flicker setup, and he afterward wrote that he felt that his soul was being sucked away down the wires. So much for Descartes.

We could move in several directions from here. One is into the arts. Gordon Pask constructed an original aesthetic theory based on the idea that human beings actually find pleasure and satisfaction in performative adaptation to others, human or nonhuman. In the early 1950s, his famous Musicolour machine was an instance of this. Musicolour translated a musical performance into a light show, but its defining feature was that its parameters evolved as a function of what had gone before, so that it was impossible to gain a cognitive overview of the linkage between sounds and lights. The performer thus had continually to adapt to the machine just as it adapted to him or her, and the overall performance was a dynamic and decentered joint product of the human and the nonhuman—literally a staging of the relational brain and self, now in the realm of the arts and entertainment. Here I could make two observations: The first is that here we can see clearly that what is at stake is not simply *ideas* about the brain and the self. Distinct and specific projects and forms of life hang together with these ideas—*different ways to live*. Again, this

197

observation serves to thematize the straitened character of both the Cartesian self and the human sciences, now aesthetics, that conspire to naturalize these selves. The other observation is that the strangeness of Pask's work is manifest in the fact that no one, not even Pask, was sure what a Musicolour machine was. He later wrote of trying "to sell it in any possible way: at one extreme as a pure art form, at the other as an attachment for juke boxes." Much the same could be said of the Beat writer and artist Brion Gysin's attempt to market flicker machines as a performative substitute for the living room TV.

Another direction in which we could travel is madness. Madness for the cyberneticians was just another of those altered states the performative brain could get into, as usual elicited by specific technologies of the self. Walter drove his robot tortoises mad by placing them in contradictory setups in which their conditioning pointed them to contradictory responses. He also cured them with other setups that he analogized to the brutal psychiatry of his day: shock, sleep therapy, and lobotomy. Gregory Bateson refined this picture in his story of the double bind as a contradictory social situation to which the symptoms of schizophrenia were an unfortunate adaptation. Here what interests me most is that, at Kingsley Hall in the second half of the 1960s, R. D. Laing and his colleagues put this decentered and performative image of schizophrenia into practice, in a community where psychiatrists and the mad (as well as artists and dancers) lived together on a par rather than in the rigidly hierarchic relations of the traditional mental hospital. Kingsley Hall was another technology of the self—both an antidote to the double bind for sufferers, and, as Laing put it, a place where the mad could teach the sane to go mad—where new kinds of self could emerge. Again, Kingsley Hall makes the point that it is not just ideas that are at stake here, but other forms of life too. And something of the strangeness of this other form of life is caught up by the label *antipsychiatry* that attached to the Bateson-Laing enterprise. A style of adaptive architecture, associated with the Archigram group, as well as Cedric Price and Gordon Pask, likewise found itself described as *antiarchitecture*. I find these links from the non-Cartesian performative and adaptive brain to these strange forms of life fascinating.

The third axis we can explore under this heading is "alternative spiritualities." The decentering that goes with the adaptive brain of course pushes us in the direction of Eastern spirituality. Instead of the centered and unchangeable soul, one finds a self that evolves and becomes in the thick of things, and this just is a Buddhist analysis of the self. One can plunge into this further. Here is a diagram drawn by Gordon Pask in connection with his work on cybernetic machines for entertainment and education. It is labeled "two views of minds and media." Both views are decentered, focusing on the relationality of communication. One diagram enshrines a conventional view of this process and shows minds communicating with one another through some medium—say, words traveling through the air. But Pask wrote that "I have a hankering" for the other view, in which minds are somehow "embedded" in an all-pervasive communicational medium.

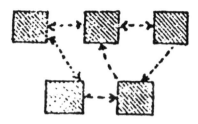

Fig. 1 ▧ Organisms ----→ Media as channels of communication

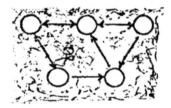

Fig. 2 ◯ Individuals --→ Communication as program sharing and linguistic interaction between individuals. Medium (M) as shading

diagrams: minds and media (1977)

These diagrams seem quite innocuous unless one immerses oneself in the sort of scientific/spiritual literature found in the *Journal of the Society for Psychical Research*, when the occult significance of diagram (b) becomes clear. The idea behind diagram (b) is that the brain is the organ of a strange sense, unrecognized in the West, capable of accessing some other nonhuman and intrinsically spiritual realm that one may as well call "universal mind." One finds this idea in Ashby's notebooks from the early 1930s. In the passage where he admits to himself that he should be a spiritualist, he sketches out precisely the idea of the brain as a sort of hypersensitive (by virtue of its material complexity) radio receiver, uniquely open to signals in a spiritual ether. Over the years, one finds this image endlessly elaborated in attempts to understand phenomena like ESP, which become much more plausible if they have their own medium in which to happen, and in the ideas

199

of "evolutionary consciousness" which one finds in important branches of New Age philosophy.

If Pask's diagram of minds and media remains philosophical and representational, Aldous Huxley made a different connection to the spiritual realm in making sense of his mescaline experience. In the beautiful description of the phenomenology of psychedelic drugs that he gave in *The Doors of Perception*, Huxley appealed to Buddhist imagery to convey the intensity of his experiences—seeing the dharma body of the Buddha in the hedge at the bottom of the garden is the image that sticks in my mind. So here the altered states induced by chemical technologies of the nonmodern self are immediately identified with those other altered states induced by Buddhist and more generally mystical technologies of the self. Interestingly, Huxley even offers an explanation of why mystical experiences are so rare in terms of the key concept of cybernetics, adaptation. His famous theory of the brain as a "reducing valve" elaborates the idea that evolutionary processes have set us up to perceive the world in directly functional and performative terms. Mescaline and other technologies of the self then serve to undo this focused and performative stance, at least for a while, allowing us to latch onto the world in other ways.

Finally, I can just note that the references so far to *siddhis* and strange performances point directly not just to Eastern philosophy but also to Eastern spiritual practices—to nonmodern technologies of the self again. If you really want to know about *siddhis*, a place to start is with Mircea Eliade's big book, *Yoga: Immortality and Freedom* (1958). This intensely scholarly tome surveys the history and substance of the whole range of Indian yogic traditions, and singles out *tantric* yoga as the form that emphasized bodily techniques, altered states, and strange performances—the *siddhis*—as well as magic and alchemy. Stafford Beer, as I said, practiced and taught tantric yoga—he lived all this stuff.

In all these ways, then, the adaptive brain of cybernetics extended into a distinctly and integrally spiritualized set of understandings and forms of life, running from psychedelic explorations of consciousness to strange yogic performances. The oddity of it all against the backdrop of, say, mainstream contemporary Christianity, is manifest. Again we are reminded of the straitened and impoverished conceptions of the self and the spirit that the modern West affords us and that we act out in our daily lives, and of the complicity of the modern social and human sciences in this narrowing and constriction of thought and action.

HYLOZOISM

So far I have been dwelling on cybernetics as a science of the performative brain, in contrast to the more familiar cognitive version. Now I should recognize that the cyberneticians did not deny the brain its cognitive capacity. Rather, they wanted *to put cognition in its place*. Like me in *The Mangle of Practice*, they argued for a *performative epistemology*, in which knowledge and representation are seen as intimately engaged in performance, as revisable components of performance, having to do with getting along better or worse in the world, rather than as something especially human and having to do with making accurate maps and winning arguments. Beyond that, however, the cybernetic focus on the adaptive brain—the brain that helps us get along with the unknown and unknowable—in turn thematized what one might call the *performative excess* of the world in relation to our cognitive capacity—precisely the ability of the world always to surprise us with novel behavior.

This explicit recognition of the performative excess of the world feeds into my last topic, which I refer to by the slippery word *hylozoism*. Hylozoism, for me, refers to a kind of spiritually charged wonder at the performativity and agency of matter, and Stafford Beer was certainly a hylozoist under this definition. He wrote poems on the computational power of the Irish Sea as indefinitely exceeding our own. "*Nature* is (let it be clear that) *nature* is in charge," he wrote in 1977. What interests me most, again, is that this hylozoism was not just a philosophical position, an idea of what the world is like. Again, the cyberneticians elaborated it in all sorts of practices, including engineering and the arts.

In modern engineering, the dominant approach is a version of what Martin Heidegger called *enframing*. The world is materially reformed and reconfigured to try to accomplish some preconceived goal according to a preconceived plan. Beer and Pask developed a quite different approach that one could associate with *revealing*, not enframing—an open-ended exploratory approach of *finding out* what the world can offer us. Perhaps the best way to grasp this is via the notion that whatever one wants in the world, it's already there, somewhere in nature. I think here of the craziest and most visionary project I have ever come across in the history of technology: Beer and Pask's attempt to construct nonrepresentational *biological computers*. The idea is simple enough once you see it. Ashby had argued for the idea of the brain as an organ of performative adaptation, and Beer stood this idea on its head: any adaptive system can function as a brain. In the late 1950s and early 1960s, Beer and Pask then embarked on a long search through the space of adaptive systems, running from pond ecosystems to electrochemically deposited metal threads as some sort of substitute for human factory managers.[7] They failed, but the problem lay in getting adaptive systems to care about our projects rather than any difficulties of principle. Once more the contrast between this sort of hylozoist

---

[7] There is a close resemblance between this idea of substituting biological computers for human managers and the transhumanist project of downloading human consciousness into a digital computer. The axis of differentiation, besides the very different substrates involved, is that what gains "cybernetic immortality" in biological computing is not the conscious, reasoning brain of the manager but his or her preconscious, performative and adaptive capabilities.

engineering and that taught in engineering schools is manifest; this time we would have to blame the modern natural sciences and IT strategies, rather than the social sciences, for conspiring with the narrowing of our imagination of the world itself, against which biological computing stands out.

We can see hylozoist parallels in the arts to this style of cybernetic engineering. Brian Eno said he was indebted to Stafford Beer's *Brain of the Firm* for innovative changes in his music in the 1970s. If classical music consists in the reproduction of a preconceptualized score, Eno's generative music consists, as he once put it, in "riding the dynamics" of unpredictable algorithms and *finding out* what emerges, as if the music was already there, now in the domain of computational systems. In the realm of what used to be called sculpture, Garnet Hertz built a robot very similar to Grey Walter's tortoises, but with the electronics replaced by an optically and mechanically coupled giant Madagascan cockroach, and exhibited it as an art object.

picture: roach robot

The artist Eduardo Kac has done much the same with biorobots and genetically modified animals, and Andy Gracie's artwork explores the dynamic possibilities of interfering with natural processes of growth and adaptation. My favorite example of hylozoist art, however, is biofeedback music. Developed by people like Alvin Lucier, biofeedback music consists in extracting naturally occurring electrical rhythms from the brain and using them to control soundmaking equipment. Once more we arrive at the hylozoist idea that it's all already there in nature; there is no need for that long trip through the centuries of compositional development in the history of the West—all you need is a few electrodes and wires. And yet again, the strangeness of this sort of performance is evident. As James Tenney (1995, 12) put it: "Before [the first performance of Lucier's *Music for a Solo Performer*] no one would have thought it necessary to define the word 'music' in a way which allowed for such a manifestation; afterwards some definition could not be avoided."

It is also worth noting that biofeedback is historically related to Grey Walter's EEG research and originated as a technique for interfering with one's own brainwaves. It was taken up in the sixties as a technique for achieving the same sort of transcendental inner states as meditation and psychedelic drugs, and performances of biofeedback music often entailed the achievement of such altered states by performers (individually or collectively) and the audience. So this new sort of music was directly performative as itself a technology of the self for achieving altered states and nonmodern subject positions.[8]

To wrap things up, I want to say that, in elaborating a conception of the brain as adaptive and performative, the history of cybernetics dramatizes visions of the self and spirituality and the arts and engineering and the world that go far beyond those prevalent in contemporary society and the mainstream sciences, and that cybernetics acted out those visions in all sorts of strange, surprising, and wonderful projects. As I have said several times, I take it that this sort of ontological theater points up the narrowness of our hegemonic forms of life and the role of the natural, as well as the social sciences, in closing down our imagination and naturalizing this constriction.

References

Beer, Anthony Stafford. *Transit.* Limited Edition, Private Circulation. Cardiff, Wales: CWRW Press, 1977.

Eliade, Mircea. *Yoga: Immortality and Freedom.* New York: Bollingen Foundation, 1958.

Huxley, Aldous. *The Doors of Perception.* New York: Harper & Brothers, 1954.

---

[8] There are many threads that one could follow in exploring the theme of hylozoism in the arts and science including the role of the camera obscura in the extreme realism of Vermeer's paintings (which apparently include reflections of the camera itself); Bernard Palissy's amazing techniques for turning living creatures into pottery; Pamela Smith's writings, which suggest that much of what is usually taken to be alchemical symbolism is actually a literal description of the mediaeval vermilion synthesis; Galison's account of the history of the bubble chamber, with C. T. R. Wilson trying to create real meteorological phenomena in his early cloud chambers; and D'Arcy Thompson on the nineteenth-century science of inkdrops.

Huxley, Aldous. *Heaven and Hell.* New York: Harper & Brothers, 1956.

Lindsay, David. *Voyage to Arcturus.* 1920. Reprint, Lincoln, NE: University of Nebraska Press, 2002.

Murphy, Michael. *The Future of the Body: Explorations into the Further Evolution of Human Nature.* New York: Tarcher, 1992.

Pickering, Andrew. *The Mangle of Practice: Time, Agency, and Science.* Chicago: University of Chicago Press, 1995.

Pickering, Andrew. "Beyond Design: Cybernetics, Biological Computers and Hylozoism," *Synthese* 168 (2009): 469-91.

Pickering. Andrew. *The Cybernetic Brain: Sketches of Another Future.* Chicago: University of Chicago Press, 2010.

Stapledon, Olaf. *Last and First Men.* 1931. Reprint, New York: Dover, 1968.

Walter, W. Grey. *The Living Brain.* New York: W. W. Norton & Co., 1953.

Chapter Thirteen

Transhumanism: Threat or Menace?
A Response to Andrew Pickering

by Michael LaTorra

ACKNOWLEDGEMENTS

I would like to thank Natasha Vita-More for her dedication and tireless efforts in arranging for this essay and others to appear in this publication, Metanexus Institute for producing this online periodical, *The Global Spiral*, Dr. Hava Tirosh-Samuelson of Arizona State University for hosting the events on transhumanism (one of which I was privileged to attend in 2007), and the John Templeton Foundation, whose generous support underwrote the workshops.

INTRODUCTION

Transhumanism is often misrepresented. By accident or design, this movement—a movement that aims at improving the lot of humanity through longer life spans, greater material abundance, enhanced abilities, new powers, and a wealth of opportunities extending beyond current biological limits—has often been depicted as a villain without redeeming qualities. Rather than considering transhumanism on its own terms, we are often given a false choice: is transhumanism a threat or a menace?

Upon first reading Prof. Pickering's papers,[1] I was delighted to find that he is opposed to the "freezing and narrowing" of the definition of what it means to be human. Soon, however, I became discouraged when I encountered his claim that the expansive, liberating goals that I know to be the essence of transhumanism were, according to his ill-informed view, actually just the sort of freezing and narrowing he decried. I was at first puzzled as to how he could have so badly misunderstood actual existing transhumanism.

THE PUZZLING TRUTH

The answer to my puzzlement proved easy to find. Pickering admits that, before being invited to speak at the "Transhumanism and the Meanings of Progress" workshop held on the campus of Arizona State University in April 2008, he "knew almost nothing about this movement."[2] And although he "had intended to write a paper just for the meeting," he never got around to doing so; instead he submitted a paper about his work on the history of cybernetics, which he fixed up a bit since it "touches on some relevant issues." Yet despite his unfamiliarity with the reality of transhumanism or the persons involved in it, he declared, "Yes, I'm starting not to like transhumanism."[3]

Since Pickering fails to mention any primary sources written by transhumanists, one must assume that his research was limited to reading the single secondary source he cites.[4] One wonders at such a small data set, given the large amount of primary transhumanist literature available, most of it easily found on the Internet.[5]

---

[1]   Andrew Pickering, "Brains, Selves and Spirituality in the History of Cybernetics," *The Global Spiral* 9, no. 3 (2008). http://www.metanexus.net/magazine/tabid/68/id/10545/Default.aspx. Andrew Pickering, "The Science of the Unknowable: Stafford Beer's Cybernetic Informatics," *Working Papers from Centre for STS Studies* (2006). http://webcache.googleusercontent.com/search?q=cache:1WDpMC8YxPAJ:sts.imv.au.dk/arbejdspapirer/WP6.pdf+%22Stafford+Beer%22+%22Tantric%22&hl=en&ct=clnk&cd=3&gl=us.

[2]   Pickering, "Brains, Selves and Spirituality in the History of Cybernetics."

[3]   Pickering, "Brains, Selves and Spirituality in the History of Cybernetics." (NOTE: Comment: "Yes, I'm starting not to like transhumanism.")

[4]   Hava Tirosh-Samuelson, "Facing the Challenges of Transhumanism," *The Global Spiral* 8, no. 7 (2007). http://www.metanexus.net/magazine/tabid/68/id/10169/Default.aspx.

[5]   See for example Max More, "The Diachronic Self: Identity, Continuity, Transformation," (PhD diss., University of Southern California, 1995), available at http://www.maxmore.com/disscont.htm; Nick Bostrom, "Existential Risks:

The narrowness of his research is particularly troubling when one notes that on the selfsame *Global Spiral* Web site, where Pickering's paper appears, one also finds "The Compatibility of Religious and Transhumanist Views of Metaphysics, Suffering, Virtue and Transcendence in an Enhanced Future" by Prof. James Hughes, who, just a year prior to Pickering's presentation, had delivered his paper in the same venue.

Mind Uploading: Cybernetic Immortality or Mind Emulation?

Contrary to the claim made in Pickering's paper, uploading is not the transfer of consciousness to a computer. By this statement, I am not asserting that it is impossible for consciousness to exist in a computer or other nonhuman substrate. Rather, I am saying that consciousness is not an object or energy that could be moved from one location in space to another. If consciousness is defined as a process of the brain, then uploading is the emulation of that process by a computer. Uploading an intellect from a brain to a computer is similar to the copying of data structures from one CD (compact disc) to another, or a data file from one computer to another, like synchronizing an iPod with an iTunes library. At the end of the copying process, there are two copies rather than one. Similarly, uploading is brain emulation, not mind or consciousness transfer.

Analyzing Human Extinction Scenarios and Related Hazards," *Journal of Evolution and Technology* 9 (2002), available at http://www.nickbostrom.com/existential/risks.html; A. Sandberg, "Transhumanist Resources," (2002), available at http://www.aleph.se/Trans/index-2.html; D. Pearce, "The Hedonistic Imperative," (2004), available at http://www.hedweb.com/hedab.htm; James J. Hughes, *Citizen Cyborg: Why Democratic Societies Must Respond to the Redesigned Human of the Future* (Boulder, CO: Westview Press, 2004); Aubrey de Grey and Michael Rae. *Ending Aging: The Rejuvenation Breakthroughs That Could Reverse Human Aging in Our Lifetime.* 1st ed. New York: St. Martin's Press, 2007; Natasha Vita-More, "Designing Human 2.0 (Transhuman), Äì Regenerative Existence," *Artifact* 2, no 3. (2008): 145-152; Humanity Plus, *H+ magazine*, (2008), available at http://www.hplusmagazine.com/; IEET—*Institute for Ethics and Emerging Technologies*, (2008), http://www.ieet.org/.

And uploading is not the aim of all transhumanists. Many transhumanists envision enhanced, nonaging, long-lived bodies that include implanted technologies.[6], [7] - the "shuffling off the material form of the human body . . . exemplifies the transhuman aspiration" is simply, plainly, flatly untrue as a blanket statement.

To his credit, Pickering gives the caveat early in his paper that "transhumanists might not have a single agreed upon position" with regard to uploading and cybernetic immortality. Then without bothering to confirm his supposition—which is in fact a correct one—Pickering proceeds to "narrow [his] definition of transhumanism down to the goal of 'cybernetic immortality.'" That is narrow indeed! It flies in the face of the facts about transhumanist beliefs.

Such narrowness may be convenient for Pickering, but it comes at the cost of violating the truth about transhumanism. Like the man who loses his keys in a dark alley and then walks some distance onto a well-illuminated sidewalk to look for them, Pickering prefers to work where the light is better for him rather than where the real object of his search is to be found.

Pickering claims that transhumanists seek immortality. While the term *immortality* is sometimes used casually by transhumanists, most of us are scientifically literate, philosophically informed, and technologically savvy enough to know that indefinitely expanded lifetimes—not guaranteed immortality—is the maximum possibility. We might aim for immortality, but we can never be sure we have achieved it. Even if one were to live ten billion years, one could still die in the next hour. No one can know with certainty how long he or she will live.

IRONIC AGREEMENT

Despite the thinness of Pickering's research into transhumanism, there is much value in the positions he actually holds with regard to human potential. The irony here is that Pickering endorses the real aims of transhumanism while wrongly believing that he is opposing transhumanist goals. If only he had "done his homework" by researching the topic more carefully before writing about it, Pickering might be praising transhumanism rather than disparaging it.

---

[6]   Aubrey de Grey and Michael Rae, *Ending Aging: The Rejuvenation Breakthroughs That Could Reverse Human Aging in Our Lifetime*, 1st ed. (New York: St. Martin's Press, 2007).

[7]   Natasha Vita-More, "Designing Human 2.0 (Transhuman),Äì Regenerative Existence," *Artifact* 2, no. 3 (2008). Mihail C. Roco and William Sims Bainbridge, *Converging Technologies for Improving Human Performance: Nanotechnology, Biotechnology, Information Technology and Cognitive Science* (Dordrecht; Boston: Kluwer Academic Publishers, 2003). World Transhumanist Association, (2008), http://www.transhumanism.org/index.php/WTA/index/

Quite perceptively, Pickering writes that "different technologies, different material set-ups, indeed elicit different inner states." What is not clear from his brief discussion of "technologies of the self" (a concept he takes from Foucault) is how Pickering views the relationships or definitions of self, being, consciousness, and essence. Which are senior, or prior, and which are derivative? Pickering claims that belief in "essence" is a transhumanist notion. This came as a surprise to me, as I cannot recall the term appearing very often in my many years of corresponding with other transhumanists, attending conferences, reading transhumanist writings, and writing my own.[8]

I would agree with Pickering that a "self" emerges from material conditions. However, as Pickering realizes, material conditions are not static. In writing about the concept of emergence, Pickering says, "we have to expect new selves to be continually bubbling up in our dealing with the material world, even dealings that aim to hold the self constant."

This is true, in my view, and perhaps to a greater extent than Pickering implies or recognizes. The self is a pattern, not an entity or an irreducible object that merely changes. The pattern that we call a self at any instant is merely the successor state of previous instances of that pattern. It maintains continuity by displaying a high degree of similarity to previous pattern states.

Like many transhumanists, I maintain that a self pattern could even manifest in a sufficiently complex body (or machine) that is not human at all. Mind uploading, then, is copying the pattern that is self into a different platform (i.e., substrate or body).

SPIRITUALITY AND TRANSHUMANISM

In his discussion of explorations of consciousness, yogic *siddhis* (powers), dissolution of the self (or as I would put it, seeing the transient nature of the self), Tantric yoga, and union with the divine, Pickering moves far from topics that most transhumanists choose to discuss but with which I happen to be completely at home.

In addition to being a transhumanist academic, I am an ordained Soto Zen Buddhist priest [ZCLC, 2008]. I know what Pickering is talking about when he discusses Buddhism and other forms of Eastern spirituality. I am even familiar with the enneagram, which I learned in the same esoteric school as John Lilly, whom Pickering mentions.[9]

---

8   Michael LaTorra, "Trans-Spirit: Religion, Spirituality and Transhumanism," *Journal of Evolution and Technology* 14 (2005). http://www.jetpress.org/volume14/latorra. html. Robin Hanson, James Hughes, Michael LaTorra, David Brin and Giulio Prisco, "The Hanson-Hughes Debate On 'The Crack of a Future Dawn,'" *Journal of Evolution and Technology* 16 (2007). http://www.jetpress.org/v16/hanson.html.

9   Pickering, "The Science of the Unknowable: Stafford Beer's Cybernetic Informatics."

My experience of personal training and spiritual practice under the direction of qualified teachers—my very existence—puts the lie to Pickering's claim that transhumanists seek to "engineer . . . out of existence" all of the aforementioned extraordinary practices, performances, experiences, states, and conditions.[10]

Being Human or Just Being?

What does it mean to be human? Along with other transhumanists, I would prefer to put the question this way: what does it mean to be a conscious, thinking, sentient being? Stated this way, the question is much broader, and it does not discriminate on the basis of the body type, human, machine, or other.

If members of an intelligent extraterrestrial species were to travel through the vast distances of interstellar space and land on Earth, coming in peace and bearing gifts of knowledge and high technology, how should we greet them? Would we discriminate against them because they are not human, even though their level of technology and science far exceed our own? Or would we accept them (albeit cautiously at first) as fellow beings? If we would accept intelligent aliens as being on par with ourselves, why not accept transhuman cyborgs or posthuman beings of whatever sort if they were peaceful and benevolent?

Conclusion

Transhumanism is neither a threat nor a menace. It is the promise of a better future for us and for generations yet unborn. Accept the gifts it has to offer. Or at least allow others to do so. The freedom to grow is the freedom to transform. Transhumanism is the opportunity to transform life, liberty, and the pursuit of happiness beyond current human limits.

References

Bostrom, Nick. "Existential Risks: Analyzing Human Extinction Scenarios and Related Hazards," *Journal of Evolution and Technology* 9 (2002).

---

[10]   Michael LaTorra and Laozi, *A Warrior Blends with Life : A Modern Tao* (Berkeley, Calif.: North Atlantic Books, 1993). LaTorra, "Trans-Spirit: Religion, Spirituality and Transhumanism."

De Grey, Aubrey and Michael Rae. *Ending Aging: The Rejuvenation Breakthroughs That Could Reverse Human Aging in Our Lifetime.* 1st ed. New York: St. Martin's Press, 2007.

Hanson, Robin, et al. "The Hanson-Hughes Debate On 'The Crack of a Future Dawn.'" *Journal of Evolution and Technology* 16, no. 1 (2007): 99-126. http://www.jetpress.org/v16/hanson.html.

Hughes, James J. *Citizen Cyborg: Why Democratic Societies Must Respond to the Redesigned Human of the Future.* Boulder, CO: Westview Press, 2004.

LaTorra, Michael. "Trans-Spirit: Religion, Spirituality and Transhumanism." *Journal of Evolution and Technology* 14, no.1 (2005): 39-53.http://www.jetpress.org/volume14/latorra.html.

LaTorra, Michael, and Laozi. *A Warrior Blends with Life: A Modern Tao.* Berkeley, Calif.: North Atlantic Books, 1993.

More, Max. "The Diachronic Self: Identity, Continuity, Transformation." PhD diss., University of Southern California, 1995.

Pearce, D. "The Hedonistic Imperative." http://www.hedweb.com/hedab.htm.

Pickering, Andrew. "Brains, Selves and Spirituality in the History of Cybernetics." *The Global Spiral* 9, no. 3 (2008). http://www.metanexus.net/magazine/tabid/68/id/10545/Default.aspx.

Pickering, Andrew. "The Science of the Unknowable: Stafford Beer's Cybernetic Informatics." *Working Papers from Centre for STS Studies* (2006). http://webcache.googleusercontent.com/search?q=cache:1WDpMC8YxPAJ:sts.imv.au.dk/arbejdspapirer/WP6.pdf+%22Stafford+Beer%22+%22Tantric%22&hl=en&ct=clnk&cd=3&gl=us.

Roco, Mihail C., and William Sims Bainbridge. *Converging Technologies for Improving Human Performance: Nanotechnology, Biotechnology, Information Technology and Cognitive Science.* Dordrecht; Boston: Kluwer Academic Publishers, 2003.

Sandberg, A. Transhumanist Resources. http://www.aleph.se/Trans/index-2.html

Tirosh-Samuelson, Hava. "Facing the Challenges of Transhumanism." *The Global Spiral* 8, no. 7 (2007). http://www.metanexus.net/magazine/tabid/68/id/10169/Default.aspx.

Vita-More, Natasha. "Designing Human 2.0 (Transhuman), Äì Regenerative Existence." *Artifact* 2, no. 3 (2008): 145-52.

IV. H-: CRITICAL PERSPECTIVES ON TRANSHUMANISM

Chapter Fourteen

Wrestling with Transhumanism

by N. Katherine Hayles

Transhumanism for me is like a relationship with an obsessive and very neurotic lover. Knowing it is deeply flawed, I have tried several times to break off my engagement, but each time, it manages to creep in through the back door of my mind. In *How We Became Posthuman*,[1] I identified an undergirding assumption that makes possible such predictions as Hans Moravec's transhumanist fantasy that we will soon be able to upload our consciousness into computers and leave our bodies behind. I argued that this scenario depends on a decontextualized and disembodied construction of information. The disembodied information Claude Shannon formalized as a probability function, useful for specific purposes, has been expanded far beyond its original context and inappropriately applied to such phenomena as consciousness.[2] With this argument, I naively thought that I had dismissed transhumanism once and for all, exposing its misapprehensions to my satisfaction and delivering a decisive blow to its aspirations. But I was wrong. Transhumanism has exponentially more adherents today than it did a decade ago when I made this argument, and its influence is clearly growing rather than diminishing, as this essay collection itself testifies.

There are, of course, many versions of transhumanism, and they do not all depend on the assumption I critiqued. But all of them, I will argue, perform decontextualizing moves that oversimplify the situation and carry into the new millennium some of the most questionable aspects of capitalist ideology. Why

---

[1]   N. Katherine Hayles, *How We Became Posthuman: Virtual Bodies in Cybernetics, Literature, and Informatics* (Chicago, Ill.: University of Chicago Press, 1999).

[2]   Claude E. Shannon and Warren Weaver, *The Mathematical Theory of Communication* (Urbana: University of Illinois Press, 1949).

then is transhumanism appealing despite its problems? Most versions share the assumption that technology is involved in a spiraling dynamic of coevolution with human development. This assumption, known as technogenesis, seems to me compelling and indeed virtually irrefutable, applying not only to contemporary humans but also to *Homo sapiens* across the eons, shaping the species biologically, psychologically, socially, and economically. While I have serious disagreements with most transhumanist rhetoric, the transhumanist community is one that is fervently involved in trying to figure out where technogenesis is headed in the contemporary era and what it implies about our human future. This is its positive contribution, and from my point of view, why it is worth worrying about.

How can we extract the valuable questions transhumanism confronts without accepting all the implications of transhumanist claims? One possibility is to embed transhumanist ideas in deep, rich, and challenging contextualizations that reintroduce the complexities it strips away. The results reframe the questions, leading to conclusions very different from those most transhumanists embrace. In these encounters, transhumanism serves as the catalyst—or better, the irritant—that stimulates a more considered and responsible view of the future than it itself can generate.

As a literary scholar, I consider the locus classicus for reframing transhumanist questions to be science fiction and speculative fiction, jointly signified by "SF." To initiate my inquiry, I will focus on the critical area of reproduction: reproduction of individuals through children, reproduction of the species through technology as well as biology, and reproduction of psychological, philosophical, social, and economic institutions that facilitate and/or threaten the continued existence of humans as a species. To see why reproduction is at the center of transhumanist concerns, we need only consider the rhetoric of the *singularity*, a term introduced by SF writer and mathematician Vernon Vinge to indicate a decisive break in which advanced technology catapults us into a future qualitatively different from all previous human experience. Within a few years, Vinge predicts, we will confront a change comparable to the rise of life on earth: "the precise cause of this change is the imminent creation by technology of entities with greater than human intelligence."[3] So different will our future be, the story goes, that it is impossible for us accurately to predict it from our position on this side of the break. Insofar as reproduction implies continuities between past and future, it challenges the idea of a cataclysmic break while simultaneously acting as a privileged site for visions of radical ruptures and transformations. Reproduction, then, is where the rubber hits the road—where issues of what will change and what will endure are imagined, performed, and contested.

Before demonstrating that SF recontextualizes crucial issues surrounding reproduction, I will find it useful to review briefly the ideologies implicit in

---

[3]   Vernor Vinge, "The Singularity," http://kuoi.com/~kamikaze/doc/vinge.html.

transhumanist rhetoric. Transhumanism, sometimes signified by "<H" or "H+," is an international movement dedicated to the proposition that contemporary technosciences can enhance human capabilities and ameliorate or eliminate such traditional verities as mortality. It holds that human evolution is incomplete and that we have a responsibility to further our evolution through technology. As a sample of transhumanist rhetoric, consider the following passage from Max More, a prominent movement spokesperson:

> We seek to void all limits to life, intelligence, freedom, knowledge, and happiness. Science, technology and reason must be harnessed to our extropic values to abolish the greatest evil: death. Death does not stop the progress of intelligent beings considered collectively, but it obliterates the individual. No philosophy of life can be truly satisfying which glorifies the advance of intelligent beings and yet which condemns each and every individual to rot into nothingness. Each of us seeks growth and the transcendence of our current forms and limitations. The abolition of aging and, finally, all causes of death, is essential to any philosophy of optimism and transcendence relevant to the individual.[4]

Nick Bostrom, a philosopher at Oxford University and one of transhumanism's more thoughtful practitioners, gives a two-fold definition on the World Transhumanist Association Web site:

> (1) The intellectual and cultural movement that affirms the possibility and desirability of fundamentally improving the human condition through applied reason, especially by developing and making widely available technologies to eliminate aging and to greatly enhance human intellectual, physical, and psychological capacities. (2) The study of the ramifications, promises, and potential dangers of technologies that will enable us to overcome fundamental human limitations, and the related study of the ethical matters involved in developing and using such technologies.[5]

As these examples illustrate, transhumanist rhetoric concentrates on individual transcendence; at transhumanist Web sites, articles, and books, there is a conspicuous absence of considering socioeconomic dynamics beyond the individual. Bostrom,

---

4   Max More, "Transhumanism: Towards a Futurist Philosophy," http://www.maxmore. com/transhum.htm/.

5   Nick Bostrom, "What Is Transhumanism? FAQ," http://www.transhumanism.org/index. php/w/faq2.

for example, writes of "making widely available technologies to eliminate aging," but what this would do to population growth, limited resources, and the economics of the young supporting the old are not considered.

Transhumanists recognize, of course, that contemporary technoscience is not an individual enterprise, typically requiring significant capitalization, large teams of workers, and extensive networks of knowledge exchange and distribution, but these social, technoscientific, and economic realities are positioned as if they are undertaken for the sole benefit of forward-thinking individuals. In addition, there is little discussion of how access to advanced technologies would be regulated or of the social and economic inequalities entwined with questions of access. The rhetoric implies that everyone will freely have access (as in the quotation cited above), or at least that transhumanist individuals will be among the privileged elite that can afford the advantages advanced technologies will offer. How this will play out for the large majority of people living in developing countries that cannot afford access and do not have the infrastructure to support it is not an issue. Indeed, the rhetoric often assumes that, as Iain Banks puts in his transhumanist far-future novel *Look to Windward*,[6] the Age of Scarcity is a passing phase in human evolution that our descendants will leave far behind, with death, hunger, disease, and other afflictions brought under control and subject to the whim of individual choice.

Resisting these utopian visions are the sociological, philosophical, and psychological complexities (a constellation that Iain Banks has usefully called "metalogy"[7]) that operate, at their most fraught, with reproduction. Consistent with the transhumanist emphasis on the individual, reproduction typically figures in transhumanist rhetoric as the reproduction of the individual through cloning, cryogenic suspension, radical life extension, and uploading human consciousness into a computer. In all these versions, the rhetoric assumes that the individual will maintain his identity intact. As Hans Moravec's fantasy scenario of uploading consciousness in *Mind Children* makes clear, not only is identity preserved but the uploaded consciousness is also represented as seamlessly continuous with the embodied mind.[8] Whether a reproduced consciousness would in fact be identical (or even similar) is a point of intense interrogation in SF. In Greg Egan's *Permutation City*, for example, an uploaded consciousness finds the awareness that it has become a computer program unbearable, and all such consciousnesses commit suicide (or try to) within fifteen minutes of coming to awareness.[9]

---

[6] Iain Banks, *Look to Windward* (New York: Pocket Books, 2001).

[7] Iain Banks, *Look to Windward* (London: Orbit, 2000), 83."Metalogical . . . is short for psycho-physio-philosophical,"

[8] Hans P. Moravec, *Mind Children: The Future of Robot and Human Intelligence* (Cambridge, Mass.: Harvard University Press, 1988), 109-10.

[9] Greg Egan, *Permutation City* (London: Millennium, 1995).

Equally controversial are issues surrounding the reproduction of the species. Transhumanist rhetoric assumes that "we" will become citizens of a transhuman future, an assumption existing in uneasy tension with the decisive break implied by the singularity. Who or what will be left behind, and what global conflicts might result from class and economic disparities are seldom discussed. When such issues are entertained, as in Moravec's claim that intelligent machines will be our evolutionary successors and that we will embrace them as "mind children," the rhetoric implies that these silicon progeny will inspire the same emotional investment, love, and pride that (sometimes) accompanies biological reproduction. Whether deep-seated responses evolved through millennia of biological reproduction would map seamlessly onto intelligent machines created through entirely different mechanisms is typically not a concern.

The metalogical (i.e., the psychological, physiological, and philosophical) contextualizations SF performs draw thee assumptions into question. In Philip K. Dick's *Do Androids Dream of Electric Sheep?* the issues surrounding reproduction are enacted in multiple ways, including through the surrogacy of animal procreation.[10] Rick Deckard's argument with his neighbor about whether it is immoral to own more than one animal when others (like him) own none is precipitated by the neighbor's announcement that his Percheron mare is pregnant. A similar dialogue occurs when Deckard negotiates with Rachel Rosen for part of Scrappy the owl's brood—until he realizes that the owl is a mechanical replica, biological owls having been extinct for decades. These minor incidents serve as a backdrop to the major issue of human reproduction. Deckard dons a lead codpiece when he goes outside to protect his gonads from the radioactive dust that has covered the planet since World War Terminus. He undergoes regular testing and has so far managed to maintain a sperm count that allows him to be classified "normal" within the limits defined by law; but thousands fail each month as their reproductive (and intellectual) capacities plummet below the line, condemning them to the category of "specials," who are not allowed to emigrate off-planet and can look forward only to further decline. The biological reproductive future of humankind appears doomed; their evolutionary successors will clearly be the androids, now so sophisticated and intelligent that they already surpass human capabilities in many respects.

In sharp contrast to Moravec's vision of a humanity that embraces its postbiological successors, humans in Dick's novel cling to every possible vestige of superiority, however spurious, and ruthlessly oppress the androids, condemning them to lives of slavery in the hellish conditions of Mars and other off-world colonies. Humans will not, it appears, go gently into that good night. Ridley

---

10   Philip K. Dick, *Blade Runner*, 1st Ballantine Books ed. (New York: Ballantine, 1982). Originally published under the title, *Do Androids Dream of Electric Sheep?*

Scott's brilliant film adaptation[11] picks up on this theme, representing Roy Baty, leader of the rebellious androids, as the errant son of Tyrell, CEO of the company that created him and the other Nexus-6 androids. Although the androids do not manage to wrest a longer life span from their "father" and eventually are all killed, as they are in Dick's novel, the novel makes clear that this postbiological species will nevertheless triumph as humans fade from the scene, victims of their own environmental folly.

The empathic (and viciously competitive) bond in the film between father and postbiological child plays out differently in the novel, with empathy partitioned among species and alleged to be possible only with humans and animals, with androids positioned outside and exterior to this privileged emotion. This ideological configuration, promoted by the government as a justification for human superiority and android oppression, is confounded when Deckard realizes he feels empathy for at least some androids. The resulting ethical and psychological complexities entwine reproduction with political ideology, species identification with cross-species empathy, and the individual with global dynamics that dictate the outcome of the war, regardless of individual contests such as those waged by Deckard.

When the child is not an android but a biological progeny, the prospect of a transhuman future is, if possible, even more contentious. Novels exploring the parent-biological child relationship range from Arthur C. Clarke's *Childhood's End*,[12] in which the children become a successor species, to Vernon Vinge's near-future world in *Rainbows End*,[13] where the generations are separated only by technological expertise and quickness in adapting to it. At the passionate end of the spectrum is Greg Bear's *Darwin's Radio* and the sequel, *Darwin's Children*.[14] Rather than imagine a future in which technology creates a postbiological future, Bear speculates that the human genome can function as a nonconscious genetic engineer of sorts, responding to global factors such as "stress" by activating an ancient human endogenous virus (significantly nicknamed "SHEVA") that causes genetic mutations in fetuses. In ironic inversion of the AIDS virus, SHEVA infects only couples in monogamous committed relationships and has

---

[11]   Ridley Scott, Hampton Fancher, David Webb Peoples, Michael Deeley, Harrison Ford, Rutger Hauer, Sean Young, Edward James Olmos, M. Emmet Walsh, Daryl Hannah, Vangelis, Philip K. Dick, Warner Bros., Ladd Company, Nelson Entertainment (Firm) and Van Wert Collection (University of Pennsylvania), *Blade Runner*, videorecording, Nelson Entertainment [S.l.], 1982.

[12]   Arthur Charles Clarke, *Childhood's End* (New York: Ballantine Books, 1953).

[13]   Vernor Vinge, *Rainbows End*, 1st ed. (New York: Tor, 2006).

[14]   Greg Bear, *Darwin's Children*, 1st ed. (New York: Del Rey/Ballantine Books, 2003). Greg Bear, *Darwin's Radio*, 1st ed. (New York: Ballantine Pub. Group, 1999).

its epicenter in the U.S. and Europe, while Africa is not nearly as hard hit. With the threat looming close to home, emotional tensions are exacerbated when the mutational process causes a two-step pregnancy. The first fetus, initially mistaken as the virus's final product, is horribly malformed by conventional standards, with rudimentary appendages, a Cyclopean head formation, a functional ovary, and virtually no brain. It invariably aborts at the end of the first trimester, and images of the miscarried fetuses cause worldwide panic among pregnant women and their partners. The first fetus's purpose, it turns out, is to release an egg that initiates a second pregnancy without further fertilization from sperm. The emotional thumbscrews are tightened when male partners refuse to believe that their women could become pregnant for a second time without having sex with other men, and violence against women spikes worldwide. Further complicating these dynamics is the possibility, trumpeted by the dangerously ambitious governmental functionary Mark Augustine, that the SHEVA virus is activating other ancient retroviruses in the human genome, releasing a pandemic of diseases unknown for millennia. The resulting worldwide riots, corporate intrigue, and global panic lead to unprecedented crises in which the civil rights of SHEVA children and their parents are shredded.

Against this backdrop is set the drama of Mitch and Kaye, who knowingly have a SHEVA child, Stella Nova (the new species, they decide, should be named *Homo sapiens novus*). Stella evokes from them the traditional desire to protect, nurture, and love her, so the tension here is not so much between the parents and child as between the family unit and the society that fears, stigmatizes, and hunts them. Although Bear could be accused of sensationalism—insofar as he relies on the raw emotional impact of aborted fetuses, children born dead with monstrous deformities, and societal witch hunts—he nevertheless recognizes the inherent tensions, conflicts, and social upheavals that would be unleashed by the appearance of a new generation of children so superior to their parents that they will obviously be the successor species, spelling the eventual doom of *Homo sapiens sapiens*.

Perhaps the most explicit SF confrontation with transhumanist philosophy occurs in Nancy Kress's novella "Beggars in Spain," later expanded to a novel and a sequel. Kenzo Yagai is the text's philosopher-economist who serves as the fictional counterpart to Ayn Rand, often cited on transhumanist Web sites as one of the founding thinkers of the movement.[15] Initially infatuated

---

15   Ayn Rand, writer and philosopher, is the author of *The Fountainhead* (1947), *Atlas Shrugged* (1953), and with Nathaniel Branden, *The Virtue of Selfishness* (1954). Having read Ayn Rand myself in college, I assumed that she would be ancient history to today's college students, but I was surprised when most of my students (in a 100-person lecture class) had read her.

with Rand's extreme individualism, its concomitant ideology of free market capitalism unhampered by regulation, and a Darwinian survival-of-the-fittest, in which the fit are those who can most effectively exploit the free market, Kress became disenchanted with Rand's objectivist philosophy[16] and wrote "Beggars in Spain" in rebuttal.[17] In Yagaiist philosophy,[18] the contract freely entered into by individuals is seen as the basis for a good society, in part because it is an advance over social systems based on coercion. The premise is tested by embedding it in a reproductive context in which Roger Camden, self-made millionaire and confirmed Yagaiist, arranges for a genetic intervention that will yield a daughter (intelligent, blond, long-legged, attractive) who will not need to sleep. Unexpectedly, however, his wife (a bit player in Camden's life) conceives twins: Leisha, the engineered baby, is one of the Sleepless; while Alice is a "normal" child who requires sleep.

The matchup allows the effects of this seemingly minor genetic alteration— eliminating the need for sleep—to be explored and dramatized. While Alice progresses at the usual rate, Leisha, apple of her father's eye, zooms ahead of her

---

[16] Hans Persson and Tommy Persson, "Interview with Nancy Kress," http://www.lysator. liu.se/lsff/mb-nr28/Interview_with_Nancy_Kress.html. In "Interview with Nancy Kress," Carina Björklind asks Kress about Ayn Rand: "The thing about Ayn Rand, with whom I was enraptured when I was in my early twenties as so many people are, and who I eventually outgrew, as many people do, is that although there's something very appealing about her emphasis on individual responsibility, that you should not evade reality, you should not evade responsibility, you should not assume that it's up to the next person to provide you with your life . . . but . . . pushed to its really logical conclusion, objectivism, Ayn Rand's philosophy, lacks all compassion, and even more fundamental, it lacks recognition of the fact that we are a social species and that our society does not exist of a group of people only striving for their own ends . . . but groups of people co-operating for mutual ends, and this means that you don't always get what you want and your work does not always benefit you directly,"

[17] Nancy Kress, *Beggars in Spain* (New York: William Morrow, 1993) xii. In the preface to the novel version of *Beggars in Spain*, Nancy Kress writes that "I was nagged by the feeling that Leisha's story had only begun. I wanted to explore the long-range economic effects of creating a favored class of people in a United States becoming increasingly polarized between rich and poor. I also wanted to work out my reactions to other writers' philosophies: to Ayn Rand's belief that no human being owes anything to any other except what is agreed to in a voluntary contract."

[18] Nancy Kress, "Beggars in Spain," *The Best of the Best. Volume 2, 20 Years of the Best Short Science Fiction Novels*, ed. Gardner R. Dozois, 1st ed. (New York: St. Martin's Griffin, 2007).

twin intellectually. She is Camden's "special" (i.e., "real") daughter not only because he paid for her genetic alteration but also because she buys in wholeheartedly to her father's Yagaiist doctrine of individual achievement, allowing him to reproduce ideologically as well as genetically. As with other SF interventions, Kress does not allow the narrative to remain focused entirely on the individual but rather sketches a broader social context. The Sleepless form networks among themselves as they encounter increasing resentment and sanctions from the majority Sleepers, who contend that the Sleepless have unfair advantages because they have, in effect, 33 percent more time at their disposal in which to study, learn, and achieve. The social landscape in which Leisha grows up is rife with conflicts between "normal" humans and the transhuman Sleepless, who, as they grow up, prove to be not only highly intelligent and high achieving but also resistant to aging, with life expectancies measured in hundreds rather than decades of years. Already numbering in the hundred thousands, the Sleepless in a dozen generations appear to be on track to become the successor species to *Homo sapiens sapiens* (perhaps as *Homo sapiens sleepless*).

Despite the growing tensions, Leisha struggles to retain ties to Sleepers, including her sister Alice. The eponymous "beggars in Spain" represent a strong challenge to that desire. Her Sleepless friend Tony argues that high-achieving Sleepless have more to offer than Sleepers and, in the face of increasing prejudice against them, should withdraw to form their own society. He asks her if she would give money to a beggar in Spain; Leisha says yes. Then what about two beggars, three, a hundred, a thousand? The lesson Tony means to teach is to show that the basis for a shared society—that is, the contract that reciprocally benefits both participants—breaks down when those who have nothing to give outnumber those who have much to give, for any contract must then be unequal and hence unfair to the privileged.

Of course, there would be other ways to interpret the conundrum, for example, deciding that it shows the limitations of the contract as a basis for social interactions. This is the interpretation Leisha eventually chooses, replacing the contract and the individualistic ideology that underwrites it, with an "ecology of help" in which assistance is extended even to those who cannot reciprocate in kind. This modest intervention stops short of a wholesale critique of Rand's objectivism, however, for in this view, society is still based on exchanges between willing partners, with the modification that the exchange may be unequal and indirect, circling through a network before benefits are returned to the giver. That a system might be based on entirely different principles than exchange remains unthought and unarticulated. Despite this limitation, the story, poignantly conceived and skillfully written, shows that reproduction is deeply enmeshed with visions of a transhumanist future and the ethical and social issues it raises.

More startling in its probing implications is James Patrick Kelly's novella "Mr. Boy."[19] This fine example of SF grotesque inverts the usual perspective; rather than exploring the dynamics between a parent and transhuman child, it focuses on the tensions between a transhuman parent and child. The protagonist is a twenty-five-year-old male who, at his mother's behest, has his genes periodically "stunted" so that his body remains, emotionally and physically, that of a twelve-year-old boy. Situated in a posthuman future in which his constant companion is a robot and his best friend has had himself "twanked" so that he resembles a dinosaur, Mr. Boy inhabits the site of the mother—literally. She has had her body transformed into a three-quarter scale replica of the Statue of Liberty, and Mr. Boy resides within the multistory edifice. He communicates with his mother via her "remotes," robots that carry out specific functions indicated by their names, "Nanny," "Cook," "Greeter," and the sex couple, "Lovey" and "Dear," who express and perform Mom's erotic urges in a room wired to Liberty's head, presumably the site of her conscious (and unconscious) thoughts.

In this grotesque tale, life and death are systemically confused, each blending into and contaminating the other. Mr. Boy calls the hospital staff that oversee his stunting "stiffs," and his prized porn collection consists entirely of images of the dead—preferably with their teeth showing. While his friend Stennie practices for his first real-life romantic encounter with a girlfriend by having sex with "Lovey," Mr. Boy, who sets up the encounter with his mother's remote and watches while it proceeds, confesses, "I had always found sex kind of dull." Turning instead to his corpse porn, he associates the "soft wet slap of flesh against flesh" with "my mother's brain, up there in the head where no one ever went" (179). The mother is thus both eroticized and "boring," absent and present, permissive and imprisoning, presumably alive and yet inanimate. The conflicted and perverse contexts of reproduction represented here point to the ways in which advanced technology has been (mis)used to disrupt the age-old order of things: the mother, instead of watching her son grow up, intervenes to keep him forever on the child side of puberty; the man, trapped within a boy's body, finds excitement in the dead and is bored by procreation; the separation in which a man leaves his mother behind to find a mate is forestalled because he continues literally to live within his mother's body, as if still in the womb.

Weary of being stunted, Mr. Boy begins to see his life in a different perspective when he meets Tree, a young woman whose parents are "realists," hard-core resistors who reason that "first came clothes, then jewelry, fashion, makeup, plastic surgery, skin tints, and hey jack! here we are up to our eyeballs in the delusions of 2096 (172)," careening down the slippery slope to gene twanking and uploading consciousness into a computer. The irony of being trapped within Liberty comes to a head (so to

---

19   James Patrick Kelly, "Mr. Boy," *The Best of the Best. Volume 2, 20 Years of the Best Short Science Fiction Novels*, ed. Gardner R. Dozois, 1st ed. (New York: St. Martin's Griffin, 2007).

speak) when Mr. Boy discovers there is nothing in the head; his mother had died years ago and has been running her operation as an uploaded consciousness. After a final confrontation with Mom, Mr. Boy takes back his given name, "Peter," and finally leaves her, preferring to walk away rather than go through the court proceedings that would enable him to claim his family inheritance by declaring her legally dead, uploaders not being considered persons and so having no legal rights.

One need not agree with Francis Fukuyama that transhumanism is the "world's most dangerous idea" to appreciate the critiques of transhumanism enacted in these science fictions.[20] When advanced technologies come together with reproduction to reconfigure metalogical dynamics at every level, from the individual to the family to the nation-state and globalized society, it is impossible to predict accurately all the consequences or to trammel them up, as transhumanist rhetoric implies, using reason, technology, and science. As science fictions interrogated have shown, evolution has twisted together biology and culture in strands of enormous complexity, and cutting some strands of advanced technologies or rearranging them into patterns altogether different almost certainly will entail unanticipated consequences and corollary changes in other areas whose association with the primary changes were not even known. At issue are the emotional dynamics of population change as people confront the possibility that *Homo sapiens sapiens* may not be the terminus of evolutionary processes, of parents engendering children so different from them they can scarcely make contact over the generation gap, of children contemplating parents whose closely held assumptions are no longer viable in a posthuman future. Each of these scenarios involves complexities for which the transhumanist philosophy is simply not able to account or to understand, much less to explain. Reason is certainly needed, but so are emotion, systemic analysis, ecological thinking, and ethical consideration. As Pynchon's narrator in *Gravity's Rainbow* observes: "Everything is connected."

I do not necessarily agree with Fukuyama's argument that we should outlaw such developments as human cloning with legislation forbidding it (not least because he falls back on "human nature" as a justification), but I do think we should take advantage of every available resource that will aid us in thinking through, as far as we are able, the momentous changes in human life and culture that advanced technologies make possible—and these resources can and should include SF fictions. The framework in which transhumanism considers these questions is, I have argued, too narrow and ideologically fraught with individualism and neoliberal philosophy to be fully up to the task. It can best serve by catalyzing questions and challenging us to imagine fuller contextualizations for the developments it envisions. Imagining the future is never a politically innocent or ethically neutral act. To arrive at the future we want, we must first be able to imagine it as fully as we can, including all the contexts in which its consequences will play out.

---

[20]   Francis Fukuyama, "Transhumanism," *Foreign Policy* no. 144 (2004): 42-43.

REFERENCES

Banks, Iain. *Look to Windward*. New York: Pocket Books, 2001.

Banks, Iain. *Look to Windward*. London: Orbit, 2000.

Bear, Greg. *Darwin's Children*. 1st ed. New York: Del Rey/Ballantine Books, 2003.

Bear, Greg. *Darwin's Radio*. 1st ed. New York: Ballantine Pub. Group, 1999.

Bostrom, Nick. "What Is Transhumanism?: FAQ." http://www.transhumanism.org/index.php/w/faq2.

Clarke, Arthur Charles. *Childhood's End*. New York: Ballantine Books, 1953.

Dick, Philip K. *Blade Runner*. 1st Ballantine Books ed. New York: Ballantine, 1982.

Egan, Greg. *Permutation City*. London: Millennium, 1995.

Fukuyama, Francis. "Transhumanism." *Foreign Policy* no. 144 (2004): 42-43.

Hayles, N. Katherine. *How We Became Posthuman: Virtual Bodies in Cybernetics, Literature, and Informatics*. Chicago, Ill.: University of Chicago Press, 1999.

Kelly, James Patrick. "Mr. Boy." *The Best of the Best. Volume 2, 20 Years of the Best Short Science Fiction Novels*. Ed. Dozois, Gardner R. 1st ed. New York: St. Martin's Griffin, 2007: 158-203.

Kress, Nancy. *Beggars in Spain*. New York: William Morrow, 1993.

Kress, Nancy. "Beggars in Spain." *The Best of the Best. Volume 2, 20 Years of the Best Short Science Fiction Novels*. Ed. Dozois, Gardner R. 1st ed. New York: St. Martin's Griffin, 2007: 204-60.

Moravec, Hans P. *Mind Children: The Future of Robot and Human Intelligence*. Cambridge, Mass.: Harvard University Press, 1988.

More, Max. "Transhumanism: Towards a Futurist Philosophy." http://www.maxmore.com/transhum.htm/.

Persson, Hans, and Tommy Persson. "Interview with Nancy Kress." http://www.lysator.liu.se/lsff/mb-nr28/Interview_with_Nancy_Kress.html.

Scott, Ridley, et al. *Blade Runner*. Perf. Harrison Ford, Rutger Hauer, Sean Young, Edward James Olmos, M. Emmet Walsh, Daryl Hannah. Videorecording. Nelson Entertainment [S.l.], 1982.

Shannon, Claude Elwood, and Warren Weaver. *The Mathematical Theory of Communication*. Urbana: University of Illinois Press, 1949.

Vinge, Vernor. *Rainbows End*. 1st ed. New York: Tor, 2006.

Vinge, Vernor. "The Singularity." http://kuoi.com/~kamikaze/doc/vinge.html.

Chapter Fifteen

Cybernetics Is Antihumanism: Advanced Technologies and the Rebellion Against the Human Condition

by Jean-Pierre Dupuy

FOREWORD

I chose the topic of my contribution after I discovered, first with amazement, then with wonder, N. Katherine Hayles's beautiful book *How We Became Posthuman: Virtual Bodies in Cybernetics, Literature, and Informatics*.[1] Amazement because she and I worked on the same fairly confidential corpus, in particular the proceedings of the Macy conferences, which were the birthplace of cybernetics and, I have claimed, of cognitive science; we celebrate the same heroes, in particular Warren McCulloch, Heinz von Foerster, and Francisco Varela; and, in spite of these shared interests and passions, we apparently never heard of each other. She and I live and work worlds and languages apart. The world is still far from being a close-knit village. Wonder at realizing how from the same corpus we could arrive at interpretations that, although compatible or even complementary, are so richly diverse or even divergent.

My book on the Macy conferences and the origins of cybernetics and cognitive science, *Sur l'origine des sciences cognitives*, was first published in French in 1985;[2]

---

[1]   N. Katherine Hayles, *How We Became Posthuman: Virtual Bodies in Cybernetics, Literature, and Informatics* (Chicago, Ill.: University of Chicago Press, 1999).

[2]   Jean-Pierre Dupuy, *L'essor de la première cybernétique (1943-1953)*, Paris, Ecole Polytechnique, Cahiers du CREA, 7, 1985.

a second and completely revised edition followed in 1994;[3] the first English-language edition, an extensively revised and amplified version of the latter, came out in 2000.[4] It is with shame that I acknowledge that during all this time, I never came across Ms. Hayles's work, published in book form in 1999. It is with great sadness that I realize that there is no longer any way that I could ask my two great friends, Heinz von Foerster and Francisco Varela, two men of communication, why they never put us in touch. The Chilean neurophilosopher Francisco Varela was the cofounder of the theory of autopoietic systems; he chose to come to France and work in my research institution after he was expelled from his country. Heinz von Foerster, a Viennese Jewish immigrant to the United States, after serving as secretary to the Macy conferences, went on to found what was to be called second-order cybernetics. Francisco and Heinz play important roles in the story that I tell in my book. The former passed away in 2000, the latter in 2002. I miss them both terribly.

My book seeks to disabuse readers of a number of ideas that I consider mistaken. Cybernetics calls to mind a series of familiar images that turn out on closer inspection to be highly doubtful. As the etymology of the word suggests, cybernetics is meant to signify control, mastery, governance—in short, the philosophical project associated with Descartes, who assigned mankind the mission of exercising dominion over the world and over mankind itself. Within the cybernetics movement, this view was championed by Norbert Wiener—unsurprisingly, perhaps, since it was Wiener who gave it its name. But this gives only a very partial, if not superficial, idea of what cybernetics was about, notwithstanding that even a philosopher of such penetrating insight as Heidegger was taken in by it.

In my work, I have relied on the notion, due to Karl Popper, of a *metaphysical research program*, which is to say a set of presuppositions about the structure of the world that are neither testable nor empirically falsifiable, but without which no science would be possible. For there is no science that does not rest on metaphysics, though typically it remains concealed. It is the responsibility of the philosopher to uncover this metaphysics and then to subject it to criticism. What I have tried to show is that cybernetics, far from being the apotheosis of Cartesian humanism, as Heidegger supposed, actually represented a crucial moment in its demystification and indeed in its deconstruction. To borrow a term that has been applied to the structuralist movement in the human sciences, cybernetics constituted a decisive step in the rise of *antihumanism*. Consider, for example, the way in

---

3   Jean-Pierre Dupuy, Aux origines des sciences cognitives, Paris, La Découverte, 1994.

4   Jean-Pierre Dupuy, The Mechanization of the Mind (Princeton: Princeton University Press, 2000). A revised paperback edition has been published by the MIT Press under the title On the Origins of Cognitive Science. The Mechanization of the Mind (2010).

which cybernetics conceived the relationship between man and machine. The philosophers of consciousness were not alone in being caught up in the trap set by a question such as "will it be possible one day to design a machine that thinks?" The cybernetician's answer, rather in the spirit of Molière, was "Madame, you pride yourself so on thinking. And yet, you are only a machine!" The aim of cognitive science always was—and still is today—the mechanization of the mind, not the humanization of the machine.

"Continental" political philosophy has yet to acknowledge the notion of posthumanism. On the other hand, the notion of antihumanism has been debated for at least four decades. My contribution will bear on the latter only. My hope is that our workshop will enable us to explore the possible connections between the two notions and, beyond, perhaps bridge the gap between two cultural worlds so far apart.

1. HEIDEGGER'S ERROR

I will start with a classic question: can the idea that we have of the human person, which is to say, of ourselves, survive the forward march of scientific discovery? It is a commonplace that from Copernicus to molecular biology, and from Marx to Freud along the way, we have had steadily to abandon our proud view of ourselves as occupying a special place in the universe and to admit that we are at the mercy of determinisms that leave little room for what we have been accustomed to consider our freedom and our reason. Is not cognitive science now in the process of completing this process of disillusionment and demystification by showing us that just where we believe we sense the workings of a mind, there is only the firing of neural networks, no different in principle than an ordinary electric circuit? The task in which I have joined with many others, faced with reductive interpretations of scientific advance of this sort, has been to defend the values proper to the human person, or, to put it more bluntly, to defend humanism against the excesses of science and technology.

Heidegger completely inverted this way of posing the problem. For him it was no longer a question of defending humanism but rather of indicting it. As for science and technology, or rather "technoscience" (an expression meant to signify that science is subordinated to the practical ambition of achieving mastery over the world through technology), far from threatening human values, they are in Heidegger's view the most striking manifestation of them. This dual reversal is so remarkable that it deserves to be considered in some detail, even—or above all—in a reflection on the place of cybernetics in the history of ideas, for it is precisely cybernetics that found itself to be the principal object of Heidegger's attack.

In those places where Heideggerian thought has been influential, it became impossible to defend human values against the claims of science. This was particularly true in France, where structuralism—and then poststructuralism—reigned supreme over the intellectual landscape for several decades before taking refuge in the literature departments of American universities. Anchored in the thought of the three great Germanic "masters of suspicion"—Marx, Nietzsche, and Freud—against a common background of Heideggerianism, the human sciences à la française made antihumanism their watchword,[5] loudly celebrating exactly what humanists dread: the death of man. This unfortunate creature, or rather a certain image that man created of himself, was reproached for being "metaphysical." With Heidegger, "metaphysics" acquired a new and quite special sense, opposite to its usual meaning. For positivists ever since Comte, the progress of science had been seen as forcing the retreat of metaphysics; for Heidegger, by contrast, technoscience represented the culmination of metaphysics. And the height of metaphysics was nothing other than cybernetics.

Let us try to unravel this tangled skein. For Heidegger, metaphysics is the search for an ultimate foundation for all reality, for a "primary being" in relation to which all other beings find their place and purpose. Where traditional metaphysics (ontotheology) had placed God, modern metaphysics substituted man. This is why modern metaphysics is fundamentally humanist, and humanism fundamentally metaphysical. Man is a subject endowed with consciousness and will: his features were described at the dawn of modernity in the philosophy of Descartes and Leibniz. As a conscious being, he is present and transparent to himself; as a willing being, he causes things to happen as he intends. Subjectivity, both as theoretical presence to oneself and as practical mastery over the world, occupies center stage in this scheme—whence the Cartesian promise to make man "master and possessor of nature." In the metaphysical conception of the world, Heidegger holds: everything that exists is a slave to the purposes of man; everything becomes an object of his will, fashionable as a function of his ends and desires. The value of things depends solely on their capacity to help man realize his essence, which is to achieve mastery over being. It thus becomes clear why technoscience, and cybernetics in particular, may be said to represent the completion of metaphysics. To contemplative thought—thought that poses the question of meaning and of being, understood as the sudden appearance of things, which escapes all attempts at grasping it—Heidegger opposes "calculating" thought. This latter type is characteristic of all forms of planning that seek to attain ends by taking circumstances into account. Technoscience, insofar as it constructs mathematical models to better establish its mastery over the causal organization of the world, knows only calculating thought. Cybernetics is precisely that which calculates—computes—in order to govern, in

---

[5]   This point is clearly established by Luc Ferry and Alain Renaut, *French Philosophy of the Sixties: An Essay on Antihumanism*, trans. Mary H. S. Cattani, (Amherst, NY: University of Massachusetts Press, 1990).

the nautical sense (Wiener coined the term from the Greek *xvbepvntns*, meaning "steersman"): it is indeed the height of metaphysics.

Heidegger anticipated the objection that would be brought against him: "Because we are speaking against humanism people fear a defense of the inhuman and a glorification of barbaric brutality. For what is more *logical* than that for somebody who negates humanism nothing remains but the affirmation of inhumanity?"[6] Heidegger defended himself by attacking. Barbarism is not to be found where one usually looks for it. The true barbarians are the ones who are supposed to be humanists, who, in the name of the dignity that man accords himself, leave behind them a world devastated by technology, a desert in which no one can truly be said to dwell.

Let us for the sake of argument grant the justice of Heidegger's position. At once an additional enigma presents itself. If for him cybernetics really represented the apotheosis of metaphysical humanism, how are we to explain the fact that the human sciences in France, whose postwar development I have just said can be understood only against the background of Heidegger's philosophy, availed themselves of the conceptual toolkit of cybernetics in order to deconstruct the metaphysics of subjectivity? How is it that these sciences, in their utter determination to put man as subject to death, each seeking to outdo the other's radicalism, should have found in cybernetics the weapons for their assaults?

From the beginning of the 1950s—which is to say, from the end of the first cybernetics—through the 1960s and 1970s, when the second cybernetics was investigating theories of self-organization and cognitivism was on the rise, the enterprise of mechanizing the human world underwent a parallel development on each side of the Atlantic. This common destiny was rarely noticed, perhaps because the thought of any similarity seemed almost absurd: whereas cognitive science claimed to be the avant-garde of modern science, structuralism—followed by poststructuralism—covered itself in a pretentious and often incomprehensible philosophical jargon. What is more, it was too tempting to accuse French deconstructionists of a fascination with mathematical concepts and models that they hardly understood. But even if this way of looking at the matter is not entirely unjustified, it only scratches the surface. There were very good reasons, in fact, why the deconstruction of metaphysical humanism found in cybernetics an ally of the first order.

At the beginning of the 1940s, a philosopher of consciousness such as Sartre could write, "The inhuman is merely . . . the mechanical."[7] Structuralists hastened

---

6   Martin Heidegger, "Letter on Humanism," in *Basic Writings*, ed. David Farrell Krell (New York, Harper and Row, 1977), 225.

7   This phrase is found in the review Sartre wrote in 1943 of Albert Camus's *The Stranger*, "Explications de *l'Etranger*," reprinted in Critiques littéraires (*Situations I*), (Paris, Gallimard, 1947); available in English in *Literary and Philosophical Essays*, trans. Annette Michelson (New York: Criterion Books, 1955).

to adopt this definition as their own while reversing the value assigned to its terms. Doing Heidegger one better, they made a great show of championing the inhuman—which is to say the mechanical.[8] Cybernetics, as it happened, was ready to hand, having come along at just the right moment to demystify the voluntary and conscious subject. The will? All its manifestations could apparently be simulated, and therefore duplicated, by a simple negative feedback mechanism. Consciousness? The "Cybernetics Group"[9] had examined the Freudian unconscious, whose existence was defended by one of its members, Lawrence Kubie, and found it chimerical. If Kubie often found himself the butt of his colleagues' jokes, it was not because he was thought to be an enemy of human dignity. It was rather because the postulation of a hidden entity, located in the substructure of a purportedly conscious subject, manifesting itself only through symptoms while yet being endowed with the essential attributes of the subject (intentionality, desires, beliefs, presence to oneself, and so on), seemed to the cyberneticians nothing more than a poor conjuring trick aimed at keeping the structure of subjectivity intact.

It is remarkable that a few years later the French psychoanalyst Jacques Lacan, along with the anthropologist Claude Lévi-Strauss and the Marxist philosopher Louis Althusser (one of the founders of structuralism), should have adopted the same critical attitude toward Freud as cybernetics. The father of psychoanalysis had been led to postulate an improbable "death wish"—"beyond the pleasure principle," as he put it—as if the subject actually desired the very thing that made him suffer, by voluntarily and repeatedly placing himself in situations from which he could only emerge battered and hurt. This compulsion (*Zwang*) to repeat failure Freud called *Wiederholungszwang*, an expression translated by Lacan as *automatisme de répétition*, which is to say the "*automatism* of repetition." In so doing he replaced the supposed unconscious death wish with the senseless functioning of a machine, the unconscious henceforth being identified with a cybernetic automaton. The alliance of psychoanalysis and cybernetics was neither anecdotal nor fortuitous: it corresponded to a radicalization of the critique of metaphysical humanism.

There was a deeper reason for the encounter between the French *sciences de l'homme* and cybernetics, however. What structuralism sought to conceive—in the anthropology of Lévi-Strauss, for example, and particularly in his study of systems of exchange in traditional societies—was a subjectless cognition, indeed cognition without mental content. Whence the project of making "symbolic thought" a mechanism peculiar not to individual brains but to "unconscious" linguistic structures that automatically operate behind the back, as it were, of unfortunate

---

[8]   "To render philosophy inhuman"—thus the task Jean-François Lyotard set himself in 1984.

[9]   This expression is borrowed from Steve Heims's indispensable book, *The Cybernetics Group* (Cambridge, Mass.: MIT Press, 1991).

human "subjects," who are no more than a sort of afterthought. "It thinks" was destined to take the place once and for all of the Cartesian cogito. Now cognition without a subject was exactly the unlikely configuration that cybernetics seemed to have succeeded in conceiving. Here again the encounter between cybernetics and structuralism was in no way accidental. It grew out of a new intellectual necessity whose sudden emergence appears in retrospect as an exceptional moment in the history of ideas.

2. THE SELF-MECHANIZED MIND

It is time to come back to our enigma, which now may be formulated as a paradox. Was cybernetics the height of metaphysical humanism, as Heidegger maintained, or was it the height of its deconstruction, as certain of Heidegger's followers believe? To this question I believe it is necessary to reply that cybernetics was both things at once, and that this is what made it not only the root of cognitive science, which finds itself faced with the same paradox - but also a turning point in the history of human conceptions of humanity. The title I have given to this section—the self-mechanized mind—appears to have the form of a self-referential statement, not unlike those strange loops the cyberneticians were so crazy about, especially the cyberneticians of the second phase. But this is only an appearance: the mind that carries out the mechanization, and the one that is the object of it are two distinct (albeit closely related) entities, like the two ends of a seesaw, the one rising ever higher in the heavens of metaphysical humanism as the other descends further into the depths of its deconstruction. In mechanizing the mind, in treating it as an artifact, the mind presumes to exercise power over this artifact to a degree that no psychology claiming to be scientific has ever dreamed of attaining. The mind can now hope not only to manipulate this mechanized version of itself at will, but also to reproduce and manufacture it in accordance with its own wishes and intentions. Accordingly, the technologies of the mind, present and future, open up a vast continent upon which man now has to impose norms if he wishes to give them meaning and purpose. The human subject will therefore need to have recourse to a supplementary endowment of will and conscience in order to determine, not what he can do, but what he ought to do—or, rather, what he ought not to do. These new technologies will require a whole set of ethics to be elaborated, ethics not less demanding than those that are slowly being devised today in order to control the rapid development and unforeseen consequences of new biotechnologies. But to speak of ethics, conscience, the will—is this not to speak of the triumph of the subject?

The connection between the mechanization of life and the mechanization of the mind is plain. Even if the Cybernetics Group snubbed biology, to the great displeasure of John von Neumann, it was of course a cybernetic metaphor that enabled molecular biology to formulate its central dogma: the genome operates like a computer program. This metaphor is surely not less false than the analogous metaphor that structures the cognitivist paradigm. The theory of biological self-organization, first opposed to the cybernetic paradigm during the Macy conferences before later being adopted by the second cybernetics as its principal model, furnished then—and still furnishes today—decisive arguments against the legitimacy of identifying DNA with a "genetic program." Nonetheless—and this is the crucial point—even though this identification is profoundly illegitimate from both a scientific and a philosophical point of view, its technological consequences have been considerable. Today, as a result, man may be inclined to believe that he is the master of his own genome. Never, one is tempted to say, has he been so near to realizing the Cartesian promise: he has become—or is close to becoming—the master and possessor of all of nature up to and including himself.

Must we then salute this as yet another masterpiece of metaphysical humanism? It seems at first altogether astonishing, though after a moment's reflection perfectly comprehensible, that a German philosopher following in the tradition of Nietzsche and Heidegger, Peter Sloterdijk, should have recently come forward, determined to take issue with the liberal humanism of his country's philosophical establishment, and boldly affirmed that the new biotechnologies sound the death knell for the era of humanism. Unleashing a debate the like of which is hardly imaginable in any other country, this philosopher ventured to assert: "The domestication of man by man is the great unimagined prospect in the face of which humanism has looked the other way from antiquity until the present day." And to prophesy:

> It suffices to clearly understand that the next long periods of history will be periods of choice as far as the [human] species is concerned. Then it will be seen if humanity, or at least its cultural elites, will succeed in establishing effective procedures for self-domestication. It will be necessary, in the future, to forthrightly address the issue and formulate a code governing anthropological technologies. Such a code would modify, a posteriori, the meaning of classical humanism, for it would show that *humanitas* consists not only in the friendship of man with man, but that it also implies . . . , in increasingly obvious ways, that man represents the supreme power for man.[10]

But why should this "superhuman" power of man over himself be seen, in Nietzschean fashion, as representing the death of humanism rather than its apotheosis?

---

[10] Peter Sloterdijk, "On the Rules of the Human Fleet" (paper delivered at a conference on Heidegger at Elmau Castle, Upper Bavaria, July 17, 1999, and presented as a reply to Heidegger's "Letter on Humanism").

For man to be able, as subject, to exercise a power of this sort over himself, it is first necessary that he be reduced to the rank of an object, able to be reshaped to suit any purpose. No rising can occur without a concomitant lowering, and vice versa.

Let us come back to cybernetics and, beyond that, to cognitive science. We need to consider more closely the paradox that an enterprise that sets itself the task of naturalizing the mind should have as its spearhead a discipline that calls itself artificial intelligence. To be sure, the desired naturalization proceeds via mechanization. Nothing about this is inconsistent with a conception of the world that treats nature as an immense computational machine. Within this world man is just another machine—no surprise there. But in the name of what, or of whom, will man, thus artificialized, exercise his increased power over himself? In the name of this very blind mechanism with which he is identified? In the name of a meaning that he claims is mere appearance or phenomenon? His will and capacity for choice are now left dangling over the abyss. The attempt to restore mind to the natural world that gave birth to it ends up exiling the mind from the world and from nature. This paradox is typical of what the French sociologist Louis Dumont, in his magisterial study of the genesis of modern individualism, called

> the model of modern artificialism in general, the systematic application of an extrinsic, imposed value to the things of the world. Not a value drawn from our belonging to the world, from its harmony and our harmony with it, but a value rooted in our heterogeneity in relation to it: the identification of our will with the will of God (Descartes: man makes himself master and possessor of nature). The will thus applied to the world, the end sought, the motive and the profound impulse of the will are [all] foreign. In other words, they are extra-worldly. Extra-worldliness is now concentrated in the individual will.[11]

The paradox of the naturalization of the mind attempted by cybernetics, and today by cognitive science, then, is that the mind has been raised up as a demigod in relation to itself.

Many of the criticisms brought against the materialism of cognitive science from the point of view either of a philosophy of consciousness or a defense of humanism miss this paradox. Concentrating their (often justified) attacks on the weaknesses and naïveté of such a mechanist materialism, they fail to see that it invalidates itself by placing the human subject outside of the very world to which he is said to belong. The recent interest shown by cognitive science in what it regards as the "mystery" of consciousness seems bound to accentuate this blindness.

---

[11]   Louis Dumont, *Essays on Individualism: Modern Ideology in Anthropological Perspective* (Chicago: University of Chicago Press, 1986).

3. THE NANOTECHNOLOGICAL DREAM

I want now to broach not so much the intellectual evolution of cognitive science itself as its embodiment by new technologies, or, as one should rather say, its instantiation by ideas for new technologies. For the moment at least these technologies exist only as projects, indeed in some cases, only as dreams. But no matter that many such dreams will acquire physical reality sooner or later, the simple fact that they already exist in people's minds affects how we see the world and how we see ourselves.

Since my book was first published, I have thought a great deal about the philosophical foundations of what is called the NBIC convergence—the convergence of nanotechnology, biotechnology, information technology, and cognitive science—and about the ethical implications of this development.[12] Here I have found many of the same tensions, contradictions, paradoxes, and confusions that I discerned first within cybernetics, and then within cognitive science. But now the potential consequences are far more serious because we are not dealing with a theoretical matter, a certain view of the world, but with an entire program for acting upon nature and mankind.

In searching for the underlying metaphysics of this program, I did not have far to look. One of the first reports of the National Science Foundation devoted to the subject, entitled "Converging Technologies for Improving Human Performance," summarizes the credo of the movement in a sort of haiku:

> If the Cognitive Scientists can think it,
> The Nano people can build it,
> The Bio people can implement it, and
> The IT people can monitor and control it.[13]

---

[12]   See Jean-Pierre Dupuy, "Some Pitfalls in the Philosophical Foundations of Nanoethics," *Journal of Medicine and Philosophy* 32, no. 3 (2007): 237-261; Jean-Pierre Dupuy, "Complexity and Uncertainty: A Prudential Approach to Nanotechnology," in John Weckert et al., eds., *Nanoethics: Examining the Social Impact of Nanotechnology* (Hoboken, N.J.: John Wiley and Sons, 2007), 119-131; Jean-Pierre Dupuy, "The double language of science, and why it is so difficult to have a proper public debate about the nanotechnology program," Foreword to Fritz Allhoff and Patrick Lin, eds., *Nanoethics: Emerging Debates* (Dordrecht: Springer, 2008); and Jean-Pierre Dupuy and Alexei Grinbaum, "Living with Uncertainty: Toward a Normative Assessment of Nanotechnology," *Techné* (joint issue with *Hyle)* 8, no. 2 (2004): 4-25.

[13]   Mihail C. Roco and William Sims Bainbridge, *Converging Technologies for Improving Human Performance: Nanotechnology, Biotechnology, Information Technology, and Cognitive Science* (Washington, D.C.: National Science Foundation, 2002), 13.

Note that cognitive science plays the leading role in this division of labor, that of thinker—not an insignificant detail, for it shows that the metaphysics of NBIC convergence is embedded in the work of cognitive scientists. It comes as no surprise, then, that the contradictions inherent in cognitive science should be found at the heart of the metaphysics itself.

One of the main themes of my book is the confrontation between Norbert Wiener and John von Neumann: Wiener embodying the ideas of control, mastery, and design; von Neumann the ideas of complexity and self-organization. Cybernetics never succeeded in resolving the tension, indeed the contradiction, between these two perspectives; more specifically, it never managed to give a satisfactory answer to the problems involved in realizing its ambition of *designing* an autonomous, self-organizing machine. Nanotechnology—whose wildest dream is to reconstruct the natural world that has been given to us, atom by atom—is caught up in the same contradiction.

The most obvious element of the nanotechnological dream is to substitute for what François Jacob called bricolage, or the tinkering of biological evolution, a paradigm of *design*. Damien Broderick, the Australian cultural theorist and popular science writer, barely manages to conceal his contempt for the world that human beings have inherited when he talks about the likelihood that "nanosystems, designed by human minds, will bypass all this Darwinian wandering, and leap straight to *design success*."[14] One can hardly fail to note the irony that science, which in America has had to engage in an epic struggle to root out every trace of creationism (including its most recent avatar, "intelligent design") from public education, should now revert to a logic of design in the form of the nanotechnology program—the only difference being that now it is mankind that assumes the role of the demiurge.

Philosophers, faced with the ambition of emerging technologies to supersede nature and life as the engineers of evolution, the designers of biological and natural processes, may suppose that they are dealing with an old idea: Descartes' vision of science as the means by which man may become the master and possessor of nature. Again, however, this is only part of a larger and more complicated picture. As another influential visionary, the American applied physicist Kevin Kelly revealingly remarked, "It took us a long time to realize that the power of a technology is proportional to its inherent *out-of-controlness*, its inherent ability to surprise and be generative. In fact, unless we can worry about a technology, it is not revolutionary enough."[15] With NanoBioConvergence, a novel conception of engineering has indeed been introduced. The engineer, far from seeking mastery over nature, is now meant to feel that his enterprise will be crowned by success

---

[14]   Damien Broderick, *The Spike: How Our Lives Are Being Transformed by Rapidly Advancing Technologies* (New York: Forge, 2001), 118.

[15]   See Kevin Kelly, "Will Spiritual Robots Replace Humanity by 2100?" in *The Technium,* a work in progress, http://www.kk.org/thetechnium.

only to the extent that the system component he has created is capable of surprising him. For whoever wishes ultimately to create a self-organizing system—another word for life—is bound to attempt to reproduce its essential property, namely, the ability to make something that is radically new.

In her masterful study of the perils facing mankind, *The Human Condition* (1958), of which we are celebrating the fiftieth anniversary, Hannah Arendt brought out the fundamental paradox of our age: whereas the power of mankind to alter its environment goes on increasing under the stimulus of technological progress, less and less do we find ourselves in a position to control the consequences of our actions. I take the liberty of giving a long quotation here whose pertinence to the subject at hand cannot be exaggerated—keeping in mind, too, that these lines were written fifty years ago:

> To what extent we have begun to *act into nature*, in the literal sense of the word, is perhaps best illustrated by a recent casual remark of a scientist [Wernher von Braun, December 1957] who quite seriously suggested that "*basic research is when I am doing what I don't know what I am doing.*"

> This started harmlessly enough with the experiment in which men were no longer content to observe, to register, and contemplate whatever nature was willing to yield in her own appearance, but began to prescribe conditions and to provoke natural processes. What then developed into an ever-increasing skill in *unchaining elemental processes*, which, without the interference of men, would have lain dormant and perhaps never have come to pass, has finally ended in a veritable art of "*making*" nature, that is, of creating "natural" processes which without men would never exist and which earthly nature by herself seems incapable of accomplishing . . . .

> [N]atural sciences have become exclusively sciences of process and, in their last stage, *sciences of potentially irreversible, irremediable "processes of no return"* . . . [16]

The sorcerer's apprentice myth must therefore be updated: it is neither by error nor terror that mankind will be dispossessed of its own creations, but by *design*—which henceforth is understood to signify not mastery, but nonmastery and out-of-controlness.

---

[16]   Hannah Arendt, *The Human Condition* (Chicago: University of Chicago Press, 1958), 231.

4. THE REBELLION AGAINST THE HUMAN CONDITION

Arendt began the same, decidedly prescient book with the following words:

> The human artifice of the world separates human existence from all mere animal environment, but life itself is outside this artificial world, and through life man remains related to all other living organisms. For some time now, a great many scientific endeavors have been directed toward making life also "artificial," toward cutting the last tie through which even man belongs among the children of nature . . . .

> This future man, whom the scientists tell us they will produce in no more than a hundred years, seems to be possessed by a *rebellion against human existence* as it has been given, a free gift from nowhere (secularly speaking), which he wishes to exchange, as it were, for something he has made himself.[17]

The nanotechnological dream that began to take shape only a few decades after the utterance of Arendt's prophesy amounts to exactly this revolt against the finiteness, the mortality of the human condition. Human life has an end, for it is promised to death. But not only do the champions of NBIC convergence oppose themselves to fate by promising immortality; they quarrel with the very fact that we are born. Their revolt against the given is therefore something subtler and less visible, something still more fundamental, than the revolt against human mortality, for it rejects the notion that we should be brought into the world for no reason.

"Human beings are ashamed to have been born instead of made." Thus the German philosopher Günther Anders (Arendt's first husband and himself a student of Heidegger) characterized the essence of the revolt against the given in his great book, published in 1956, *Die Antiquiertheit des Menschen*—The Antiquatedness (or Obsolescence) of the Human Being.[18] One cannot help recalling here another philosophical emotion: the nausea described by Jean-Paul Sartre, that sense of forlornness that takes hold of human beings when they realize that they are not the foundation of their own being. The human condition is ultimately one of freedom; but freedom, being absolute, runs up against the obstacle of its own contingency, for we are free to choose anything except the condition of being *un*free. Discovering that we have been *thrown* into the world without any reason, we feel abandoned.

---

[17] Ibid., 2-3.

[18] Günther Anders, *Die Antiquiertheit des Menschen: über die Seele im Zeitalter der zweiten industriellen Revolution*, vol. 1 (Munich: Beck, 1980), 21-97.

Sartre acknowledged his debt to Günther Anders in expressing this idea by means of a phrase that was to become famous: man is "to freedom condemned."[19]

Freedom, Sartre held, never ceases trying to "nihilate" that which resists it. Mankind will therefore do everything it can to become its own maker - to owe its freedom to no one but itself. But only things are what they are; only things coincide with themselves. Freedom, on the other hand, is a mode of being that never coincides with itself since it ceaselessly projects itself into the future, desiring to be what it is not. Self-coincidence is what freedom aspires to and cannot attain, just as a moth is irresistibly attracted to the flame that will consume it. A *metaphysical self-made man,* were such a being possible, would paradoxically have lost his freedom, and indeed would no longer be a man at all, since freedom necessarily entails the impossibility of transforming itself into a thing. Thus, Anders's notion of "Promethean shame" leads inexorably to the obsolescence of man.

Had they lived to see the dawn of the twenty-first century, Sartre and Anders would have found this argument resoundingly confirmed in the shape of the NBIC convergence—a Promethean project, if ever there was one. For the aim of this distinctively metaphysical program is to place mankind in the position of being the divine maker of the world, the demiurge, while at the same time condemning human beings to see themselves as out of date.

At the heart of the nanotechnological dream, we therefore encounter a paradox that has been with us since the cybernetic chapter in the philosophical history of cognitive science—an extraordinary paradox arising from the convergence of opposites, whereby the overweening ambition and pride of a certain scientific humanism leads directly to the obsolescence of mankind. It is in the light, or perhaps I should say the shadow, of this paradox that all "ethical" questions touching on the engineering of mankind by mankind must be considered.

5. "PLAYING GOD" VERSUS THE BLURRING OF FUNDAMENTAL DISTINCTIONS

In 1964, Norbert Wiener published an odd book with the curious title *God and Golem, Inc.: A Comment on Certain Points where Cybernetics Impinges on Religion.* In it one finds this:

> God is supposed to have made man in His own image, and the propagation of the race may also be interpreted as a function in which one living being makes another in its own image. In our desire to glorify God with respect to man and Man with respect to matter, it is thus natural

---

[19]   Jean-Paul Sartre, *L'Existentialisme est un humanisme*, (Paris, Nagel, 1946).

to assume that machines cannot make other machines in their own image; that this is something associated with a sharp dichotomy of systems into living and non-living; and that it is moreover associated with the other dichotomy between creator and creature. Is this, however, so?[20]

The rest of the book is devoted to mobilizing the resources of cybernetics to show that these are false dichotomies and that, in truth, "machines are very well able to make other machines in their own image."[21]

In recent years, the enterprise of "making life from scratch" has been organized as a formal scientific discipline under the seemingly innocuous name of *synthetic biology*. In June 2007, the occasion of the first Kavli Futures Symposium at the University of Greenland in Ilulissat, leading researchers from around the world gathered to announce the convergence of work in synthetic biology and nanotechnology, and to take stock of the most recent advances in the manufacture of artificial cells. Their call for a global effort to promote "the construction or redesign of biological systems components that do not naturally exist" evoked memories of the statement that was issued in Asilomar, California, more than thirty years earlier, in 1975, by the pioneers of biotechnology.

Like their predecessors, the founders of synthetic biology insisted not only on the splendid things they were poised to achieve, but also on the dangers that might flow from them. Accordingly, they invited society to prepare itself for the consequences, while laying down rules of ethical conduct for themselves.[22] We know what became of the charter drawn up at Asilomar. A few years later, this attempt by scientists to regulate their own research had fallen to pieces. The dynamics of technological advance and the greed of the marketplace refused to suffer any limitation.

Only a week before the symposium in Ilulissat, a spokesman for the ETC Group, an environmental lobby based in Ottawa that has expanded its campaign against genetically modified foods to include emerging nanotechnologies, greeted the announcement of a feat of genetic engineering by the J. Craig Venter Institute in Rockville, Maryland, with the memorable words, "For the first time, God has competition." In the event, ETC had misinterpreted the nature of the achievement.[23]

---

[20]   Norbert Wiener, *God and Golem, Inc.: A Comment on Certain Points where Cybernetics Impinges on Religion* (Cambridge, Mass.: The MIT Press, 1964), 12.

[21]   Ibid., 13.

[22]   The Ilulissat Statement, "The Merging of Bio and Nano: Towards Cyborg Cells" (presented at Kavli Futures Symposium, June 11-15, 2007, Ilulissat, Greenland).

[23]   Carole Lartigue's JCVI team had succeeded in "simply" transferring the genome of one bacterium, *Mycoplasma mycoides,* to another, *Mycoplasma capricolum,* and showing that the cells of the recipient organism could function with the new genome. In effect, one species had been converted into another.

But if the Ilulissat Statement is to be believed, the actual synthesis of an organism equipped with an artificial genome ("a free-living organism that can grow and replicate") will become a reality in the next few years. Whatever the actual timetable may turn out to be, the process of fabricating DNA is now better understood with every passing day, and the moment when it will be possible to create an artificial cell using artificial DNA is surely not far off.

The question arises, however, whether such an achievement will really amount to *creating life*. In order to assert this much, one must suppose that between life and nonlife there is an absolute distinction, a critical threshold, so that whoever crosses it will have shattered a taboo, like the prophet Jeremiah and like Rabbi Löw of Prague in the Jewish tradition, who dared to create an artificial man, a *golem*. In the view of its promoters and some of its admirers, notably the English physicist and science writer Philip Ball,[24] synthetic biology has succeeded in demonstrating that no threshold of this type exists: between the dust of the earth and the creature that God formed from it, there is no break in continuity that permits us to say (quoting *Genesis* 2:7) that He breathed into man's nostrils the breath of life. And even in the event that synthetic biology should turn out to be incapable of fabricating an artificial cell, these researchers contend, it would still have had the virtue of depriving the prescientific notion of life of all consistency.

It is here, in the very particular logic that is characteristic of dreams, that nanotechnology plays an important symbolic role. It is typically defined by the scale of the phenomena over which it promises to exert control—a scale that is described in very vague terms, since it extends from a tenth of a nanometer[25] to a tenth of a micron. Nevertheless, over this entire gamut, the essential distinction between life and nonlife loses all meaning. It is meaningless to say, for example, that a DNA molecule is a living thing. At the symbolic level, a lack of precision in defining nanotechnology does not matter; what matters is the deliberate and surreptitious attempt to blur a fundamental distinction that until now has enabled human beings to steer a course through the world that was given to them. In the darkness of dreams, there is no difference between a living cat and a dead cat.

Once again, we find that science oscillates between two opposed attitudes: on the one hand, vainglory, an excessive and often indecent pride; and on the other, when it becomes necessary to silence critics, a false humility that consists in denying that one has done anything out of the ordinary, anything that departs from the usual business of normal science. As a philosopher, I am more troubled by the false humility, for in truth it is this, and not the vainglory, that constitutes the height of pride. I am less disturbed by a science that claims to be the equal

---

24   See Philip Ball, "Meanings of 'life,'" Editorial, *Nature* 447 (28 June 2007): 1031-1032. The subtitle is "Synthetic biology provides a welcome antidote to chronic vitalism."

25   A nanometer is one-billionth of a meter.

of God than by a science that drains one of the most essential distinctions known to humanity since the moment it first came into existence of all meaning: the distinction between that which lives and that which does not, or, to speak more bluntly, between life and death.

Let me propose an analogy that is more profound, I believe, than one may at first be inclined to suspect. With the rise of terrorism in recent years, specifically in the form of suicide attacks, violence on a global scale has taken a radically new turn. The first edition of this book belongs to a bygone era, which ended on September 11, 2001. In that world, even the most brutal persecutor expressed his attachment to life, because he killed in order to affirm and assert the primacy of his own way of living. But when the persecutor assumes the role of victim, killing himself in order to maximize the number of people killed around him, all distinctions are blurred, all possibility of reasoned dissuasion is lost, all control of violence is doomed to impotence. If science is allowed, in its turn, to continue along this same path in denying the crucial difference that life introduces in the world, it will, I predict, prove itself to be capable of a violence that is no less horrifying.

Among the most extreme promises of nanotechnology, as we have seen, is immortality (or "indefinite life extension," as it is called). But if there is thought to be no essential difference between the living and the nonliving, then there is nothing at all extraordinary about this promise. Yet again, Hannah Arendt very profoundly intuited what such a pact with the devil would involve:

> The greatest and most appalling danger for human thought is that what we once believed could be wiped out by the discovery of some fact that had hitherto remained unknown; for example, it could be that one day we succeed in making men immortal, and everything we had ever thought concerning death and its profundity would then become simply laughable. Some may think that this is too high a price to pay for the suppression of death.[26]

The ETC Group's premonitory observation—"For the first time, God has competition"—can only strengthen the advocates of the NBIC convergence in their belief that those who criticize them do so for religious reasons. The same phrases are always used to sum up what is imagined to be the heart of this objection: human beings do not have the right to usurp powers reserved to God alone; *playing God* is forbidden. Often it is added that this taboo is specifically "Judeo-Christian."

Let us put to one side the fact that this allegation wholly misconstrues the teaching of the Talmud as well as that of Christian theology. In conflating them

---

[26] Hannah Arendt, *Journal de pensée (1950-1973)*, 2 vols., translated by Sylvie Courtine-Denamy (Paris: Seuil, 2005), 1.

with the ancient Greek conception of the sacred—the gods, jealous of men who have committed the sin of pride, *hubris,* send after them the goddess of vengeance, Nemesis—it forgets that the Bible depicts man as cocreator of the world with God. As the French biophysicist and Talmudic scholar Henri Atlan notes with regard to the literature about the Golem:

> One does not find [in it], at least to begin with, the kind of negative judgment one finds in the Faust legend concerning the knowledge and creative activity of men "in God's image." Quite to the contrary, it is in creative activity that man attains his full humanity, in a perspective of *imitatio Dei* that allows him to be associated with God, in a process of ongoing and perfectible creation.[27]

Within the Christian tradition, authors such as G. K. Chesterton, René Girard, and Ivan Illich see Christianity as the womb of Western modernity, while arguing that modernity has betrayed and corrupted its message. This analysis links up with the idea, due to Max Weber, of the desacralization of the world—its famous "disenchantment"—in regarding Christianity, or at least what modernity made of it, as the main factor in the progressive elimination of all taboos, sacred prohibitions, and other forms of religious limitation.

It fell to science itself to extend and deepen this desacralization, inaugurated by the religions of the Bible, by stripping nature of any prescriptive or normative value. It is utterly futile, then, to accuse science of being at odds with the Judeo-Christian tradition on this point. Kantianism, for its part, conferred philosophical legitimacy on the devaluation of nature by regarding it as devoid of intentions and reasons, inhabited only by causes, and by severing the world of nature from the world of freedom, where the reasons for human action fall under the jurisdiction of moral law.

Where, then, is the ethical problem located, if in fact there is one here? It clearly does not lie in the transgression of this or that taboo sanctioned by nature or the sacred, since the joint evolution of religion and science has done away with any such foundation for the very concept of a moral limitation, and hence of a transgression. But that is precisely the problem. For there is no free and autonomous human society that does not rest on some principle of self-limitation. We will not find the limits we desperately need in the religions of the Book, as though such limits are imposed on us by some transcendental authority, for these religions do nothing more than confront us with our own freedom and responsibility.

The ethical problem weighs more heavily than any specific question dealing, for instance, with the enhancement of a particular cognitive ability by one or another

---

[27]   Henri Atlan, *Les étincelles du hasard,* vol. 1: *Connaissance spermatique* (Paris: Seuil, 1999), 45.

novel technology. But what makes it all the more intractable is that, whereas our capacity to act into the world is increasing without limit, with the consequence that we now find ourselves faced with new and unprecedented responsibilities, the ethical resources at our disposal are diminishing at the same pace. Why should this be? Because the same technological ambition that gives mankind such power to act upon the world also reduces mankind to the status of an object that can be fashioned and shaped at will; the conception of the mind as a machine—the very conception that allows us to imagine the possibility of (re)fabricating ourselves—prevents us from fulfilling these new responsibilities. Hence my profound pessimism.

6. ALCMENA'S PARADOX

To pay Heinz von Foerster a final homage, I would like to conclude by recounting a very lovely and moving story he told me, one that has a direct bearing on the arguments developed here.

The story takes place in Vienna toward the end of 1945, and it concerns another Viennese Jew, the psychiatrist Viktor Frankl, whose celebrated book *Man's Search for Meaning* was to be published the following year. Frankl had just returned to Vienna, having miraculously survived the Auschwitz-Birkenau camp; in the meantime, he had learned that his wife, his parents, his brother, and other members of his family had all been exterminated. He decided to resume his practice. Here, then, is the story as my friend Heinz told it:

> Concentration camps were the setting for many horrific stories. Imagine then the incredulous delight of a couple who returned to Vienna from two different camps to find each other alive. They were together for about six months, and then the wife died of an illness she had contracted in the camp. At this her husband lost heart completely, and fell into the deepest despair, from which none of his friends could rouse him, not even with the appeal "Imagine if she had died earlier and you had not been reunited!" Finally he was convinced to seek the help of Viktor Frankl, known for his ability to help the victims of the catastrophe.

> They met several times, conversed for many hours, and eventually one day Frankl said: "Let us assume God granted me the power to create a woman just like your wife: she would remember all your conversations, she would remember the jokes, she would remember every detail: you could not distinguish this woman from the wife you lost. Would you like me to do it?" The man kept silent for a while, then stood up and said, "No thank you, doctor!" They shook hands; the man left and started a new life.

> When I asked him about this astonishing and simple change, Frankl explained, "You see, Heinz, we see ourselves through the eyes of the other. When she died, he became blind. But when he *saw* that he was blind, he could see!"[28]

This, at least, is the lesson that von Foerster drew from this story—in typical cybernetic fashion. But I think that another lesson can be drawn from it, one that extends the first. What was it that this man suddenly saw, which he did not see before? The thought experiment that Frankl invited his patient to perform echoes one of the most famous Greek myths, that of Amphitryon. In order to seduce Amphitryon's wife, Alcmena, and to pass a night of love with her, Zeus assumes the form of Amphitryon.

> All through the night, Alcmena loves a man whose qualities are in every particular identical to those of her husband. The self-same description would apply equally to both. All the reasons that Alcmena has for loving Amphitryon are equally reasons for loving Zeus, who has the appearance of Amphitryon, for Zeus and Amphitryon can only be distinguished numerically: they are two rather than one. Yet it is Amphitryon whom Alcmena loves and not the god who has taken on his form. If one wishes to account for the emotion of love by appeal to arguments meant to justify it or to the qualities that lovers attribute to the objects of their love, what rational explanation can be given for that "something" which Amphitryon possesses, but that Zeus does not, and which explains why Alcmena loves only Amphitryon, and not Zeus?[29]

When we love somebody, we do not love a list of characteristics, even one that is sufficiently exhaustive to distinguish the person in question from anyone else. The most perfect *simulation* still fails to capture something, and it is this something that is the essence of love—this poor word that says everything and explains nothing. I very much fear that the spontaneous ontology of those who wish to set themselves up as the makers or recreators of the world know nothing of the beings who inhabit it, only lists of characteristics. If the nanobiotechnological dream were ever to come true, what still today we call love would become incomprehensible.

---

28   Translated from the German ("Wir sehen uns mit den Augen des anderen. . . . Als er aber erkannte, daß er blind war, da konnte er sehen!"). See Heinz von Foerster, "Mit den Augen des anderen," in *Wissen und Gewissen. Versuch einer Brücke*, S. J. Schmidt, ed., Frankfurt, 1993; 350-363.

29   Monique Canto-Sperber, "Amour," in Monique Canto-Sperber, ed., *Dictionnaire d'éthique et de philosophie morale,* 4th edition (Paris: Presses Universitaires de France, 2004), 41.

REFERENCES

Anders, Günther. *Die Antiquiertheit des Menschen: über die Seele im Zeitalter der zweiten industriellen Revolution*, vol. 1. Munich: Beck, 1980.

Arendt, Hannah. *The Human Condition*. Chicago: University of Chicago Press, 1958.

Arendt, Hannah. *Journal de pensée (1950-1973)*, 2 vols. Translated by Sylvie Courtine-Denamy. Paris: Seuil, 2005.

Atlan, Henri. *Les étincelles du hasard*, vol. 1: *Connaissance spermatique*. Paris: Seuil, 1999.

Ball, Philip. "Meanings of 'Life': Synthetic Biology Provides a Welcome Antidote to Chronic Vitalism." Editorial. *Nature* 447 (2007): 1031-1032.

Broderick, Damien. *The Spike: How Our Lives Are Being Transformed by Rapidly Advancing Technologies*. New York: Forge, 2001.

Dumont, Louis. *Essays on Individualism: Modern Ideology in Anthropological Perspective*. Chicago: University of Chicago Press, 1986.

Dupuy, Jean-Pierre. Aux origines des sciences cognitives. Paris: La Découverte, 1994.

————. "Complexity and Uncertainty: A Prudential Approach to Nanotechnology." In *Nanoethics: Examining the Social Impact of Nanotechnology*, edited by John Weckert et al., 119-131. Hoboken, N.J.: John Wiley and Sons, 2007.

————. "The Double Language of Science, and Why It Is So Difficult to Have a Proper Public Debate about the Nanotechnology Program." Foreword to *Nanoethics: Emerging Debates*, edited by Fritz Allhoff and Patrick Lin. Dordrecht: Springer, 2008.

————. *L'essor de la première cybernétique (1943-1953)*. Paris: Ecole Polytechnique, Cahiers du CREA, 7, 1985.

————. *On the Origins of Cognitive Science: The Mechanization of the Mind*. Boston: The MIT Press, 2009.

————. "Some Pitfalls in the Philosophical Foundations of Nanoethics." *Journal of Medicine and Philosophy* 32, no. 3 (2007): 237-261.

Dupuy, Jean-Pierre and Alexei Grinbaum. "Living with Uncertainty: Toward a Normative Assessment of Nanotechnology." *Techné* (joint issue with *Hyle)* 8, no. 2 (2004): 4-25.

Ferry, Luc and Alain Renaut. *French Philosophy of the Sixties: An Essay on Antihumanism*. Trans. Mary H. S. Cattani. Amherst, NY: University of Massachusetts Press, 1990.

Hayles, N. Katherine. *How We Became Posthuman: Virtual Bodies in Cybernetics, Literature, and Informatics*. Chicago, Ill.: University of Chicago Press, 1999.

Heidegger, Martin. "Letter on Humanism." In *Basic Writings*, edited by David Farrell Krell, 225. New York, Harper and Row, 1977.

Heims, Steve. *The Cybernetics Group*. Cambridge, Mass.: MIT Press, 1991.

Ilulissat Statement, The. "The Merging of Bio and Nano: Towards Cyborg Cells." Presented at Kavli Futures Symposium, June 11-15, 2007, Ilulissat, Greenland.

Kelly, Kevin. "Will Spiritual Robots Replace Humanity by 2100?" *The Technium*. http://www.kk.org./thetechnium/.

Sartre, Jean Paul. "Explications de *l'Etranger.*" Reprinted in Critiques littéraires (*Situations I*), Paris, Gallimard, 1947. Available in English in *Literary and Philosophical Essays*, trans. Annette Michelson. New York: Criterion Books, 1955.

Sartre, Jean-Paul. *L'Existentialisme est un humanisme*. Paris: Nagel, 1946.

Sloterdijk, Peter. "On the Rules of the Human Fleet." Paper delivered at a conference on Heidegger at Elmau Castle, Upper Bavaria, on July 17, 1999.

Roco, Mihail C. and William Sims Bainbridge. *Converging Technologies for Improving Human Performance: Nanotechnology, Biotechnology, Information Technology, and Cognitive Science*. Washington, D.C.: National Science Foundation, 2002. von Foerster, Heinz. "Mit den Augen des anderen." In *Wissen und Gewissen. Versuch einer Brücke*, edited by S. J. Schmidt, 350-363. Frankfurt, 1993.

Wiener, Norbert. *God and Golem, Inc.: A Comment on Certain Points where Cybernetics Impinges on Religion*. Cambridge, Mass.: The MIT Press, 1964.

Chapter Sixteen

Millennialism at the Singularity: Reflections on the Limits of Ray Kurzweil's Exponential Logic

by William Grassie

Imagine billions of nanobots, tiny computerized machines smaller than your red blood cells, travelling through your body, inserted in your brain, all communicating internally with each other and externally with machines outside of your body. These nanobots could repair damaged cells in your body, destroy cancer cells, eliminate pathogens, provide optimum nutrition, eliminate unhealthy chemicals, regulate your hormones on command, and reset the telomeres on your chromosomes so that you might live forever at your optimal "biological" age. Should you swim underwater or climb Mount Everest, these nanobots will provide you with oxygen. All the while these billions of nanobots would be enhancing your mental capacities to that of a supercomputer, with the content of the entire Internet at your ready access. Your sensory capacities would be similarly enhanced, enabling heightened powers of perception, sensation, and pleasures. All of this would be inside of "you," even as "you" would be connected outside to a cybernetic utopia. Oh, by the way, these trillions of nanobots will also reproduce and evolve.

If Ray Kurzweil[1] is right, and there is a persuasive argument to suggest he might be, then this blending of supermachines, enhanced brains, and immortal bodies will

---

[1] "Ray Kurzweil has been described as "the restless genius" by the Wall Street Journal, and "the ultimate thinking machine" by Forbes. *Inc.* magazine ranked him number 8 among entrepreneurs in the United States, calling him the "rightful heir to Thomas Edison," and PBS included Ray as one of sixteen "revolutionaries who made America," along with other inventors of the past two centuries. As one of the leading inventors of our time, Ray was the principal developer of the first CCD flatbed scanner, the first omnifont optical character recognition, the first print-to-speech reading machine for

be achieved by 2045. Thirty-five years is not such a long time, so with some luck and good health, most readers alive today will see whether these predictions are true. Kurzweil and his disciples call this "the Singularity," because it will be a new threshold in evolution, a tipping-point when "transbiological" and "postbiological" civilization takes off. The good news is that the superhuman "you" can live forever through rejuvenation technologies and computer enhancements. The bad news is that there may be some really bad news along the way.

After two days and twenty-six speakers at the Singularity Summit 2009, I am still not sure whether the end is near or whether we are on the cusp of a great new beginning. Eight hundred technophiles[2] and a smattering of venture capitalists

---

the blind, the first text-to-speech synthesizer, the first music synthesizer capable of re-creating the grand piano and other orchestral instruments, and the first commercially marketed large-vocabulary speech recognition. Ray's Web site Kurzweil AI.net has over one million readers. Among Ray's many honors, he is the recipient of the $500,000 MIT-Lemelson Prize, the world's largest for innovation. In 1999, he received the National Medal of Technology, the nation's highest honor in technology, from President Clinton in a White House ceremony. And in 2002, he was inducted into the National Inventors' Hall of Fame, established by the U.S. Patent Office. He has received sixteen honorary doctorates and honors from three U.S. presidents. Ray has written five books, four of which have been national best sellers. *The Age of Spiritual Machines* has been translated into nine languages and was the number 1 best-selling book on Amazon in science. Ray's recent book, *The Singularity is Near*, was a New York Times best seller, *and has been the #1 book on Amazon in both science and philosophy. His newest book, TRANSCEND: Nine Steps to Living Well Forever*, coauthored with Terry Grossman, MD, builds on the science behind radical life extension to present a practical plan for achieving optimal health and longer life." See http://www.rayandterry.com/transcend/kurzweil.shtml

2   I confess to also being a technophile, albeit with a schizophrenic streak. A child of the Apollo Space Program, I studied astronomy and launched Estes rockets in the backyard. In elementary school, I was indoctrinated with filmstrips courtesy of the Atomic Energy Commission, as well as regular "duck and cover" air raid drills courtesy of civil defense preparedness. In high school, I maxed out on advanced calculus and laser holography in the physics lab. As a freshman at Middlebury College, I took a computer programming course, the only such course offered there in 1975, programming in Basic on a hot, new PDP 11. Along the way, however, I was introduced to the examined life and ethical imperatives. So I wandered away from science and technology to studying politics, philosophy, and religion in search of the good life and the just society in what I increasingly came to understand is a dangerous moment in the natural history of our planet and the cultural evolution of our species. I still love my toys though and love the company and stimulation of other technophiles. The older the boys, the more expensive

gathered in New York City in early October for the two-day conference organized by the Singularity Institute for Artificial Intelligence (SIAI), whose purpose is to contemplate the trajectory of exponential developments in genomics, nanotechnology, and robotics, with the goal of predicting and shaping our evolutionary future.[3] Many in attendance, Kurzweil not the least, hoped to radically extend and enhance their brains and life expectancy, perhaps even "curing death." All of this will be mediated in part by the exponential growth in computer technology, as witnessed in the last forty years and predicted to dramatically accelerate. Ray Kurzweil's 2005 book *The Singularity Is Near* lays out the case for what is now being referred to as "the Singularity movement." He is predicting a probable dramatic "phase transition" in the fields of artificial general intelligence (AGI) and genomics, nanotechnology, and robotics (GNR).

Douglas Hofstadter, the Pulitzer Prize Winning author of *Gödel, Escher, Bach* (1979), says of the Singularity enthusiasts:

> If you read Ray Kurzweil's books and Hans Moravec's, what I find is that it's a very bizarre mixture of ideas that are solid and good with ideas that are crazy. It's as if you took a lot of very good food and some dog excrement and blended it all up so that you can't possibly figure out what's good or bad. It's an intimate mixture of rubbish and good ideas, and it's very hard to disentangle the two, because these are smart people; they're not stupid.[4]

What I propose to do in this essay is to try to create a rudimentary intellectual centrifuge to see if I can separate the probable rubbish from the definitely good food for thought. I will do so first on the level of the science to see whether these predictions are plausible. Along the way, I will discuss the challenges of computational finitude, complexity, the limits of exponential logic, the misuse of metaphors, and the dangers of category mistakes. I will then analyze the "Singularity movement" as a quasi-religious endeavor with its own secular salvation story, torn between premillennialist and postmillennialist interpretations of evolution and the human prospect comparable to Jewish and Christian chiliastic movements throughout history.

---

the toys!

[3] See http://www.singularitysummit.com, http://www.singinst.org/, and http://singularityu.org/.

[4] Greg Ross and Douglas R. Hofstadter, "An Interview with Douglas Hofstadter," American Scientists, http://www.americanscientist.org/bookshelf/pub/douglas-r-hofstadter. Douglas R. Hofstadter, *Gödel, Escher, Back: An Eternal Golden Braid* (New York: Vintage Books, 1979).

∞

Kurzweil proposes a Law of Accelerating Returns woven into the fabric of the universe, the evolution of biological complexity, the development of human culture, and the trajectory of technological innovation. What this means is that we are surfing a wave of exponential growth, although our minds and cultures are oriented toward linear processes and gradual changes. The "magic" of exponentiality is that innovations begin slowly at first and then "take-off" on a steep, accelerating curve. In his book and in his lectures, Kurzweil discusses a number of logarithmic plots of technological innovation (i.e., linear representations of exponential trends):

- The Countdown to the Singularity (Life to PCs) (p.17)
- Paradigm Shifts (p.19)
- Canonical Milestones (p. 20)
- Growth in US Phone Industry by revenues and phone calls per day (p. 48)
- Growth in Cell Phone Subscribers (p.49)
- Mass Use of Inventions (p. 50)
- Dynamic RAM in computers (p. 57)
- Dynamic RAM price (p. 58)
- Average Transistor Price (p. 59)
- Microprocessor Clock Speed (p. 61)
- Microprocessor Cost (p. 62)
- Transistors per Microprocessor (p. 63)
- Processor Performance (MIPS) (p. 64)
- DNA Sequencing Cost (p. 73)
- Growth in Genebank (p. 74)
- Magnetic Data Storage (p.76)
- Price-Performance of Wireless Devices (p. 77)
- Internet Hosts (p. 78)
- Internet Data Traffic (p.80)
- Internet Backbone Bandwidth (p.81)
- Decreasing Size of Mechanical Devices (p. 82)
- Nano-related Patents (p. 84)
- Real Gross Domestic Product (p. 98)
- Per-Capita GDP (p. 99)
- Noninvasive Brain Scanning (p. 159)
- Brain Scanning Reconstruction Time (p. 160)

Taken separately and together, these trends are very impressive. If these trajectories continue, as Kurzweil argues they will, then humanity is riding a very big wave of technological innovation in multiple and interrelated fields of science and engineering (GNR plus AGI). Within ten to twenty years time, we should have a pretty good assessment of whether this really is an evolutionary tsunami. And if we make it to 2045 without crashing, the world will certainly be significantly, perhaps singularly, different.

Critic Jaron Lanier referred to this fixation on the exponentials as "the fetishizing of Moore's Law" and argues that the difficulty of writing software will thwart these hyperbolic predictions.[5] Sun Microsystem founder Bill Joy wrote an impassioned plea for restraint in a now infamous *WIRED* cover story entitled "Why the Future Doesn't Need Us?"[6] Far from a utopia, Joy worried that the GNR revolution was a misanthropic nightmare leading to the extinction of our species, not to mention his own children's lives. Others wonder whether the supersession of our species by immortal and superintelligent postbiological entities would be such a bad thing.[7] Kurzweil knows his critics and addresses each of their points to varying degrees of satisfaction in his lectures and in his book.[8] Let's review some of the most salient arguments presented by Singularity skeptics.

∞

The first problem in these Singularity predictions lies with the very nature of computation. There are known limits to computation. Computer scientists know that sometimes even very simple problems cannot be solved by the very nature of the problem. As David Harel at the Weizmann Institute of Science explains in his book *Computers Ltd.: What They Really Can't Do* (2000):

> . . . we shall see interesting and important problems for which there
> simply are no algorithms, and it doesn't matter how smart we are,
> or how sophisticated and powerful our computers, our software, our
> programming languages and our algorithmic methods . . . .
> These facts have deep philosophical implications, not only on the limits
> of machines like computers, but also on our own limits as beings with
> finite mass. Even if we were given unlimited amounts of pencil and
> paper, and unlimited lifespan, there would be well defined problems

---

[5]   Jaron Lanier, "One-Half of a Manifesto: Why Stupid Software Will Save the Future from Neo-Darwinian Machines," *WIRED* 8.12 (1999).

[6]   Bill Joy, "Why the Future Doesn't Need Us," *WIRED* 8.04 (1999).

[7]   Michel Houellebecq's dark novel, *The Elementary Particle*, presents human life as so absurd and pathetic that the Singularity is a welcome end to our species's self-induced misery and hypocrisy. See Michel Houellebecq, *The Elementary Particle*, trans. Frank Wynne (New York: Alfred Knopf, 2000).

[8]   See chapter nine "Response to Critics" Ray Kurzweil, *The Singularity Is Near: When Humans Transcend Biology* (New York: Penguin Books, 2005).

we could not solve. It is also important to stress that this is not just about computing, by brain or by machine. It is a fact about knowing. In a strong sense, what we can compute is what we are able to figure out by careful step-by-step processes from what we already know. The limits of computation are the limits of knowledge.[9]

This is a very technical discussion in computer science, but the short of it is that many problems simply don't compute.[10] There are also other theoretical and practical limits to computation. These are called intractable problems because they "require hopelessly large amounts of time even for relatively small inputs . . ."[11] Computer encryption depends on this second fact. It may be that the genome, in dynamic relationship with proteins and its environment, is in some sense "encrypted." It may be that the mind-brain is similarly "encrypted." In which case, we will never be able to fully understand, let alone reliably control life and mind no matter how exponentially our scientific knowledge grows nor how fast technological know-how accelerates.[12]

The second problem that could scuttle the hopes and fears of the Singularity prophets is the nature of chaos and complexity.[13] This is both a computational problem as well as a biological and engineering problem. When you design a program or model a complex natural phenomena with too many feedback loops and too many input variables and parameters, you quickly meet the proverbial "butterfly effect," in which minor variations in initial conditions can ripple through the system with widely variable, unpredictable, and unintended results. Complex distributed systems

---

[9]   David Harel, *Computers Ltd.: What They Really Can't Do* (New York: Oxford University Press, 2000), 27-28.

[10]   On the question of limits to science, see also John D. Barrow, *Impossibility: The Limits of Science and the Science of Limits* (New York: Oxford University Press, 1999).

[11]   Harel, *Computers Ltd.: What They Really Can't Do*, 79.

[12]   For an introduction to computational limits, see Ibid. For an understanding of genomic expression as a complex biological system, see Scott F. Gilbert and David Epel, *Ecological Developmental Biology: Integrating Epigenetics, Medicine, and Evolution* (Sunderland, MA: Sinauer Associates, 2009). See also my review of Gilbert and Epel's book, William J. Grassie, "Post-Darwinism: The New Synthesis," Metanexus Institute, http://www.grassie.net/articles/2009_postdarwinism.html. Roger Penrose, *The Emperor's New Mind: Cencerning Computers, Minds and the Laws of Physic* (New York: Oxford University Press, 1989). ———, *Shadows of the Mind: A Search for the Missing Science of Consciousness* (New York and Oxford: Oxford University Press, 1994).

[13]   James Gleick, *Chaos: Making a New Science* (New York: Penguin, 1987).

can be incredibly resilient, true, but they can also be incredibly fragile. It is hard to know in advance. While some complex systems can be represented mathematically with simple reiterative formula, it is a big leap of faith to think that all chaotic and complex systems can be thus represented, understood, and controlled.[14] This then is the "useless arithmetic" problem, for instance, as detailed by Orrin Pilky and Linda Pilkey-Jarvis in their book *Useless Arithmetic: Why Environmental Scientists Can't Predict the Future* (2007).[15] For better or worse, the same principles apply to other complex distributed systems.[16] The genome (which requires also proteomics, developmental biology, and a whole lot more) and the mind-brain (which requires bodies, nature, cultures, and a whole lot more) strike me as likely candidates for irreducible complexity. Instead of an exponential explosion, we should more likely anticipate asymptotic limits to many sciences in the twenty-first century, limits set by chaos, complexity, and computational finitude as determined by the real complexity of natural entities that we hope to understand.[17]

The third problem has to do with the challenges of writing software. Jaron Lanier lays out this argument in his essay "One Half of a Manifesto" with the subtitle "Why stupid software will save the future from neo-Darwinian machines." Lanier writes,

> This breathtaking vista (the Singularity) must be starkly contrasted with the Great Shame of computer science, which is that we don't seem to be

---

[14] This is the view presented in Stephen Wolfram, *A New Kind of Science* (Champaign, IL: Wolfram Media, 2002). Wolfram acknowledges that there will be irreducibly complex entities in nature that we can control or predict or adequately model.

[15] Orrin H. Pilkey and Linda Plkey-Jarvis, *Useless Arithmetic: Why Environmental Scientists Can't Predict the Future* (New York: Columbia University Press, 2007). See also my review of their book, William J. Grassie, "Useless Arithmetic and Inconvenient Truths: A Review," *Metanexus Global Spiral* (2007), http://www.metanexus.net/Magazine/tabid/68/id/9854/Default.aspx.

[16] See Kevin Kelly, *Out of Control: The New Biology of Machines, Social Systems, and the Economic World* (New York: Addison-Wesley, 1994). See also my book review William J. Grassie, "Wired for the Future: Kevin Kelly's Techno-Utopia," *Terra Nova: Nature and Culture* 2, no. 4 (1997).

[17] Gleick, *Chaos: Making a New Science*. Kelly, *Out of Control: The New Biology of Machines, Social Systems, and the Economic World*. Brian Castellani and Frederic William Hafferty, *Sociology and Complexity Science: A New Field of Inquiry* (Berlin: Springer Verlag, 2009). Brian Castellani, "Map of Complexity Science," http://www.art-sciencefactory.com/complexity-map_feb09.html. Grassie, "Wired for the Future: Kevin Kelly's Techno-Utopia."

able to write software much better as computers get much faster . . . . If
anything, there's a reverse Moore's law observable in software.[18]

Lanier discusses software "brittleness," "legacy code," "lock-in," and "other
perversions" that work counter to the logic of Kurzweil's exponential vision. It turns
out there is also an exponential growth curve in programming and IT support jobs,
as more and more talent and hours are drawn into managing, debugging, translating
incompatible databases, and protecting our exponentially better, cheaper, and more
connected computers. This exponential countertrend suggests that humanity will
become "a planet of help desks" long before the Singularity.

Fourth, when computer programs are designed to simulate natural processes,
for instance the human brain, you get layers of abstraction from the real thing.
Science works best by simplifying and isolating processes, but that does not
mean that reality is actually simple, isolatable, or adequately represented in this
manner. In addition to the "useless arithmetic" problem, we have a problem of
representation, which in this case may be too simplistic and too abstracted from
reality. A. N. Whitehead warns of "the fallacy of misplaced concreteness," on the
one hand, and the imperative to "seek simplicity and distrust it," on the other hand.[19]
The map is not the terrain, and the details that matter depend on the context and
cannot always be known in advance. It seems to me that the Singularity prophets
have underestimated both of these problems.

The fifth problem is the fallacy of exponential logic. It is hard to imagine
any earth-bound natural process including humans and human technologies
that can grow exponentially forever. Whether it is a pair of aphids on potted
plants in my office or the rapid growth in the Chinese economy, nothing can
grow exponentially for all that long on the relevant time scale without running
into some stark limitations. We have lived through an extraordinary century of
exponential growth—population, economic growth, energy consumption, water
usage, mining, manufacturing, domesticated plants and animals, technological
and scientific advance, publishing and media. How long can this continue? Instead
of an exponential explosion into the new age of spiritual machines, we are more
likely to have an economic and environmental implosion.[20] The actual history of

---

18   Lanier, "One-Half of a Manifesto: Why Stupid Software Will Save the Future from
      Neo-Darwinian Machines."

19   "The fallacy of misplaced concreteness" is from Alfred North Whitehead, *Science
      and the Modern World* (New York: Free Press, [1925] 1967), 51. "Seek simplicity and
      distrust it" is from ———, *The Concept of Nature* (Cambridge: Cambridge University
      Press, 1926), 163.

20   J. Robert McNeill, *Something New under the Sun: An Environmental History of the
      Twentieth-Century World* (New York: W. W. Norton & Company, 2000).

civilizations and the evolution of life involve periods of collapse disrupting the overall trend toward complexification. I will revisit this question below, because that fear is very much part of the Singularity movement's self-understanding, as it should be for all of us today.

One rough measure of complexity is energy density flow. Astronomer Eric Chaisson has estimated the comparative energy density flow of different entities in the universe, measured as the amount of free energy flowing through a system in respect to its mass over time, in this case measured as erg per seconds per grams (erg s^{-1} g^{-1}). Earth's climasphere, which consists of the atmosphere and oceans, has roughly a hundred times the energy density flow of a typical star or galaxy. Through photosynthesis, plants achieve an energy density flow roughly a thousand times more than that of a star. The human body is sustained by a daily food intake resulting in an energy density flow about 20,000 times more than that of a typical star.

Remember that we are comparing the ratio of energy consumed to mass of the objects. So here is another way to think of this. If a human body could be scaled up to the mass of our sun, it would be 20,000 times more luminous (assuming it could obtain enough food energy!). The human brain, which consumes about 20 percent of our energy intake while constituting about 2 percent of our body weight, has an energy density flow 150,000 times that of a typical star. And finally, modern human civilization has an energy density ratio some 500,000 times that of a typical star.[21] Energy density flows turn out to be a useful way to think about emergent complexity, but also the exponential trajectory of energy consumption in Kurzweil's nanobot postbiological, transhuman complexity.[22]

There is an important caveat to the fallacy of exponential logic, because disembodied information, if such a thing exists, can conceivably grow exponentially forever. Information, in this view, would not be subject to the second law of thermodynamics and the limitations of space-time and matter-energy. We do not, however, have an adequate definition of information (or complexity) across different scientific disciplines. We do not really know what disembodied information would really mean except as some Platonic mystification. It may be that computer scientists, mathematicians, and

---

[21]   Eric Chaisson, *Cosmic Evolution: The Rise of Complexity in Nature* (Cambridge, MA: Harvard University Press, 2001), 139.; ———, *Epic of Evolution : Seven Ages of the Cosmos* (New York: Columbia University Press, 2006), 293-96.; David Christian, *Maps of Time: An Introduction to Big History* (Berkeley: University of California Press, 2004).

[22]   Kurzweil certainly knows this and has done some interesting calculations on the energy requirements, which he envisions coming largely through more efficient harnessing of solar energy, perhaps on the scale of the solar system collection devices rather than merely Earth-bound collectors.

theoretical physicists are prone to such disembodied mystifications, more so than, say, chemists, geologists, and physicians, which leads to the next point.

Metaphors matter in science. An apt metaphor can lead to interesting insights as well as major category mistakes. Certainly the real revolution in science in the last thirty years has been the advent of ever more powerful and cheaper computer technology. We can now collect and analyze large datasets, create new models and simulations, build new tools, and conduct research and collaboration over the Internet. This has been a Kuhnian revolution in science, a paradigm shift not just in one discipline, but in all of the sciences as well as practically every other aspect of human life. The metaphors of computer science have now been adopted in diverse disciplines, from psychology to economics, from cell biology to cosmology. A metaphor is a comparison of two unlike entities. Metaphors can be symbolically profound, but are not literally true. Metaphors enrich language and thought, but if we become literal fundamentalists, we are sadly and sometimes tragically mistaken.

So my sixth point is to deconstruct the metaphors upon which artificial intelligence, life extension technology, nanotechnology, robotics, and genomics are all based—the idea that life and mind are machines that can be reverse engineered. Human engineering is pretty fantastic stuff, but I doubt whether anything that humans have ever designed approaches the biochemical complexity of a single cell. Let me quote Bill Bryson's description of a simple prokaryotic cell from his book *A Short History of Nearly Everything* (2003, 2005):

> Blown up to a scale at which atoms were about the size of peas, a cell would be a sphere roughly half a mile across, and supported by a complex framework of girders called the cytoskeleton. Within it, millions upon millions of objects—some the size of basketballs, others the size of cars—would whiz about like bullets. There wouldn't be a place you could stand without being pummeled and ripped thousands of times every second from every direction. Even for its full-time occupants the inside of a cell is a hazardous place. Each strand of DNA is on average attacked or damaged once every 8.4 seconds—ten thousand times in a day—by chemicals and other agents that whack into or carelessly slice through it, and each of these wounds must be swiftly stitched up if the cell is not to perish.

> The proteins are especially lively, spinning, pulsating and flying into each other up to a billion times a second. Enzymes, themselves a type of protein, dash everywhere, performing up to a thousand tasks a second. Like greatly speeded-up worker ants, they busily build and rebuild molecules, hauling a piece off this one, adding a piece to that one. Some monitor passing proteins and mark with a chemical those that are irreparably damaged or flawed. Once so selected, the doomed proteins

proceed to a structure called a proteasome, where they are stripped down and their components used to build new proteins. Some types of protein exist for less than half an hour; others survive for weeks. But all lead existences that are inconceivably frenzied.[23]

Bryson's vivid trope for describing the trillions of biochemical reactions per second in a simple prokaryotic cell does not even begin to approach the real nanotech-level, informational, and developmental complexity of this smallest unit of life. A typical such cell contains 20,000 different types of proteins, each with capacities to fold and unfold in specific context to accomplish specific tasks. A small cell contains perhaps 100 million protein molecules. The adult human body contains some 10 trillion (10^{13}) large Eukaryotic cells. All of these cells began as a single fertilized egg in your mother's womb, a single cell with 23 chromosomes, some 70,000 genes, and 3 billion base pairs, a single cell that replicated, initially exponentially, and along the way differentiated into 210 tissue types in their proper organs performing their proper function.

Can a computer model the complexity inside of a single cell, let alone the complexity of the entire brain of some hundred billion neurons (10^{11}) connected together in a tangled web of over one hundred trillion synaptic connections (10^{14}). What details are we necessarily going to exclude from these models? If we follow Bryson's lead and blow an entire human brain up to a scale where each atom would be the size of a pea, then suddenly the only human creation that might compare to the informational complexity of the brain would be the entire global economy shrunk to the size of a brain. Nobody designed and nobody controls the global economy, even though we try to influence it as best we can as differentially empowered participants with different interests, motivations, and expectations.

But wait, a disembodied brain is a useless mush of grey matter. For a human brain to realize its extraordinary abilities—for instance, in the extraordinary intelligence, creativity, and concern manifested by the speakers and conferees at the Singularity Summit—requires in its ontogeny and phylogeny an entire body and an evolved history. A brain requires a network of nerves and a metabolism. It requires vocal chords and oppositional thumbs. The brain must evolve and develop in natural environments rich in semiotic and semantic meanings. It requires the nurture of families, communities, and civilizations from which it acquires language, tools, and purpose. The brain, much like the genome, does absolutely nothing by itself. When separated from this messy matrix of embodied relationships—top down,

---

[23]   Bill Bryson, *A Short History of Nearly Everything: Special Illustrated Edition* (New York: Broadway Books, [2003] 2005), 477-78.

bottom up, side to side—the brain really has no capacities at all, computational or otherwise.

In a profound ontological sense, the human body-brain-mind-spirit is an emergent phenomenon in which the whole is "exponentially" more than the sum of its parts. Different levels of analysis are necessary for different kinds of scientific and philosophical questions that we might ask about body-brain-mind-spirit. Reductionistic approaches to the neurosciences and artificial intelligence can quickly become category mistakes, as silly as trying to use particle physics to interpret a novel, evolutionary psychology to ascertain the truth-value of physics, or life extension technology to realize the meaning of life. Metaphors matter. It is time to jettison the machine metaphor.

I have nothing in principle against scientists pushing the envelope up to and, if possible, beyond the asymptotes, trying to reduce complex problems into more manageable levels, building all kinds of models and simulations, trying to enhance and extend human health and well-being, as well as that of other species and our environments, building ever more intelligent, efficient, and useful prosthetic devices, machines that change what we know, how we live, and in a profound sense also who we are. By all means, push the envelope! I think society should spend more resources, not less on these issues, including educating children and adults alike about this remarkable cosmic, chemical, geological, biological, cultural, and technological evolutionary adventure in which we are now so consequentially participating. My hope, however, is that by doing so our species and science itself will become less hyperbolic and more humble, more appreciative in a religious sense that nature, including our own embodied human nature, turns out to be fantastically super.

∞

In the critical analyses above we are "saved" from the Singularity by the bite of complexity and the fallacy of misplaced concreteness. This, however, is not something we should necessarily be celebrating with a sigh of relief because, as several of the speakers pointed out, without technological innovation our economy is in big trouble. We have become addicted to exponential growth measured in annual returns on our investments and annual growth in GNP. Most of the people in the world will do just fine in the short-term implementing off-the-shelf twentieth-century technologies and, in the process, realizing huge economic gains. In the United States and in Western Europe, however, we face an innovation crisis because technology turns out to be the source of our most important economic growth in the last fifty years, even as manufacturing has moved to cheaper labor markets and less regulated environmental protections.

All forms of credit—treasuries, bonds, mortgages, student loans, credit cards—involve claims on the future. If our economies stop growing, then the credit markets will collapse. The ability to repay creditors depends on things getting better every year or making exponential sacrifices at some future date. If you don't have future growth, then the claims of the future can't be painlessly met. When credit markets collapse, value collapses; and with it, the stock market, production, commerce, exchange, employment, and the tax base also all collapse. Modern global capitalism is based on a series of positive self-reinforcing feedback loops, which, as we learned in 2008, can quickly turn into negative self-reinforcing feedback loops. Such a future economic collapse is likely to bring out the worst in our human nature, including fascist, collectivist, xenophobic, totalitarian, and chauvinist political movements, which ideological extremes will be amplified by our global media and empowered with incredibly destructive weapons. If the world is suddenly filled with more magnitudes of desperately impoverished humans, then you can be sure that it will also be bad for the environment. The message is "without the Singularity we are doomed."

At the Summit, entrepreneur and venture capitalist Peter Thiel explored seven different catastrophic scenarios for the future and argued that "the Singularity is not happening quickly enough." This is most worrisome because of the way an economic downturn would reverberate through the political economy.[24] Of course, at a certain point, sooner or later, this view of infinite exponential economic growth is really just a giant Ponzi scheme on a global scale. If the Pied Piper is not eventually paid, we will lose our children or children's children. Perhaps information, innovation, and creativity can somehow break free of resource limitations and the second law of thermodynamics, in which case we can dematerialize economic growth and innovate ourselves incrementally or exponentially into a better world. That is the sixty-trillion-dollar economic, evolutionary, and metaphysical question on which the future hinges. I find myself torn between the Singularity movers and shakers, and the Environmentalist wailers and moaners. The optimists always seem to win, but they may be tragically wrong. It is a question most people living today will confront in a dramatic and extremely personal fashion in the short-term horizon before 2045. Fortunately, my predictions tend to be wrong; and in this case, I would be happy to be proven wrong.

The Singularitarians, however, have a lot more than these mundane economic worries to contemplate. As genomic techniques become more widely available, it will be increasingly easy to synthesize new diseases. A graduate student might decide on a lark to cross the flu virus with AIDS, foolishly creating a highly contagious, stealthy, and deadly epidemic. Bioterrorists might concoct even more dangerous designer pathogens. The world could be visited by out-of-control pandemics, killing billions in a matter of weeks or months. In response to these existential threats, governments will invade privacy and create surveillance and

---

[24] Peter Thiel is president of Clarium, a global macro hedge fund. He is also the founder and chairman of Palantir Technologies, a national security software firm, and a founding investor and board member of Facebook. He was founder and CEO of PayPal.

control mechanisms to preemptively defend themselves, techniques that will then also help totalitarian governments consolidate power. Self-replicating nanobots might get out of control like an invasive weed species, turning our rich, green planet into "gray goo." Superintelligent AGIs might just decide to be done with those pesky humans, perhaps keeping a few biological specimens of our species in their zoos, along with the databases of our DNA for future confabulations.

In every case, argued Kurzweil and the others at the Singularity Summit, the appropriate response to the threat is to accelerate developing the very technology that might do us in. We need to develop DNA interference and new antiviral techniques to deal with new designer pathogens and bioterrorism. We need to develop "blue goo" nanobots that will control bad "gray goo" nanobots in the environment and in our bodies, much like the T cells in our immune system. We need to decentralize the new technologies and energy systems in order to protect our civil liberties. We need to try to program our best human values into these GNR devices such that when the day comes, they will embody the best of human civilization and human values. The Singularity, we are told, is an inevitability, so all we can do is try to speed it up and bend it more to our liking.[25]

∞

What does it mean to *program* our best human values? What are those values? Who decides? How do humans typically do such "value programs" in our children, in our civilizations, in our machines? What does it mean to say that machines have values? There is a lot more going on with the Singularity movement than just science and technology.

The Singularity Institute's Web site describes their "core values" with these words: "Set a high standard of integrity and honesty, preserve rationalist values, and maintain strict ethics." It then lists the following "commitments":

- SIAI will not enter any partnership that compromises our values.
- Technology developed by SIAI will not be used to harm human life.
- The challenge, opportunity, and risk of artificial intelligence is the common concern of all humanity. SIAI will not show ethnic, national, political, or religious favoritism in the discharge of our mission.[26]

These are philosophically naïve statements. Please define *rationalist values* and *strict ethics*. If so much of this work is pursued and funded by the U.S. military, is not the technology necessarily used to "harm human life"? What does it mean

---

[25] See chapter eight in Kurzweil, *The Singularity Is Near: When Humans Transcend Biology.*

[26] http://singinst.org/aboutus/ourmission

to "not show ethnic, national, political, or religious favoritism," when many, perhaps most of these identities and differences, will be wiped out in pursuit of the Singularity?

So let's imagine some human values that we would try to program into the Singularity. It is pretty much universally the case that people everywhere prefer health to sickness, freedom to slavery, prosperity to poverty, education to ignorance, empowerment to powerlessness, pleasure to pain, justice to injustice, and living to dying. Missing from the list are three other universal preferences. Humans prefer belonging to isolation, meaning to meaninglessness, and certainty to uncertainty. We might well expand this list, for instance, easy to hard. We may disagree about the degree and interpretation of these abstract terms but not about the basic principles. How much is enough? When is enough too much? And critically, how do we decide between these universal preferences when they conflict with each other as they necessarily do in actual life? We cannot simultaneously maximize all goods. In economic terminology, we can refer to these values as "utility functions," but I can't wrap my head around what it would mean to "program" them into our technology. We do not know how to "program" these into our political system, though I believe the best attempts to do so are through some form of limited government, with checks and balances, something on a continuum between libertarianism and democratic socialism.

Historically, these values have been "encoded" within civilization by a multivariable, multilevel phenomenon, which we label "religion," lots of different religions. There is a tragic disconnect between the worlds of religion and the domains of science, so the Singularity is not off to a good start because the vast majority of valuing humans know very little about modern science and the existential threats that we have just discussed.

Of course, anytime we talk about the future, our hopes or our fears, we are in the realm of religions. You can dress it up with science and mathematics, technology and innovation, but it is still faith of a sort that can no more be proven than a belief in God or in an afterlife. Projecting a utopic or dystopic future is a kind of religious activity that changes how we think and act in the world today. Science fiction, in this view, is a genre of theological anthropology and has contemporary political consequences. Humans are profoundly teleological creatures. Broadly defined, our big hopes and big fears about the future are necessarily "religious" in nature.[27]

---

[27] For a brilliant series of lectures on the role of ideologies and utopias in human society, see Paul Ricoeur, *Lectures on Ideology and Utopia* (New York: Columbia University Press, 1986). For a philosophical analysis of conflicting ideologies, see my essay William J. Grassie, "Entangled Narratives: Competing Visions of the Good Lie," Sri Lanka Journal of the Humanities XXXIV (1&2), http://www.grassie.net/articles/2008_entangled_narratives.html.

The Singularity movement is a kind of secular religion promoting its own apocalyptic and messianic vision of the end times. In this analysis, whether or not the Singularity is plausible or realistic is no longer the point. The Singularity inevitably plays into an old trope in our culture; and it will function psychologically, politically, and culturally, much like any other chiliastic faith. On this cultural level, the Singularity movement is continuous with other messianic movements throughout human history.

In the Judeo-Christian idiom, there is a debate between premillennialists and postmillennialists revolving around whether the Messiah will come at the beginning of the messianic age or at the end of the messianic age. A modern "dispensationalist" interpretation of this messianism is found in the wildly successful *Left Behind* books, movies, and now also computer game.[28] These "dispensationalist premillennialists" see the messianic age preceded by a "rapture," followed by a period of tribulation, and ending in the utopic kingdom of God followed by the eschaton.

Will the Singularity lead to the supersession of humanity by spiritual machines? Or will the Singularity lead to the transfiguration of humanity into superhumans who live forever in a hedonistic, rationalist paradise? Will the Singularity be preceded by a period of tribulation? Will there be an elect few who know the secrets of the Singularity, a vanguard, perhaps a remnant who make it to the Promised Land? These religious themes are all present in the rhetoric and rationalities of the Singularitarians, even if the pre and postmillennialist interpretations aren't consistently developed, as is certainly the case with prescientific messianic movements.

Nowhere is this religious dimension of the Singularity movement more readily apparent than in their uncritical enthusiasm for life extension research, as if this was an obvious good. Ray Kurzweil, Aubrey de Grey, and Gregory Benford all spoke at the Summit about life extension and life enhancement technology, holding out the promise of reaching "life escape velocity," anticipating incremental improvements that lead ultimately to functional immortality. Kurzweil has written three books on nutrition, health, and immortality. A new book was just released with the title *Transcend: Nine Steps to Living Well Forever* (2009).[29] Aubrey de Grey now runs SENS Foundation (http://www.sens.org). Gregory Benford has launched a new company Genescient (http://www.genescient.com). Each has the goal of extending human life, curing death, and presumably making some money along the way.

The science of life enhancement and extension is fascinating, perhaps revolutionary, but the talks dealt very little with the actual science and instead

---

[28]   Cf. http://www.leftbehind.com and http://www.leftbehindgames.com.

[29]   Ray Kurzweil and Terry Grossman, *Trascend: Nine Steps to Living Well Forever* (New York: Rodale Press, 2009).

focused on "mythinformation."[30] Life extension medicine is the revenge of the baby boomers, who will not go softly into that dark night, who will not confront their own existential terror, who will not contemplate ancient spiritual wisdom in their "materialist" worldview. I fear that life extension technology in a materialist culture will be the ultimate killer application.

Again, I challenge the scientists to push the envelope as far as possible. We have an obligation to help and heal, to minimize suffering, to be all we can be as individuals, as a species, and as an interdependent community of many species on a planet. We could do, however, with less hype, more critical realism, more straightforward science, and certainly more humility.

Most Christians and Jews are and have long been "a-millennialists," which is to say that they interpret the messianic age as symbolic and continuous with history—past, present, and future. The lesson that most Christians and Jews derive from their own sometimes unfortunate histories is to be wary of literal messianism, apocalyptic rationalities, and utopic dreamers. Avoid "irrational exuberance" and "cynical caution." Cultivate "considered optimism" with an appreciation of the sanctity of the mundane and a transcendent trust in the future, come what may. This seems like a wise and wholesome "algorithm" to me. Of course, these dynamics and perspectives play out in other religious idioms as well. A-millennialism is thus a kind of "realized eschatology." In the Christian idiom, this is the "kingdom of God" today, so get used to it. In the Singularity idiom, we are already transhumans and postbiological. We crossed the cyborg threshold long ago. The New Age came and went; tragedy and ambiguity continue apace.[31]

As already alluded to, science fiction functions as a commentary on contemporary society, as much as about any imagined future. The Singularity

---

[30]   The term *mythinformation* was coined by Langdon Winner, *The Whale and the Reactor: A Search for Limits in an Age of High Technology* (Chicago: Chicago University Press, 1986). While dated somewhat, this book is extremely helpful in thinking philosophically and critically about technology, politics, and culture. In 2000 I helped organize a two-day conference on life extension technology. See Arthur Caplan and et al., "Extended Life, Eternal Life," John Templeton Foundation, http://www.extended-eternallife.org/frame.html. See also my essay, William J. Grassie, "Time Enough for Love," http://www.grassie.net/articles/2000_timeenough.html.

[31]   In her "Cyborg Manifesto" and other writings, UCSC philosopher Donna Haraway has explored the many tragedies and ambiguities of technoscience and global capitalism, rejecting all forms of messianism. See Donna J. Haraway, *Simians, Cyborgs and Women: The Reinvention of Nature* (New York: Routledge, 1991). ———, *Modest Witness @ Second Millennium. The Femaleman© Meets Oncomouse™.* (New York: Routledge, 1996). ———, *When Species Meet*, ed. Cary Wolfe, Posthumanities (Minneapolis: University of Minnesota Press, 2008).

movement is science fiction as social movement, but it is as much about today as anything that is going to happen in the future. In the last century, human life expectancy doubled in most parts of the world, and consequently there are now 6.7 billion of us sharing this planet. Humans are already enhanced beyond the wildest imaginations of our ancestors even a hundreds year back. The Singularity has come and gone. It continues. We are imperfect transhumans in an imperfect world. Our irrational expectation that the world should be better than it is, and that we should be better people than we are, is a window on the transcendent in the transhuman condition as it was in the merely human condition.

This is the end-time. This is the only time. This is time enough. "Time enough for love" is how Robert Heinlein put it in his 1972 science fiction classic. The book is written as a chronicle in the year 4272—part history, part fable—about the adventures of the longest living human. Lazarus Long was born in 1916 (in the old Gregorian Terran calendar) before the Great Diaspora in the twenty-third century (which marks the beginning of the new Standard Galactic calendar). Through rejuvenation technology, humans have "cured" natural death. *Homo sapiens* have multiplied exponentially and now populate the galaxy. What kind of "world" is it in which humans no longer need to die? Heinlein explores this question in the fanciful story of the life and the eventual death of the "Senior." Lazarus Long turns out to be a rogue and barbarian who discovered rather late in life that the opportunity presented in living is merely to have "time enough for love." For all his ingenuity and prowess, he was an exceptionally slow learner.[32]

Love your work and share that love with others. Love your families and share that love with your communities. Love humanity and this rich, green planet. Love God and the universe by whatever name. And trust that if life is truly good and worthy of enhancement and extension, then so too must our ultimate suffering and death somehow be an essential and necessary part of that good, even as we try to make it better. Be thankful for the food we are about to receive.

These spiritual verities with a better understanding of our evolutionary history and contemporary science will go a long way to preventing and mitigating existential threats in the twenty-first century. Science literacy for religions and religious literacy for science would help a lot in creating a world friendly to scientific, ecological, and humanistic values. We need to build transcending and transformational network between the old-time religions and the new kinds of sciences, connections that will not only limit but also enrich the domains of each and humanity.

As I watch my eighty-seven-year-old mother lose almost all short-term memory and my ninety-year-old stepfather slip into the deep forgetfulness of Alzheimer's, I can only hope that medical science will improve and possibly cure these diseases, such that other families need not suffer in this way. My brother and I installed an

---

[32]   Robert A. Heinlein, *Time Enough for Love* (New York: Ace Books, 1973).

iMac in their nursing home, upon which we run a continuous stream of family photos to remind them of who they are and where they come from. Dad is too far gone now, but Mom's favorite activity is to look at the random photos of her remarkable life for hours upon hours on the computer, instead of vegetating in front of the inane television. We have taken away the keyboard and the mouse, and run her computer remotely, dropping in now and then from afar to video conference with her. Some simple technology, unavailable even a decade ago, has made the end of her life and our involvement in that process so much better. And through the technology, we are able to participate in a different kind of Singularity, the generational and generative relationship between aging parents, adult children, grandchildren, and great-grandchildren. Our real hope for the future lies in a better appreciation of these intimate and embodied relationships—relationships that we now understand to also be microcosmic, mesocosmic, and macrocosmic. This is the realized Singularity and you don't need to wait.

REFERENCES

Barrow, John D. *Impossibility: The Limits of Science and the Science of Limits.* New York: Oxford University Press, 1999.

Bryson, Bill. *A Short History of Nearly Everything: Special Illustrated Edition.* New York: Broadway Books, [2003] 2005.

_____. *A Short History of Nearly Everything: Special Illustrated Edition.* New York: Broadway Books, 2003, 2005.

Caplan, Arthur et al. "Extended Life, Eternal Life." John Templeton Foundation, http://www.extended-eternallife.org/frame.html.

Castellani, Brian. "Map of Complexity Science." http://www.art-sciencefactory. com/complexity-map_feb09.html.

Castellani, Brian, and Frederic William Hafferty. *Sociology and Complexity Science: A New Field of Inquiry.* Berlin: Springer Verlag, 2009.

Chaisson, Eric. *Cosmic Evolution: The Rise of Complexity in Nature.* Cambridge, MA: Harvard University Press, 2001.

_____. *Epic of Evolution: Seven Ages of the Cosmos.* New York: Columbia University Press, 2006.

Christian, David. *Maps of Time: An Introduction to Big History.* Berkeley: University of California Press, 2004.

Gilbert, Scott F., and David Epel. *Ecological Developmental Biology: Integrating Epigenetics, Medicine, and Evolution.* Sunderland, MA: Sinauer Associates, 2009.

Gleick, James. *Chaos: Making a New Science.* New York: Penguin, 1987.

Grassie, William J. "Entangled Narratives: Competing Visions of the Good Lie." Sri Lanka Journal of the Humanities XXXIV (1&2), http://www.grassie.net/articles/2008_entangled_narratives.html.

———. "Post-Darwinism: The New Synthesis." Metanexus Institute, http://www.grassie.net/articles/2009_postdarwinism.html.

———. "Time Enough for Love." http://www.grassie.net/articles/2000_timeenough.html.

———. "Useless Arithmetic and Inconvenient Truths: A Review." *Metanexus Global Spiral* (2007), http://www.metanexus.net/Magazine/tabid/68/id/9854/Default.aspx.

———. "Wired for the Future: Kevin Kelly's Techno-Utopia." *Terra Nova: Nature and Culture* 2, no. 4 (1997): 91-101.

Haraway, Donna J. *Modest Witness @ Second Millennium. The Femaleman© Meets Oncomouse.* New York: Routledge, 1996.

———. *Simians, Cyborgs and Women: The Reinvention of Nature.* New York: Routledge, 1991.

———. *When Species Meet.* Edited by Cary Wolfe, Posthumanities. Minneapolis: University of Minnesota Press, 2008.

Harel, David *Computers Ltd.: What They Really Can't Do.* New York: Oxford University Press, 2000.

Heinlein, Robert A. *Time Enough for Love.* New York: Ace Books, 1973.

Hofstadter, Douglas R. *Gödel, Escher, Back: An Eternal Golden Braid.* New York: Vintage Books, 1979.

Houellebecq, Michel. *The Elementary Particle.* Translated by Frank Wynne. New York: Alfred Knopf, 2000.

Joy, Bill. "Why the Future Doesn't Need Us." *WIRED* 8.04, (1999).

Kelly, Kevin. *Out of Control: The New Biology of Machines, Social Systems, and the Economic World.* New York: Addison-Wesley, 1994.

Kurzweil, Ray. *The Singularity Is Near: When Humans Transcend Biology.* New York: Penguin Books, 2005.

Kurzweil, Ray, and Terry Grossman. *Trascend: Nine Steps to Living Well Forever.* New York: Rodale Press, 2009.

Lanier, Jaron. "One-Half of a Manifesto: Why Stupid Software Will Save the Future from Neo-Darwinian Machines." *WIRED* 8.12, (1999).

McNeill, J. Robert. *Something New under the Sun: An Environmental History of the Twentieth-Century World.* New York: W.W. Norton & Company, 2000.

Penrose, Roger. *Shadows of the Mind: A Search for the Missing Science of Consciousness.* New York and Oxford: Oxford University Press, 1994.

———. *The Emperor's New Mind: Concerning Computers, Minds and the Laws of Physic.* New York: Oxford University Press, 1989.

Pilkey, Orrin H., and Linda Plkey-Jarvis. *Useless Arithmetic: Why Environmental Scientists Can't Predict the Future.* New York: Columbia University Press, 2007.

Ricoeur, Paul. *Lectures on Ideology and Utopia.* New York: Columbia University Press, 1986.

Ross, Greg, and Douglas R. Hofstadter. "An Interview with Douglas Hofstadter." American Scientists, http://www.americanscientist.org/bookshelf/pub/douglas-r-hofstadter.

Whitehead, Alfred North. *Science and the Modern World.* New York: Free Press, [1925] 1967.

_____. *The Concept of Nature.* Cambridge: Cambridge University Press, 1926.

Winner, Langdon. *The Whale and the Reactor: A Search for Limits in an Age of High Technology.* Chicago: Chicago University Press, 1986.

Wolfram, Stephen. *A New Kind of Science.* Champaign, IL: Wolfram Media, 2002.

Index

The letter *n* following a page number indicates a note and the number that follows it indicates the note number.

Lightning Source UK Ltd.
Milton Keynes UK
UKOW032359200712

196351UK00001B/77/P